SPECIAL COLLECTIONS
IN LIBRARIES OF THE SOUTHEAST

SPECIAL COLLECTIONS
IN LIBRARIES OF THE SOUTHEAST

Edited by

J.B. HOWELL

With an Introduction by
Frances Neel Cheney

Published for

THE SOUTHEASTERN LIBRARY ASSOCIATION

By

HOWICK HOUSE
JACKSON, MISSISSIPPI
1978

Printed by
Star Graphics
Jackson, Mississippi

PREFACE

- The miraculous revelations of Edgar Cayce, the celebrated clairvoyant, are now systematically and sedately filed in a library in Virginia.

- Carefully preserved among priceless manuscripts in a research collection in Georgia is one Jefferson Davis whisker.

- Slides and tapes of unusual funeral customs around the world, along with books on the techniques of preparing the body for burial, comprise a mortuary science collection in Tennessee.

- The manuscripts of the works of international acclaim, on which Pearl Buck was awarded the Nobel Prize for Literature, have found a home in the library of a relatively small denominational college in West Virginia.

- There remains in South Carolina to this day the library of a society in which membership dues were paid in indigo.

All of the above statements are true. Other than that they obviously relate to Southern libraries, these diverse facts probably have only two characteristics in common — they were determined in a recent survey of special collections in the region, and they can easily be verified in this guide to the special collections in the Southeastern states.

The survey was conducted during 1977 by a special committee of the Southeastern Library Association, consisting of J. Isaac Copeland, North Carolina; David E. Estes, Georgia; Josephine Fidler, West Virginia; Michael H. Harris, Kentucky; Joseph Hipp, Florida; Ardie L. Kelly, Virginia; John David Marshall, Tennessee; Rush G. Miller, Mississippi; Laura F. Pitzer, South Carolina; and Thomas E. Skinner, Alabama. These surveyors persistently requested, prodded, and threatened their colleagues until they extracted an astounding amount of information. In time, the various listings were compiled, edited, and indexed.

A glance at the completed compendium would probably indicate that much of the material is largely of local interest. A closer look, however, would certainly reveal the unusual and the unique among the repositories of the region as well as the seemingly strange or surprising locations of a number of highly significant collections.

The editor gratefully acknowledges the assistance of all who have contributed to this directory, from the hundreds of librarians who readily or reluctantly provided the information to the ten compilers who single-handedly conducted the survey in their respective states. Special commendation is accorded Mrs. Frances Neel Cheney, not only for the Introduction which she contributed, but for her encouragement in this endeavor; to G. Sheppeard Hicks for the meticulous manner in which he prepared the three detailed indexes, providing easy access to more than 2,000 collections; and to John David Marshall for the interest he managed to maintain in this project through the tedium of many proofings.

Appreciation is also extended to Carolyn S. Newton for technical advice, and to Susan Greer, director of Secretarial Services at Mississippi College, for her assistance in both typing and photocopying.

Although additions, deletions, and condensations were necessary in many of the listings, an effort has been made to include all the essential information which was submitted. However, the Association can assume no legal responsibility for unintentional errors or omissions. Needed changes and corrections, when reported, will be filed for possible inclusion in a revised edition of this directory.

Supplementing existing sources, which are listed in the Introduction, SELA's **Special Collections in Libraries of the Southeast** should serve as a current and comprehensive guide to both the obvious and the obscure in the special collections of literally hundreds of libraries throughout the Southland.

J.B. Howell,
President
Southeastern Library Association

Mississippi College
Clinton, Mississippi
April 3, 1978

CONTENTS

Page

All I knew personally was a fine old gentleman who was a mite addled. But I've heard tell
from all of you about what he used to be like. And I want to say this. He was a fightin'
Irishman and a Southern gentleman and as loyal Confederate as ever lived. You can't get
no better combination than that. And we aint likely to see any more like him because the
times that bred men like him are as dead as he is. He was born in a furrin country but
the man we're buryin' here was more of a Georgian than any of us here mournin' him. He lived
our life, he loved our land, and, when you come right down to it, he died for our Cause
just the same as our soldiers did. He was one of us and he had our good points and our bad
points and he had our strength and he had our failings. He had our good points in that
couldn't nothin' stop him when his
mind was made up and he wasnt afraid of nothin' that walked in shoe leather. There wasnt
nothing that come to him from the outside that could lick him. He wasnt scared of the
English government that wanted to hang him, and when he come to this country and was pore
that didnt scare him a mite. He went to work and he made his money. And he wasnt scared
to tackle this section of the country when it was wild and the Injuns had just been
run out. He made a big plantation out of a wilderness. And when the war come on,
and his money began to go, he wasnt scared to be pore again. And when the Yankees
come through Tara and might of killed him or burned him out that didnt neither
he just planted his feet and stood his ground. That why I say he had our good points. There aint nothing from the
cause he could be licked from the inside. But he had our failings, too. I mean to say that
what the whole world couldnt do, his own heart could. When Mrs. O'Hara died, his heart
died, too and he was licked. And what we seen walking around here wasnt him."

        Will paused and his eyes went quietly around the silent circle of faces.
They crowd stood in the hot sun as though enchanted to the ground and what ever wrath
they had felt for Suellen was forgotten. Will's eyes rested for a moment on Scarlett's
and they crinkled slightly at the corners as though he were inwardly smiling comfort to
her. And Scarlett, who had been fighting back rising tears did feel comfort-
ed. Will was talking common sense instead of a lot of tootle about reunions in another and
better world and submitting her will to God's. And Scarlett had always found strength and

Facsimile of a Manuscript Page from
Gone With the Wind by Margaret Mitchell

(Courtesy of the Atlanta Public Library, Ella Gaines Yates, Director)

iv

INTRODUCTION

The first attempt to study all classes of research materials in the libraries of a large region was made by a group of Southeastern and Southwestern librarians in the mid-1930's. Visiting libraries in nine Southeastern states and in Arkansas, Oklahoma, and Texas, these investigators collected data, which were edited by Robert B. Downs and published by the American Library Association in 1938.

In the forty years which have intervened between the publication of Downs' **Resources of Southern Libraries** and the present directory, several related works have appeared in varied formats. "A Directory of Special Libraries in the Southeast," compiled by Paul E. Postell and published in the Fall, 1953, issue of **The Southeastern Librarian,** listed the mission of a number of special libraries, but included no scope notes. Descriptions of the special holdings of twenty research libraries in the region as of 1968 appear in **Roads to Research** by Thomas H. English. **Special Collections,** a subject approach to those libraries listed in the **American Library Directory,** is compiled periodically by Lee Ash and published by Bowker. Manuscripts in the libraries of the South, along with those of the nation as a whole, are listed in Philip M. Hamer's **Guide to Archives and Manuscripts in the United States,** published in 1961, and **The National Union Catalog, Manuscript Collections,** continuously published since 1959.

Special Collections in Libraries of the Southeast attempts to describe special collections in all types of libraries, including the holdings of special libraries, which in themselves constitute a special collection. Omitted, for the most part, are specialized governmental libraries, church libraries, school libraries, and the libraries of professional schools and colleges, such as law and medicine.

In this survey the compilers accepted the definition of **special collection,** as it is s stated in the **ALA Glossary of Library Terms:** "A collection of material of a certain form, on a certain subject, of a certain period, or gathered together for some particular reason, in a library ..." No restrictions were made on the size or richness of a particular collection, resulting in a wide variety, both in size and subject matter.

History Collections

Although it was assumed that the majority of public libraries and historical societies maintain collections of materials relating to local history and to families of the area, these are included in the directory as a reflection of the current interest in local history and genealogy. State and local history materials range in size from the great collections of nearly a million items in large state university libraries and state departments of archives and history to a modest shelf in small public libraries. An interesting development in recent years has been the concern for oral history, with many libraries, large and small, reporting tapes of recollections of local citizens. And a few libraries maintain extensive collections of photographs relating to the community and its citizens.

Special collections in other areas of history and geography are less often encountered, though a number of libraries reported holdings in Southern history and especially the period of the Civil War. Berea College specializes in the history and culture of the Southern Highlands, while Georgia State University has a collection of documents relating to organized labor, particularly to those of the trade union movement in the South.

Both the University of Miami and the University of Florida have strong collections in Latin American history; Florida State University has a research collection on Napoleon and the French Revolution. The University of Virginia has the largest colleciton on South Asia in existence; West Virginia University has special strength in East African history; and Duke has an outstanding collection of materials relating to the Philippines.

The most extensive and valuable source of materials on the history of military aviation in the United states is the Albert F. Simpson Historical Research Center at Air University, the principal repository of the historical records of the Air Force. The Rucker Agee Cartographical Collection at the Birmingham Public Library is distinguished for its early atlases and globes, together with books on surveying, navigation, geography, and travel, including works published prior to 1800.

Contributing to the materials on the social history of the region are the Afro-American collections, many of which are located at predominently Black colleges and universities. There are extensive collections at Atlanta University, emphasizing the arts and interracial cooperation; and at Fisk University, whose published volumes are augmented by the papers of such important figures as Arna Bontemps, W. E. B. DuBois, Langston Hughes, James Weldon Johnson, and others. Among many notable collections, Tuskegee Institute has the papers of Booker T. Washington and George Washington Carver.

Science and Technology Collections

Special collections in science and technology are found chiefly in libraries maintained by industry and government agencies, with a few represented in public and university libraries. In part, these collections reflect the increasing industrialization of the South.

Reported from Alabama were the history of medicine collection at the University of Alabama in Birmingham; textile technology at the Monsanto Textiles Company's Technical Center in Decatur; fertilizer research at the TVA Technical Library, Muscle Shoals; aeronautical engineering at Redstone Arsenal; aerospace at the Marshall Space Flight Center; and air power at Maxwell Air Force Base.

The University of Miami reported extensive holdings in marine and atmospheric sciences, while the Kennedy Space Center emphasizes the aerospace sciences. In Silver Springs, the Ross Allen Research Library has an interesting collection on wilderness survival and on snakes.

In Atlanta, the Center for Disease Control specializes in documents and other materials relating to communicable diseases. The Coca-Cola Company maintains distinctive archival records and realia, some of which are restricted in use. Lockheed-Aircraft Corporation in Marietta has a collection on aeronautics and related subjects, and Georgia Institute of Technology has one of the most complete collections of patents in the Southeast.

In Kentucky, there is an extensive collection relating to military history, armor equipment, weapons, and armed warfare at the U. S. Army Armor Center. Transylvania University's holdings in medical history emphasize titles published between 1800 and 1840.

In Mississippi, the Southern Forest Experiment Station of the U. S. Forestry Service in Gulfport has a collection on plant genetics, plant diseases, and destructive insects, primarily termites. The U. S. Army Engineer Waterways Experiment Station in

Vicksburg has extensive holdings in hydraulics, soil dynamics and mechanics, and related fields.

North Carolina's holdings reflect some of the industrial concerns of the state, with textile collections at the Charlotte Public Library and North Carolina State University; history of furniture at the High Point Public Library and the Bienenstock Furniture Library in High Point; and a collection on tobacco at the R. J. Reynolds Tobacco Company in Winston-Salem. Marine biology and ecology materials are found in the Atlantic Estuarine Fisheries Center in Beaufort, and a collection on lifesaving at Cape Hatteras National Seashore Research Library, which also houses the papers of the Wright Brothers.

In South Carolina, Clemson University has collected early papers of agricultural societies. Sonoco Products Company reports research materials of interest to the pulp and paper industry, and the Milliken Research Corporation supports a collection on textile technology.

Many of the specialized governmental libraries in Tennessee were not included, but Arnold Engineering Development Center reported a collection on aerospace science. The Tennessee Eastman Company in Kingsport has an extensive collection of scientific and technical materials with special emphasis on fibers, polymers, and cellulosics.

In Virginia, there is an interesting section on sport fishing in the collection of oceanography and marine biology at the Institute of Marine Science. The Mariners Museum Library collects maritime and naval history and possesses an impressive number of photographs in these fields. The U. S. Geological Survey's National Center Library in Reston has rich holdings in geology and related fields, including gems and minerals. In Richmond, Philip Morris, U. S. A. specializes on materials concerning the cigarette and tobacco industry.

Performing Arts

The region's largest collection in the performing arts is the University of Florida's Belknap Collection of more than 500,000 items, including posters, programs, popular sheet music, photographs of Ringling Circus performers, and other American ephemeral material of the past hundred years. The Collins Collection of the Dance at the Birmingham Public Library also includes programs, photographs, and memorabilia. Playbills, programs, cartoons, and pictures of play productions written by or relating to George Bernard Shaw, as well as first editions and other books, are found in the Archibald Henderson Collection of Shaviana at the University of North Carolina. The papers of the Southeastern Theater Conference, founded by Paul Green, are at the University of North Carolina at Greensboro. Memphis State University's Theatre Collection contains about 65,000 items, some dating from the 1700's, and its Circus Collection has business records of individual circuses as well as posters, films and costumes.

The Country Music Foundation in Nashville has the largest collection ever assembled in the field of country music, with 70,000 recordings, manuscripts of the American Federation of Musicians, and a large Roy Acuff Collection. Broader in scope is the Society of the Four Arts Library in Palm Beach, where the collection embraces music, drama, literature, and art, with emphasis on painting.

Women's Studies

Only a few collections in this growing field were reported, and these chiefly by women's colleges. The University of North Carolina at Greensboro's Woman's Collection emphasizes English and American works from the 17th-20th centuries, by, about, and of interest to women. Queens College in Charlotte has collected manuscripts, correspondence, photographs, and scrapbooks, dating from 1771. Randolph-Macon Woman's College has a small general collection, plus nearly 2,000 volumes of published writings by Virginia women. The University of Miami's Collection of Women's Studies consists of about 4,000 volumes, more than half of which are current titles in history, anthropology, the social sciences, literature and travel.

Children's Literature

The recent survey revealed several notable collections of children's literature, including one at the University of Florida which is particularly strong in nineteenth century British and American books for children. Another is the Lena Y. deGrummond Collection at the University of Southern Mississippi, which represents contributions from more than 800 authors and consists of literary manuscripts, correspondence, original illustrations, and first editions and children's magazines, from 1750 to the present. While not as extensive, the Lois Lenski Collection at the University of North Carolina at Greensboro contains some of her manuscripts and original illustrations as well as eighteenth and nineteenth century American children's books, a gift of Miss Lenski. Florida State University also has a Lenski Collection as well as the Shaw Poetry Collection, which is strong in nineteenth century children's periodicals and annuals.

Political and Literary Figures

Most of the papers and other materials relating to Southern political and literary figures have been collected by libraries in those states in which they have lived or served. State libraries have been particularly active in acquiring the papers of political leaders, though some public and university libraries also have collections. Senator John Bankhead's manuscripts and papers, for example, are in the Alabama Department of Archives and History, while the University of North Florida has the papers of the noted Black humanitarian, Ertha M. White.

In Georgia, the Atlanta Public Library has an exhibit collection of items relating to Margaret Mitchell. Emory University has the papers of Ralph McGill, Joel Chandler Harris, and Charles Egbert Craddock, along with those of Charles Forrest Palmer, which contain several hundred letters of Franklin and Eleanor Roosevelt. Atlanta University has a continuing collection on Countee Cullen, and Flannery O'Connor's extensive collection of manuscripts and letters is appropriately housed at her alma mater, Georgia College in Milledgeville.

In Kentucky, the Edgar Rice Burroughs Collection at the University of Louisville has a nearly complete assemblage of the first editions of the Tarzan books. The Jesse Stuart Collection at Murray State University contains about 100,000 letters, manuscripts, first editions, and other material relating to this prolific writer.

In Mississippi, the papers of Eudora Welty and William Alexander Percy are housed in the Mississippi Department of Archives and History. Additional Welty materials are found at the University of Mississippi, which also has a distinguished Faulkner collection and the papers of "Fishbait" Miller.

In North Carolina, both the Asheville Public Library and the University of North Carolina have Thomas Wolfe collections. Duke University has gone beyond the region in its collections of the papers of American writers along with a number of British authors, including Joseph Conrad, Thomas Carlyle, the Rosettis, and Sir Edmund Gosse.

In South Carolina, the Citadel has the papers of World War II General Mark Clark, Bishop Ellison Capers, L. Mendel Rivers, and Frederick Ruge, Naval Advisor to General Erwin Rommel. The papers of the president of the Continental Congress, Henry Laurens, along with those of Arthur Middleton, the Pinckney family, Joel R. Poinsett, and Dubose Heyward are among the collections of the South Carolina Historical Society. Papers of public figures in the Clemson University Library include Edgar Allan Brown, James F. Byrnes, John C. Calhoun, Ben Tillman, Ben Robertson, and others. The South Caroliniana Library at the University of South Carolina contains about 2,000,000 manuscripts, primarily personal and family papers, but also including numerous business, corporate, and institutional records. Furman University has the Furman family papers and those of state Baptist leaders. Among the significant individual and family collections at Winthrop College are the papers of Dr. David B. Johnson, Winthrop's founder and first president. These papers contain much information on higher education for women.

In Tennessee, Austin Peay State University has the papers of Dorothy Dix, known for her column of advice to the lovelorn. The Knoxville-Knox County Public Library has many collections of locally prominent persons, including the papers of Mary Utopia Rothrock, former president of the American Library Association and first president of the Southeastern Library Association. Literary manuscripts of Tennessee writers, along with the papers of Senators Estes Kefauver and Howard Baker, motion picture director Clarence L. Brown and philosopher Robert S. Hartman, are in the University of Tennessee Library. Memphis/Shelby County Public Library and Information Center has the papers of Senator K. D. McKellar and those of novelists Anne Goodwin Winslow, Harry Harrison Kroll, and Jesse Hill Ford. Fisk University, in addition to those names noted under Afro-American collections, has the papers of Charles S. Johnson, Charles W. Chesnutt, the artist Aaron Douglas, and a number of literary figures. Represented in the collection of papers at the Joint University Libraries are Donald Davidson, Andrew Lytle, Mildred Haun, Brainard Cheney, and smaller collections for Edwin Mims, Frank L. Owsley, Jesse Wills, Allen Tate, John Crowe Ransom, and Grantland Rice. The Tennessee State Library and Archives has collections relating to such notable Tennesseans as Andrew Jackson, Andrew Johnson, James K. Polk, James Robertson, and John Sevier.

In Virginia, the University of Virginia has a rich manuscript collection of nearly ten million items, including significant collections relating to Poe, Dos Passos, Faulkner, and Glasgow. In Lexington, the George C. Marshall Research Foundation Library has extensive manuscript and non-book material on the life and public service of General Marshall. The MacArthur Memorial in Norfolk includes the records, messages and private correspondence of General Douglas MacArthur. The personal library and papers of James Branch Cabell are in the library of Virginia Commonwealth University. The Woodrow Wilson Birthplace Foundation Research Library has some of the papers of President Wilson along with many other materials relating to him.

The manuscripts of a number of Pearl Buck's works are housed at West Virginia Wesleyan College in Buckhannon.

In examining the collections relating to notable political and literary figures, as reported by cooperating libraries, it is evident that with the exception of Duke and the

University of Virginia, libraries in the Southeast have not acquired collections of papers from other sections of the United States and abroad. Instead, they have made a concerted effort to collect and preserve the records of their own statesmen and men and women of letters.

Sports

Professional organizations account for some of the special collections relating to sports and sports events. Among these is the Professional Golfers Association of America, with headquarters in Lake Park, Florida, where there are 18,000 volumes on all aspects of golf, from turf care to tournaments. The Keeneland Association in Lexington, Kentucky, has a unique collection on the breeding and racing of thoroughbred horses, including many racing photographs. The National Sporting Library in Middleburg, Virginia, has papers and other materials on racing, steeple-chasing, polo, and early equine literature, dating back to the seventeenth century. All aspects of the breeding, care, racing, and marketing of pigeons are covered in a collection at the College of Charleston. William and Mary has one of the most extensive collections on dogs in North America. And, in Madison, Tennessee, the Outdoor Living Library has an unusual collection of books and other materials on wilderness survival, backpacking, camping, mountaineering, and nature crafts.

The stories behind some special collections would make most interesting reading for those who are curious as to why certain collections have found their way into particular libraries. Why, for example, does the University of Alabama happen to have one of the few complete collections of paperback pocket-size novels issued to service men during World War II? And, what moved the University of Miami to amass more than 130,000 volumes of Soviet imprints, together with complete or substantial files of 500 Soviet periodicals? And, where did Florida State University acquire its twenty-five Babylonian clay tablets and twenty-six papyrus fragments? And, how does the University of Southern Mississippi happen to have the Association of American Editorial Cartoonists Collection, with its 3,400 items by more than 200 artists? We can understand why the Choctaw Central High School in Philadelphia, Mississippi, would have an American Indian collection which emphasizes the Choctaw tribe and why the Moravian Music Foundation in Winston-Salem would have a strong collection of early church music, but how did North Carolina State acquire the Lyons Design Library with its 40,000 slides and an extensive collection on R. Buckminster Fuller?

It would be interesting to know how many collections have been named for librarians. One, at least, was noted at Appalachian State University in Boone, where the William Leonard Eury Appalachian Collection bears the name of its long-time librarian.

From the many collections bearing personal names it is evident that in developing special collections, libraries owe a great debt to a number of indefatigable scholars and others with a passionate interest in one subject and a life-long dedication to collecting material on that subject. These collections were later acquired by libraries, sometimes by purchase, often by gift.

It is hoped that this directory will achieve similar purposes to those ascribed forty years ago to Downs' **Resources of Southern Libraries:** to assist scholars and others in locating collections of interest; to describe little-known collections of value; to discover possible weaknesses in the library collections of the region; and, perhaps most importantly, to stimulate the development of special collections in the libraries of the Southeast.

Frances Neel Cheney
Professor Emerita
School of Library Science
George Peabody College for Teachers
Nashville, Tennessee

Smyrna, Tennessee
March 30, 1978

ABBREVIATIONS

ca.   Circa

R   Restricted as to access and/or use

I

SPECIAL COLLECTIONS
IN
LIBRARIES OF ALABAMA

Compiled
By
Thomas E. Skinner

ABBEVILLE

Henry County Historical Society
106 West Washington Street   36310

1   **Local History**

> ca. 100 items of books, oral history tapes, and other materials relating to Abbeville, the seat of Henry County since 1833. Included is **Bend of the Abba,** a history of Henry County families and particularly those of Abbeville, one of the oldest farming settlements in the state.

ALEXANDER CITY

Thomas D. Russell Library
Alexander City State Junior College

2   **Alabama**

> The Alexander City State Junior College, one of the newest community colleges in the state, opened in 1965. The Alabama Room of the Russell Library is being organized for a state and local history collection. Emphasis is placed on materials relating to Tallapoosa County and Alexander City, which was built on the site of one of the early towns of the Tuckabatchee, a tribe of the Creek Confederacy.

ANDALUSIA

Andalusia Public Library
212 South Three Notch Street   36420

3   **Genealogy**

> A significant collection of printed and manuscript materials covering selected counties in six Southeastern states. Included among the 200 or more items are census records, cemetery data, land grants, and bounty warrants;

the histories of 12 local families; and Wyley Ward's **Early History of Covington County.**

ANNISTON

Public Library of Anniston and Calhoun County
108 East Tenth Street   36202

4   Anniston

    Miscellaneous collection, consisting of materials on the history of Anniston, 1872 to date, including 150 items relating to the city's Diamond Jubilee, 1958; ca. 100 items concerning the Noble Family, the Noble Brothers Iron Foundry, and Noble Institute, 1886-1920; Mary Bell's scrapbooks on early Anniston, 1882-1924; and 350 pictures and information on the churches, schools, industries, and monuments of Anniston.

5   Forney, John H.

    ca. 50 items relating to Forney's career as professor of mathematics at West Point, Confederate General, and Anniston's first city engineer.

6   Pelham, John

    ca. 500 items, including correspondence, scrapbooks, and military records of this Confederate General, who served as artillery commander under "Jeb" Stuart through 60 engagements and was killed at the battle of Kelly's Ford, Virginia, in 1863.

7   Fort McClellan

    A file on the history and operation of Camp McClellan and Fort Mc-Clellan, 1917 to date, including pictures and newspapers published at this army installation.

8   Jacksonville

    Books, articles, and records of Jacksonville, Alabama, and Jacksonville State College, 1902-1952, and materials relating to the history of Benton County, 1832-1884.

9   Oxford

    A collection of correspondence, pictures, and official reports of the city of Oxford, Alabama, along with Frank J. Little's history of Oxford College, and ca. 800 items relating to Walter Stephens, Oxford historian and poet.

ATHENS

Athens State College Library
Athens   35611

10   **Limestone County**

> ca. 200 items, including books, pamphlets, and other materials relating to Athens College, which was founded in 1843, and to Limestone County, the first Alabama county to be invaded by Union troops during the Civil War. Included are ca. 900 of the early volumes added to the college library; the Journals of Thomas Hubert Hobbs, 1840-1862; and **Legendary Limestone** and **History of Limestone County** by Robert Henry Walker.

ATMORE

W. R. Holley Memorial Library
406 South Trammell Street   36502

11   **Forestry**

> Small collection of books and folders reflecting the interests of Atmore Industries, most of which relate to Southern forestry, forest reserves, and the lumber business.

12   **Scouting**

> ca. 200 books concerning scouts and scouting, including the history of scouting, handbooks, den books, packbooks, cookbooks, camping and the Merit Badge series.

AUBURN

Ralph Brown Draughon Library
Auburn University   36830

13   **Alabama Collection**

> ca. 10,000 printed volumes dealing with the history, people, geography, and other aspects of the state of Alabama. See also the Alabama materials listed in the holdings of the Auburn University Archives.

14   **Dobbins Collection**

The personal library of Charles G. Dobbins, dealing with the history and politics of twentieth-century Alabama, consists of 650 printed items.

15   **Genealogy**

A collection of ca. 600 printed volumes dealing with the genealogy of the Southern states, exclusive of Alabama.

16   **Petrie Memorial Collection**

The personal library of Dr. George Petrie, Auburn University's first graduate school dean, is comprised of ca. 6,000 printed items. It is particularly strong in the areas of Alabamiana, Southern history and literature, Reformed theology, and the history of Presbyterianism in the United States.

17   **Streit Collection**

A collection of 150 printed volumes dealing with sports, with emphasis on the Olympic games.

18   **Treasure Collection**

ca. 2,000 rare books, including a first edition of Milton's **Paradise Lost** and a set of Thomas L. M'Kenney's **History of the Indian Tribes** (1836).

Auburn University Archives
Ralph Brown Draughon Library

The manuscript holdings of the Auburn Archives consists of more than 400 collections. Notable among these are the following:

19   Civil War materials, including Thomas T. Bigbie Civil War Letters, 1863-1864; Benjamin Mason Confederate Letters, 1862-1882; Charles H. George Confederate Collection, 1860-1865; G. W. Ross Civil War Letters, 1861-1863; Captain J. Q. Burton Collection, 1864-65; Denney Confederate Collection, 1864; Stouton H. Dent Confederate Collection, 1860-1865; and the J. J. Renfroe Papers, 1863-1864.

20   Papers of military leaders, including Brigadier General Elmer H. Almquist, USA, 1955-1964; General Franklin A. Hart, USMC, 1905-1967; and Brigadier General Joseph L. Stewart, USMC, 1938-1964.

21   Papers of several Alabama legislators, including:

4

22   Andrews, George W., Congressman, 1943-1971

23   Patrick, Luther, Congressman, 1932-1956

24   Pugh, James Lawrence, Senator, 1888-1912

25   Business records, including James Mallory Plantation Journal, 1843-1892; Schuessler, Ellington, and Tucker Merchandise and Cotton Ledgers, 1880-1958; Marengo County Business Records, 1844-1925; and the Tombigbee River Shipments, 1843 and 1845.

26   Other significant collections, including WPA Historical American Building Survey, State of Alabama, 1934; Robert Jemison Collection, 1806-1891, Talladega planter and slaveholder; Petrie Collection, 1828-1945, Presbyterian ministers and educators; Alabama League of Women Voters Records, 1915-1973; and Macon County Court Records, 1837-1958.

27   **Oral History and Photographs**

More than 1,000 oral history tapes and 3,000 prints and negatives provide sound and pictorial presentations of the development of Auburn University. Along with 1,000 photographs relating to the city of Auburn, the state, and the Southland, is the J. F. Knox Collection of 45,000 glass photograph negatives of people and places in Birmingham, 1910-1973.

BESSEMER

Bessemer Hall of History
1830 Fourth Avenue, North   35020

28   **Library**

The Hall of History and West Jefferson County Historical Society's collection consists of more than 500 volumes relating particularly to the history of Alabama and Jefferson County, the development of education in this area, and local coal, iron, and steel industries. Also included are ca. 500 photographs of Bessemer and Jefferson County, historical maps of the area, and limited information on various local families.

BIRMINGHAM

Birmingham Museum of Art
2000 Eighth Avenue, North   35203

29   Library

ca. 2,000 volumes in the field of art with concentration in those areas of strength in the Museum collection of art objects — Oriental, Pre-Columbian, the decorative arts, and antique silver.

Birmingham Public Library
2020 Seventh Avenue, North   35203

30   Tutwiler Collection

A "Southern life" collection of 40,000 volumes with particular strength in state and local history of the Southeast, Southeastern genealogy, Civil War and Reconstruction studies, and Black history. The rare book holdings include significant Alabama imprints and books on travel in the South in the 18th and 19th centuries.

31   Agee, Rucker, Cartographical Collection

500 atlases, dating from 1565 to date, including the Royal edition of Blaeu's **Atlas Maior,** 1662; more than 3,000 maps with emphasis on Alabama and the Southeast, including Civil War battle maps and geological survey maps; 1,700 books on surveying, navigation, cartography, geography, and travel, 120 of which were published prior to 1800; and numerous globes.

32   Collins Collection of the Dance

1,900 cataloged items and several hundred other pieces, including pamphlets, souvenir programs, correspondence, photographs, and memorabilia. Notable among these are John Weaver's **Anatomical and Mechanical Lectures on Dancing,** 1721; **The Decorative Art of Leon Bakst,** 1913; **The Art of the Dance,** 1928, by Isadora Duncan; an autographed piano score of Delibes' "Coppelia;" and Erik Bruhn's correspondence concerning his early appearances in America.

Charles Andrew Rush Learning Center
Birmingham-Southern College   35204

33   Methodist Archives

Records of the North Alabama Conference of the United Methodist Church, 1881 to date, including conference journals, records of individual churches, the most complete file of the conference newspaper (**Methodist Christian Advocate,** 1881 to date) in existence, and various items relating to the United Methodist Church and its predecessors in the United States.

Samford University Library
800 Lakeshore Drive   35209

34   Baptist Historical Collection

The depository for the Alabama Baptist Historical Society includes original and microfilm copies of Baptist publications, particularly those relating to Alabama associations and Alabama Baptist Convention functions, records of local churches, biographical sketches of pastors, and an index for the **Alabama Baptist,** 1843-1878, 1958-1976.

35   Brantley, William H., Collection

A collection of more than 3,000 items, including Alabama books and pamphlets, state maps, Alabama newspapers and manuscripts, and Southern legal rarities. Included are substantial holdings on Indians and early travel in the South.

36   Casey, Albert E.

ca. 600 volumes supplemented by maps and manuscript materials relating to Irish history and genealogy, primarily to counties Cork and Kerry. Manuscripts consist largely of transcriptions from church registers and county records.

37   McMurtrie, Douglas C.

A significant collection, comprised of 420 items of McMurtrie books and ephemera and other materials relating to this authority on the history of books and printing.

38   Ruskin, John

480 volumes, including first and later editions of Ruskin's works and a comprehensive collection of biographical and critical materials on Ruskin.

39   Tennyson, Alfred, Lord

250 volumes, including first and distinctive editions of the writings of Tennyson along with critical works dealing with this popular Victorian poet.

40   Alabama

Extensive collection, consisting of books, manuscripts, newspapers, and maps relating to Alabama; genealogical materials, emphasizing Alabama records; and transcriptions and tapes of projects concerning Alabama folklore, mining, and rural themes.

Southern Research Institute
2000 Ninth Avenue, South   35205

41   **Thomas W. Martin Memorial Library**

A research collection, comprised of ca. 40,000 volumes, 1,000 documents and 800 serial subscriptions in the fields of the biological sciences, chemistry, physics, environmental science, engineering, and metallurgy.   **R**

Temple Emanu-El
2100 Highland Avenue   35205

42   **Carl Hess Memorial Library**

ca. 2,500 volumes of Judaica, including reference works in Hebrew and Hebrew and English, juvenile books, and fiction.

Lister Hill Library of the Health Sciences
University of Alabama in Birmingham   35294

43   **Alabama Medical History**

A collection of 10,570 documents, manuscripts, photographs, and other items relating to persons, institutions, and organizations involved in the development of medicine in Alabama in the 19th and 20th centuries.

44   **Reynolds Historical Library**

10,000 medical books and manuscripts, including correspondence of Florence Nightingale, Sir William Osler, and Louis Pasteur, and collections of Oliver Wendell Holmes and Daniel Drake. Also included is a historical dental collection.

45   **Heath, Parker, Collection**

886 volumes on ophthalmology, collected by Dr. Parker Heath of Boston.

46   **Pittman Thyroid Collection**

325 volumes, covering many aspects of thyroid medicine, contributed by Dr. James A. Pittman, dean of the University of Alabama School of Medicine.

BOAZ

Virgil B. McCain Learning Resource Center
Snead State Junior College   35957

47   **Deal, Babs H.**

72 items, including novels, short stories, articles, photographs, and bibliography, 1944-1976, of this Alabama author, who is perhaps best known for her novel, **The Reason for Roses.**

48   **Deal, Borden**

60 items, including novels, correspondence, photographs, and bibliography, 1948-1976, of other Borden Deal collections as well as articles by and about the author of **The Insolent Breed.**

49   **Huie, William B.**

140 items, comprised of fiction, non-fiction, articles, correspondence, photographs, and bibliography of this native of Hartselle, who has written **The Story of the Seabees, The Hero of Iwo Jima,** and other historical and polemical works.

50   **Wilkerson, Thom**

A collection of poetry, 1938 to date, including 146 published poems, and other materials relating to Thom Wilkerson, who received the Freedom Foundation Award in 1946 for his poem entitled, "Two Hundred Flames."

BUTLER

Choctaw County Public Library
124 North Academy Avenue   36904

51   **Local History**

In addition to ca. 100 volumes and other materials relating to Alabama, the collection includes ca. 60 volumes of local history interest, including **Alokoli** (Choctaw word for **cluster),** a comprehensive collection of Choctaw County history, people, places, and folklore, compiled by the Butler Bicentennial Committee in 1976.

CLIO

George C. Wallace Heritage Association
Clio   36017

52   Library

Beginning collection of the Heritage Association, founded in 1974, includes books and other items of local interest. The Library-Museum, now under construction, will serve as a repository for books, documents, and memorabilia donated by Governor Wallace, who graduated from Barbour County High School here.   **R**

CULLMAN

Cullman County Public Library
200 Clarke Street, NE   35055

53   Alabama

A collection of ca. 1,500 volumes relating to state and local history, including the works of two Cullman writers: Margaret Jean Jones, who has compiled two histories of Cullman County, and Anna Gregath, the author of 11 histories of families outside the state.

54   Genealogy

ca. 500 volumes, comprised of the publications of the national historical societies, local family histories, and complete census records for Cullman and surrounding counties.

DECATUR

Technical Center
Monsanto Textiles Company   35601

55   Library

A collection of 2,600 books, 3,600 periodical subscriptions, and ca. 250 microform items concerning textile technology and related fields, including chemical engineering and polymer science.

Wheeler Basin Regional Library
504 Cherry Street   35601

56   **Folk Art**

ca. 50 items, including slides, films, tapes, and transcriptions of the folk art and folklore of the area as collected by a local folklorists under the Alabama Arts and Humanities Program.

57   **Huie, William Bradford**

The Wheeler Basin Regional Library has been designated as the official repository for the papers, correspondence, and manuscripts of William Bradford Huie, who will decide when the papers will be placed there.

58   **Patillo Papers**

55 folders prepared by a local genealogist on families of the area.

EUFAULA

Eufaula Heritage Association
340 North Eufaula Avenue   36027

59   **Local History**

Concentrating on area families and historic homes, this collection of ca. 100 items includes **Historic Eufaula,** published by the Association and Anne Kendrick Walker's **Backtracking in Barbour County,** "a narrative of the last Alabama frontier."

Historic Chattahoochee Commission
118 Broad Street   36027

60   **Headquarters**

Limited in number rather than in interest, this historical collection includes the Commission's own **Archaelogical Salvage of the Walter F. George Basin of the Chattahoochee Valley** and its **Architectural Legacy of the Lower Chattahoochee Valley of Alabama and Georgia.**

FAIRHOPE

Fairhope Public Library
10 North Summit Street   36532

61   Howland, Marie

       A collection of books and papers of Marie Howland dating from the 1870's to her death in 1921. Consisting of many items dealing with 19th and 20th century utopian communities, the collection includes the novel, **Papa's Own Girl,** published in New York in 1874 and banned in Boston.

FLORENCE

Florence-Lauderdale Public Library
218 North Wood Avenue   35630

62   Dunn, Milton C., Collection

       ca. 1,000 volumes dealing with the history of the Muscle Shoals area, the Civil War, and Alabama history and genealogy.

Collier Library
University of North Alabama   35630

63   Stribling, T. S.

       A collection of papers and other materials relating to this Southern novelist, who received the Pulitzer Prize for Literature in 1933 for **The Store.**

Wesleyan Archives and Museum
University of North Alabama   35630

64   Milner Drug Store

       Along with the business records, medicines and remedies, and other inventory items of this Florence pharmacy, 1857-1901, is a dairy of the owner's trip to California in 1849.

65   Pruitt, Maurice, Collection

       Small but significant collection relating to guerrillas, bushwhackers, and buggers during and after the Civil War in Alabama and Tennessee.

FORT McCLELLAN

United States Army
Military Police School   36201

66   **Library**

ca. 17,000 volumes, 10,000 documents, and 3,000 microforms comprise a substantial collection of military history and science with emphasis on police science, criminology, and penology.   **R**

FORT RUCKER

Division 6 Library
Human Resources Research Organization   36360

67   **Stress Collection**

ca. 2,000 reports relating to human engineering, behavior modification, crisis intervention, sleep deprivation, and other causes and effects of stress.   **R**

GADSDEN

Gadsden Public Library
254 College Street   35901

68   **Alabama History and Genealogy**

A collection of ca. 900 items, including books, manuscripts, and microfilm relating to Alabama, 1540 to date, along with ca. 1,400 genealogical sources, comprised of books, manuscripts and microfilm, with special emphasis on Etowah County and the six surrounding counties from which it was formed.

69   **Lay, William Patrick**

Papers, 1890-1940, consisting of 144 items, including books, manuscripts, correspondence, scrapbooks, and pictures relating to Lay, the founder of the Alabama Power Company.

HUNTSVILLE

Huntsville-Madison County Public Library
108 Fountain Street   35804

70   **Clay, Clement Comer**

Papers, 1812-1876, 320 items, consisting primarily of letters regarding political and military affairs and family correspondence of Clay as lawyer, representative, senator, and governor of Alabama.

71 **Lewis, Mary**

Papers, 1842-1857, 54 items, including letters written by the daughter of the editor of the Huntsville **Democrat** while studying in France but gives interesting descriptions of local events in Huntsville.

72 **Zeitler, Henry B., Collection**

ca. 5,000 volumes, dating from the 1830's and relating to the social, political, religious, and military History of the United States with special emphasis on the Civil War era.

73 **Madison County**

ca. 10,000 items, emphasizing the period 1805-1865 and including published and unpublished county histories, diaries, letters, and 2,500 photographs of the area and its residents.

74 **Genealogy**

ca. 20,000 items of printed and manuscript materials, including Bible records and family histories with emphasis on Alabama, Georgia, Tennessee, and Virginia.

75 **Weeden, Maria Howard**

Papers, 1892-1904, 150 items, including correspondence, published and unpublished poetry and fiction, two original paintings, and other materials.

Eva B. Dykes Library
Oakwood College   35806

76 **Seventh-Day Adventists**

Unusual collection of materials relating to the history and beliefs of Seventh-Day Adventists in general and to the history of SDA Blacks in particular.

Library
University of Alabama in Huntsville   35807

77   **Jones, Robert E.**

Papers, 1946-1975, occupying ca. 280 linear feet, including correspondence and legislative reference materials relating to Jones, who served as representative from the 5th District of Alabama for nearly 30 years.

78   **Ley, Willy, Memorial Collection**

ca. 5,200 published items, including editions of Ley's own works in several languages; science fiction, space travel and rocketry; and paleontology.

Wyle Laboratories
7800 Governors Drive   35807

79   **Library**

A restricted research collection, consisting of ca. 3,000 volumes and 30,000 documents and films, primarily in the field of acoustics.   **R**

JACKSONVILLE

Jacksonville State University Library
North Pelham Road   36265

80   **Alabama**

A collection of ca. 2,500 books about Alabama and by Alabama authors, including a thesis by Jack Boozer on the history of Jacksonville (Alabama).

81   **Ecumenical Movement**

Complete file of the **Library of Church Unity,** compiled and edited by Alfred Thomas DeGroot.

LIVINGSTON

Julia Tutwiler Library
Livingston University   35470

15

82   **Tartt, Ruby Pickens, Collection**

A unique collection of regional folklore, consisting of ca. 5,000 manuscripts of Black folk songs, field calls, and folkways which were collected in Sumter County in the 1930's and later. Also included are Mrs. Tartt's own short stories and recordings based on her collections of folklore.

LOACHAPOKA

Lee County Historical Society
Loachapoka   36865

83   **Library**

Local history collection, comprised of histories of East Alabama and West Georgia counties, with additional files on Lee, Russell, Tallapoosa, Chambers, and Macon Counties; state genealogical periodicals; and numerous transcriptions from original Creek Confederacy records.

MARION

Bowling Library
Judson College   36756

84   **Bristow, Gwen**

Featured in the collection of papers and publications relating to the college, which was founded in 1837 and named for Ann Hasseltine Judson, are the various editions of the works of novelist Gwen Bristow, a 1924 graduate.

Baer Memorial Library
Marion Military Institute   36756

85   **Abernethy Collection**

ca. 800 volumes, 1779-1967, from the personal library of Dr. Thomas Perkins Abernethy, former chairman of the Corcoran Department of History, University of Virginia. Of particular interest in this collection of American history are the works describing travel in America in the 18th century.

MARSHALL SPACE FLIGHT CENTER

Marshall Library
George C. Marshall Space Flight Center   35812

86   NASA

A technical collection, consisting of 6,000 volumes, 80,000 documents and more than 1,000,000 microform items relating to aerospace and related fields with emphasis on the reports of the National Aeronautics and Space Administration.   **R**

MAXWELL AIR FORCE BASE

Air University Library
Maxwell Air Force Base   36112

87   Air Power

A comprehensive collection of English language materials relating to the development and employment of airpower as an instrument of national security. In addition to 340,000 books and bound journals and 500,000 map pieces, the specialized holdings include 480,000 documents produced within and for the United States Air Force and other military services. While related specifically and broadly to military operations and aeronautics, the collections are strong in the fields of education, management, and international relations.

Albert F. Simpson Historical Research Center
Air University   36112

88   Archives

As the principal repository of the historical records of the Air Force, this archival collection is comprised of the most extensive and valuable source materials on the history of military aviation in the United States. Now encompassing ca. 37,000,000 pages of historical materials, ca. 2,000,000 pages are added each year. In addition to unit histories, the collection includes reference material on the early period of military aviation, Air Corps course materials of the 1920's and 1930's, Army Air Force papers during World War II, and a large section relating to the U. S. Air Force involvement in Southeast Asia.

MOBILE

Manufacturing and Engineering Services
International Paper Company   36616

89   Information Service Library

ca. 5,000 volumes, 3,000 documents, and 1,000 pamphlets relating primarily to the pulp and paper industry, wood technology, and forest products. **R**

J. L. Bedsole Library
Mobile College   36613

90   Sellers Collection

Primarily covering the Civil War period, this collection, which occupies 2 linear feet, is comprised of letters, documents, tax records, and other historical materials.

91   Slavery Collection

In addition to a sizable collection of monographs, manuscripts, typescripts, and diaries relating to Alabama, the Library's special holdings include 6 linear feet of Antebellum and Civil War pamphlets, both for and against slavery.

Mobile Public Library
701 Government Street   36602

92   Local History

ca. 5,000 volumes covering the history of Alabama and particularly Mobile from first colonization by the French in 1699 through British, Spanish, American, and Confederate regimes to the present day. Also included is a clipping file of 600 Alabama and 600 Mobile subjects.

93   Genealogy

ca. 7,000 volumes, including genealogical records in all states; census records, 1790-1880, for all counties in the Deep South, the Middle South, New England, and elsewhere; and a large heraldry collection.

94   **Harris Collection**

1,200 books on costume along with limited editions, private press publications and books with fore-edge paintings.

Reference Library
Museum of the City of Mobile   36602

95   **Historic Documents and Records**

Numerous collections of varying size and strength, relating to all aspects of the history of Mobile and the surrounding area, including the following:

96   Farragut, David Glasgow, consisting of letters, orders, and photographs of this Union admiral, who routed the Confederate fleet in Mobile Bay and captured Forts Gaines and Morgan in 1864

97   Semmes, Raphael, comprised of letters, petitions, depositions, and other materials relating to the piracy trial of Confederate Admiral Semmes, who commanded the **Alabama** during the Civil War and later practiced law in Mobile

98   Root, Chester, consisting of commissions, orders, and correspondence of the commanding officer at Fort Bowyer during the Spanish Florida Crisis of 1819

99   Ryan, Abram J., a collection of letters, manuscripts, photographs, and rare publications of this Catholic priest and poet, who served in Mobile, 1870-1883.

100   **Fenollosa, Mary McNeil**

Papers, correspondence, manuscripts, notebooks, diaries written in Japan, photographs, and inscribed copies of all the works of this Mobile poet and author.

101   **MacKenzie, Roderick D.**

Personal papers, letters, journals, diaries, scrap books, lists of his paintings, sketches, and several etched copper plates.

102   **McMillan Collection**

Private collection of Dr. Thomas M. McMillan, comprised of thousands of Confederate documents, including references to most of the Confederate generals, Confederate medicine, and the blockade of Mobile.

Thomas Byrne Memorial Library
Spring Hill College   36608

103   Mobiliana

770 items, including a first edition of Admiral Raphael Semmes' **Memoirs of Service Afloat during the War between the States.** The collection is especially strong in the history of Mobile during the early Colonial period.

104   Rare Books

A collection of ca. 1,000 items, including two incunabula dated 1496 and 1497, and first editions of Samuel Johnson's **Dictionary of the English Language** and Webster's unabridged dictionary, published in 1828.

Library
University of South Alabama   36688

105   NAACP

ca. 400 items, including correspondence, photographs, articles, and other materials relating to the early history of the National Association for the Advancement of Colored People in the Gulf Coast Area, dating back to the 1920's.

MONROEVILLE

John Dennis Forte Library
Patrick Henry State Junior College   36460

106   Alabama

ca. 400 volumes of materials relating to the immediate area and to the state, including the Monroe County Centennial publication, which has been indexed by the librarian.

107   Forestry

A collection of ca. 100 volumes supporting the Forest Technology program which has been implemented in the lumbering center of the flat pine woods.

MONTEVALLO

Carmichael Library
University of Montevallo   35115

108   **Alabama**

ca. 900 items relating to state and local history, with emphasis upon Shelby County. Included are publications of the members of the Alabama Writers Conclave.

MONTGOMERY

Alabama Department of Archives and History
624 Washington Avenue   36104

109   In 1901, Alabama established the first state Department of Archives and History in the nation. The Department holds the non-current official records of the territory and state from 1818 to recent date. These include the executive offices, departments, commissions, bureaus and boards, the Judicial Department, the Legislature, constitutional conventions, state institutions, special commissions, the records of counties and municipalities. Also included are the Alabama military records, beginning with state militia of 1819, and selected federal records, including those of the Land Office, beginning in 1807.

110   The Alabamiana Collection is comprised of 15,000 volumes, ca. 5,000 photographs, and ca. 15,000 vertical files of biographical and other information, including the Governors of Alabama files. Various aspects of early life in Alabama are covered in the collections relating to Jabez Lamar Monroe Curry, Congressman, diplomat, and educator; Benjamin F. Perry, physician; and Albert James Pickett, planter and historian.

111   In addition to the files of official correspondence, there are 2,303 linear feet of records of churches, organizations, and businesses, including papers, manuscripts, and diaries. Notable among the manuscripts and papers are those of the following:

112   Bankhead, John Hollis, lawyer and U.S. Senator, 1931-1946

113   Bankhead, William Brockman, lawyer and member of the U.S. House of Representatives, 1917-1940, Speaker, 1936-1940

114   Bankhead, Tallulah Brockman, early correspondence of the celebrated actress from Alabama

115   Underwood, Oscar Wilder, lawyer and member, U.S. House of Representatives, 1895-1915, Democratic Floor Leader, 1911-1915, and U.S. Senator,
1915-1927.

State Planning Division
Alabama Development Office
State Capitol   36130

116   **Library**

ca. 7,000 titles, 150 serial subscriptions, and 6,200 documents, relating to
planning and development in general and specifically to local,
county/regional, and state planning and development in Alabama.

Alabama Historical Commission
725 Monroe Street   36104

117   **Library**

ca. 1,160 volumes, including books on local and county history, historic
architecture and preservation and restoration.

Alabama Public Library Service
6030 Monticello Drive   36130

118   **Alabamiana**

A collection of ca. 1,000 titles, covering the history of Alabama since
statehood, including original editions of state histories by A. J. Pickett,
Thomas Owen, and others; a complete file of the **Transactions** of the
Alabama Historical Society, and many county histories.

Alabama State University Library
915 South Jackson Street   36101

119   **Alabama State Teachers Association**

Comprised of over 100 items, this collection includes reports, journals,
pamphlets, newsletters, programs of annual sessions, yearbooks, and other
materials relating to the Alabama State Teachers Association.

Houghton Memorial Library
Huntingdon College   36106

120   **Methodist Archives**

The archives and history collection of the Alabama-West Florida Conference of the United Methodist Church is composed of correspondence, diaries, journals, minutes, and photographs of individuals and agencies of the Methodist Church in South Alabama and West Florida, 1800 to date. Included is biographical data on more than 2,500 ministers who have served churches in the Conference, records of boards and agencies, and books on the history of Methodism.

Montgomery City-County Public Library
445 South Lawrence Street   36104

121   **State and Local History**

A collection of ca. 3,000 volumes relating generally to the history of Alabama and specifically to that of Montgomery, where the provisional government of the Confederate States of America was formed by 7 seceding states in 1861.

MOUNTAIN BROOK

Emmet O'Neal Library
50 Oak Street   35213

122   **Gardening**

ca. 700 volumes covering all aspects of modern gardening in works published since 1965.

MUSCLE SHOALS

Technical Library
Tennessee Valley Authority   35660

123   **Fertilizer**

ca. 10,000 items of published materials on the history of fertilizer throughout the world, with special emphasis on fertilizers in the development of the Tennessee River Valley. Included in this collection are the volumes formerly housed in the U.S. Department of Agriculture's Fertilizer Research Center, Beltsville, Maryland.

NORMAL

J. F. Drake Memorial Learning Resources Center
Alabama Agricultural and Mechanical University   35762

124   **Black Collection**

ca. 4,500 books and a limited number of journals and microforms of material by and about Black Americans from the slavery era to the present. Included is a continuing file of Black people in areas adjacent to Madison County.

125   **Oral History**

The University's archival collection, dating back to 1875, includes taped interviews with persons born on the campus, retired professors, and citizens of the local community.

ONEONTA

Blount County Historical Society
204 Second Street, North   35121

126   **Local History**

ca. 100 items related to area history and genealogy, including the **History of Blount County,** compiled by a local surveyor in the 1850's and the **Heritage of Blount County,** a current history.

OPELIKA

Lewis Cooper Memorial Library
200 South Sixth Street   36801

127   **Genealogy**

Housed in the Library's History Room are ca. 100 genealogical reference sources, including the continuing series, "Genealogical Records of East Alabama."

PHENIX CITY

Russell County Historical Commission
Phenix City   37867

128   **Local History**

The Commission's book collection, numbering ca. 100, is maintained in the Phenix City-Russell County Library; clippings and other collections, though privately housed, are made available for serious study. These materials include a file on Fort Mitchell, which was erected near the lower capitol of the Creek Indians, and oral history tapes of interviews covering Phenix City's colorful "honky-tonk" past.

PHIL CAMPBELL

Northwest Alabama State Junior College Library
Phil Campbell   35581

129   **Alabama**

A collection of ca. 300 volumes of Alabamiana, including county histories, some genealogy, and the **Annals of Northwest Alabama.** Of special interest are the rolls of Roddy's Cavalry, a unit of the Confederate Army.

REDSTONE ARSENAL

Scientific Information Center
Redstone Arsenal   35809

130   **Library**

A highly technical collection of 22,000 volumes, 320,500 documents, and 951,000 microforms relating to aeronautical engineering, astronomy, meteorology, missiles, and related fields, including Defense Documentation Center and National Aeronautics and Space Administration microfilm collections.   **R**

USA Missile and Munitions Center
Redstone Arsenal   35809

131   **Library**

86,000 items, consisting of book and non-book materials relating to technology, electronics, and physics, along with educational media for military personnel. **R**

SELMA

Public Library of Selma and Dallas County
1113 Selma Avenue   36701

132   Local History and Genealogy

ca. 300 historical works relating to Dallas County and Selma, which boasts of a number of antebellum homes erected shortly after Lafayette's visit here in 1825. Included are John Hardy's **Selma: Her Institutions and Her Men,** published in 1879 and recently reprinted, and the detailed **Story of Selma.** Genealogical items, numbering ca. 700, include histories of local families and the series published by national historical societies.

133   Craig AFB Library

With the closing of Craig Air Force Base, four miles east of Selma, the library collection of 18,000 volumes will be transferred to the Public Library of Selma and Dallas County.

Sturdivant Museum Association
713 Mabry Street   36701

134   Library

Shelved in the front parlor and elsewhere in Sturdivant Hall, an elegant antebellum home erected in 1853, are books from 3 Old Southern libraries — Boykin, Goldsby-King, and Kaiser. The Boykin collection of several hundred volumes is a "down river" or lower Dallas County plantation library, comprised of books published between 1799 and 1900. Sturdivant Hall, now a museum, is open to the public.

SHAWMUT

Information Services
Westpoint Pepperell Research Center   36876

135   Library

A collection of ca. 6,000 volumes, 3,000 documents, and 1,000 pamphlets relating to textiles, engineering, chemistry, and other areas of interest to the textile industry.

SHEFFIELD

Reduction Research Center
Reynolds Metals Company   35669

136   Library

     ca. 1,800 volumes and 150 journal subscriptions concerning chemistry, chemical physics, and physical chemistry as related to reduction research. **R**

TALLEDEGA

Savery Library
Talladega College   35160

137   Historical Collection

     The archives of Talladega College, which was founded by two former slaves in 1867, is comprised of materials relating to Black history, education of Blacks, Negro church and religious affairs, and African missions. Also included are the papers of Eugene G. Brown, Samuel Bracy Coles, Lister L. Franklin, John Washington Goodgame, Hilton E. Hanna, William H. Holloway, E. Paul Jones, Henry C. McDowell, Leslie Richard Maye, Joseph S. Mitchell, Edwin Chambers Silsby, and Mattie Rinen Trammell.

Talladega Public Library
202 East South Street   35160

138   Local Newspapers

     A century of Talladega history is recorded in a complete file of local newspapers on microfilm, 1868-1968.

TROY

University Library
Troy State University   36081

139   Local History

     Varied collection of historical materials relating to Pike County and to Troy, including typescript of **One Hundred Fifty Years in Pike County, Alabama, 1821-1971,** by Margaret Pace Farmer, and typescript of the tape, "Sharecropping in Pike County, Alabama, in Early 1900's;" oral history tapes of recollections of older residents; and a complete file of the papers of the Pike County Historical Society.

140   Chennault Collection

ca. 450 items related primarily to Asian-American affairs, including materials regarding Claire L. Chennault, the American aviator who became an advisor to Chiang Kai-shek and formed a voluntary air corps, the "Flying Tigers," to aid China.

141   Dent, John Horry, Collection

A collection of 25 manuscript plantation journals and account books, 1851-1891, along with microfilm editions of these and other plantation records in libraries elsewhere.

142   Yoder, Paul V.

ca. 450 band scores and ca. 250 phonodisc recordings of band music, including original scores by Dr. Yoder and published scores by other composers.

TUSCALOOSA

Hugo Friedman Memorial Library
1305 24th Avenue   35401

143   Local History and Genealogy

An office collection of materials relating to the history of Tuscaloosa and area families will be transferred to the Local History Room of the new library, now under construction. Along with old Tuscaloosa newspapers are the publications and the scrapbooks of local historian, Matt Clinton.

William H. Sheppard Library
Stillman College   35401

144   Williamson, Myrtle

Papers, 1948-1960, including correspondence and the original manuscript of her book, **One Out of Four, a Personal Experience with Cancer,** published in 1960.

145   Oral History and Genealogy

A collection of the transcripts and tapes of interviews on civil rights as conducted by the predominantly Black colleges in Alabama. Also on file are papers, diaries, and correspondence concerning a number of local families, 1844-1920.

TUSCUMBIA

Helen Keller Public Library
511 North Main Street   35674

146   Keller, Helen

Along with 109 volumes in the local history collection are 59 books written by or about Miss Keller, whose home near the business district of Tuscumbia is now open to the public.

TUSKEGEE INSTITUTE

Hollis Burke Frissell Library
Tuskegee Institute   36088

147   Washington Collection

More than 25,000 items of books and journals by and about the Negro in Africa, in America, and in the Caribbean, including a complete file of **Southern Workman**, 1872-1939, and 14 editions of Booker T. Washington's **Up from Slavery** in English and foreign languages.

148   In addition to the collection which bears his name, the Library has the papers of Booker Taliaferro Washington, 1887-1915, 133 containers, including correspondence, publications, and major speeches and addresses of the founder of Tuskegee Institute.

149   Campbell, Thomas Monroe

Papers, 1914-1952, 59 containers, including manuscripts and correspondence with colleagues in rural agricultural work in the Southland and in Africa.

150   Carver, George Washington

Papers, 1896-1943, 131 containers, consisting of general correspondence, speeches, publications, experiments, reports, and other materials relating to this renowned agricultural chemist.

151   Dibble, Eugene Heriot

Papers, 1923-1968, 44 containers, including correspondence and other materials concerning his medical career, particularly as it relates to the John A. Andrew Clinical Society and the John A. Andrew Hospital.

152   Hall, Lloyd Augustus

Papers, 1947-1966, 19 containers, comprised of correspondence and reports of this chemical biologist with emphasis on his contributions in curing, preserving, and other aspects of food technology.

153   Work, Monroe Nathan

Papers, 1905-1942, 11 containers, including correspondence, publications, speeches, and awards of this outstanding Southern sociologist.

154   Southern Conference Educational Fund

Papers, 1938-1963, 155 containers of the minutes, manuscripts, and correspondence of this foundation, formerly known as the Southern Conference for Human Welfare.

155   Tuskegee Institute Lynching Reports

Papers, 1881-1966, 60 containers, comprised of books, pamphlets, statistics, and studies relating to lynching in all states.

156   Microfilm Collection

The Library maintains an extensive file of materials on microfilm, including the works of William Ellery Channing, Paul Laurence Dunbar, and Phillis Wheatley.

UNIVERSITY

Geological Survey of Alabama
Walter Bryan Jones Hall   35486

157   Library

ca. 100,000 volumes and an extensive collection of maps concerning geology and related fields, with particular emphasis on the geology of Alabama.

Tuscaloosa Metallurgy Research Laboratory
United States Bureau of Mines   35486

158   Library

A collection of ca. 5,000 volumes, 100 journal subscriptions, and 4,000 documents relating to metallurgy, clays and minerals, and chemical engineering. Included are the publications of the U.S. Bureau of Mines.

Amelia Gayle Gorgas Library
University of Alabama   35486

159   Alabama

ca. 16,000 items, comprised of books, periodicals, and ephemera published in or concerning Alabama, including works by Alabama authors, state government publications, University of Alabama materials. Concentration is on state and local history and genealogy.

160   Rare Books and Newspapers

A collection of ca. 10,000 volumes, including first editions, limited editions, autographed editions, and scarce volumes, relating primarily to historical, literary, and geographical works. In addition to an extensive pamphlet collection, dealing largely with Southern topics, there is a file of 19th century Alabama newspapers.

161   Armed Services

Comprised of 1,322 volumes, this collection of paperback pocket-size editions of novels that were issued to service men during World War II is one of the few complete collections in existence.

162   Confederate Imprints

ca. 800 items including documents of the Confederate government, books, song sheets, and broadsides printed in the Confederate States. There is also a file of Southern newspapers issued during the Confederate period.

163   Hearn, Lafcadio

151 first and later editions of the works of this 19th century Anglo-

American writer, who became a Japanese citizen. Also included are bibliographical, biographical, and critical works relating to Hearn.

164 **Jeffers, Robinson**

A collection of 60 books and papers, including manuscripts, first and limited editions of his works, and biographical, bibliographical, and critical sources relating to this American poet.

165 **Scott, Sir Walter**

108 volumes, primarily first editions of the works of Scott, the most widely read novelist in the antebellum South.

166 **Sanborn Fire Maps**

ca. 6,000 Alabama maps published by the Sanborn Map Company, illustrating buildings and materials used for insurance purposes, 1885-1943.

167 **Van Zele Collection**

A collection of 57 rare maps, with emphasis on the Southeastern states, 1585-1840, but including early maps of European countries and world maps by Ortelius, Mercator, Hondius, and Blaeu.

II

SPECIAL COLLECTIONS
IN
LIBRARIES OF FLORIDA

Compiled
by
Joseph L. Hipp

BARTOW

Polk County Historical Society
495 North Hendry Street   33830

168   Library

Historical and genealogical collection, consisting of ca. 6,000 volumes relating generally to the Southeastern states and Florida, but specifically to the Bartow area, which was settled in 1851 on the site of Fort Blount, built during the Seminole Wars.

BOCA RATON

Boca Raton Public Library
200 Northwest Second Avenue   33432

169   Floridiana

A collection of ca. 700 volumes relating to the state, including fiction and non-fiction and materials on the development of the resort city of Boca Raton, which is Spanish for rat's mouth.

170   Lincoln Collection

ca. 200 books relating to Abraham Lincoln, 16th president of the United States and the 10th president born in a Southeastern state.

S. E. Wimberly Memorial Library
Florida Atlantic University   33431

171   Pratt, Theodore

An impressive manuscript collection, occupying 28 linear feet and 171 books, comprised of the manuscripts, short stories, first and foreign editions of his novels, along with articles, speeches, correspondence, and memorabilia of this Florida author. Of special interest are 5 original animation art paintings from the movie, **The Incredible Mr. Limpet,** and a 16mm color print of the motion picture made from **The Barefoot Mailman.**

BOYNTON BEACH

Boynton Beach City Library
208 South Seacrest Boulevard   33435

172   Gardening

A general collection of ca. 450 items pertaining to home gardening with emphasis on Florida gardens.

173   Railroads

Historical records of railroading, including ca. 500 annual reports of railroad companies, 1930-1968, and Poor's **Manual of Railroads,** 1895-1915 and 1925-1930.

CAPE CANAVERAL

Florida Solar Energy Center
300 State Road 410   32920

174   Library

ca. 4,000 volumes, 100 periodical subscriptions, and extensive documents and microform items relating to solar energy, energy analysis and conservation, and other allied fields.

CLERMONT

Cooper Memorial Library
630 DeSoto Street   32711

175   Local History

Comprised of articles written by families of original settlers, first person narratives both typed and taped, old photographs and slides covering the history of Clermont, 1900-1940.

COCOA BEACH

Cocoa Beach Public Library
55 South Brevard Avenue   32911

176   **Art**

A collection of 25 oil paintings, water colors, and batiks by Cocoa Beach artists.

CORAL GABLES

Environmental Data Service
National Oceanic and Atmospheric Administration   33124

177   **Library**

The library of the Miami Branch of NOAA is comprised of ca. 2,000 volumes and 75 periodical subscriptions relating to meteorology, weather, atmospheric science, and tropical storms.

Otto G. Richter Library
University of Miami   33124

178   **Floridiana**

ca. 11,000 of the Library's 31,624 volumes of Floridiana are maintained as a special collection covering all aspects of Florida's history and culture.

179   **Contemporary Poetry**

A growing collection of ca. 3,500 items of primarily American poetry since 1960. Representative poets include Robert Bly, Charles Bukowski, Jerome Rothenberg, and Diane Wakoski.

180   **Latin America**

The G. K. Hall publication, **Catalog of the Cuban and Caribbean Library, University of Miami,** published in December, 1977, lists ca. 35,000 titles relating to Cuba, the Caribbean, Colombia, Venezuela, Mexico, and Guatemala.

181   **Marine and Atmospheric Sciences**

Covering all of the marine sciences, with emphasis on tropical studies, this collection consists of ca. 23,000 monographs and bound periodicals, 22,000 reprint items, and 43 oceanographic expedition reports.

182 Soviet

More than 130,000 volumes of Soviet imprints, primarily since 1960 along with complete or substantial files of 500 Soviet periodicals. An analysis of the subject coverage of the book collection indicate that 48 per cent pertain to technology and engineering and 45 per cent to the humanities.

183 Women's Studies

ca. 4,000 volumes, more than half of which are current titles, including areas of history, anthropology, social sciences, travel, and literature.

DAYTONA BEACH

Mary McLeod Bethune Foundation
Bethune-Cookman College   32015

184 Bethune, Mary McLeod

A collection of biographies, journal articles, clippings, microfilm copy of papers and messages, and memorabilia, dating from 1904.

Ground Systems Department
General Electric Company   32015

185 Library

ca. 16,000 volumes pertaining to aerospace, electronics, computer simulation, and other areas of technical research.   **R**

Embry-Riddle Aeronautical University Library
Regional Airport   32014

186 Riddle Research Collection

A collection of historical aviation and engineering materials, comprised of 5,000 volumes, 400 periodicals, and 10,000 NASA documents.

DELAND

duPont Ball Library
Stetson University   32720

187   **Garwood Baptist Collection**

Books, minutes, manuscripts, diaries, denominational newspapers and journals, and other materials relating to Baptist history in general and to Florida Baptist history in particular. Also included is an extensive microfilm collection of early records of Colonial and British Baptist history.

EGLIN AIR FORCE BASE

Base Library
Eglin Air Force Base   32542

188   **Library**

A collection of 42,000 volumes and 825 periodicals emphasizing aeronautics, military art and science, counter-insurgency, and aircraft and missile systems.   **R**

189   The Armament Development and Test Center Library at Eglin is comprised of ca. 15,500 books and 400 periodicals relating to aeronautics, military technology, armament munitions, and allied fields.   **R**

FORT LAUDERDALE

Systems and Data Processing Library
American Express Company   33337

190   **American Express Projects**

Documentation describing various phases of ca. 1,000-1,500 company projects from early 1973 to date, and standards manuals from various departments of the Florida and Phoenix centers.   **R**

Avionics Division
Bendix Corporation   33310

191   **Library**

ca. 600 volumes with emphasis on avionics, electronics, and engineering.

Broward County Library
1552 Gateway Drive   33310

192   **Floridiana**

A collection of ca. 2,370 titles, incorporating books about Florida, and especially historical materials relating to Broward County and Fort Lauderdale, which occupies the approximate site of a Seminole War fort erected in 1838. Also included are both juvenile and adult works by Florida authors as well as publications of local organizations.

193 Mizell Black Heritage

ca. 3,300 volumes, comprising the first organized collection of Black Heritage materials in Broward County. Emphasis is on publications of the early 1930's, reflecting the Black experience in America as expressed in various literary forms, especially fiction and poetry.

194 Talking Book/Videotapes

Along with a growing collection, currently consisting of 1,940 titles, of recorded books for the blind and physically handicapped is a series of videotapes on such popular subjects as biofeedback, ESP, and human behavior.

International Swimming Hall of Fame
1 Hall of Fame Drive   33316

195 Library

1,750 volumes and 30 periodicals relating to swimming, surfing, and other aquatic sports. Included are many rare and out-of-print editions of works on water sports.

Nova University Libraries
3301 College Avenue   33314

196 Gnotobiology

ca. 1,000 items, consisting of books and journals supporting the program of breeding germ-free animals for cancer research.

FORT PIERCE

Indian River Community College
3209 Virginia Avenue   33450

197 Area History

ca. 500 items, consisting of papers and maps, 1783 to the present, relating to the history of Fort Pierce along with Marion County, Okeechobee, St. Lucie, and Vero Beach.

198   **Heuvelmans, Martin**

Papers, depicting a citizen's battle with the Army Corps of Engineers to save the environment. Included are letters, news clippings, and manuscripts of his book, **River Killers.**

199   **Monroe, Vaughn**

ca. 300 items, consisting of musical scores and arrangements along with some of his instruments.

200   **Pierce, Benjamin K.**

Papers, 1790-1827, ca. 300 items, consisting of letters and other materials along with Lewis K. Burbey's notes on this Revolutionary War soldier and governor of New Hampshire.

St. Lucie-Okeechobee Regional Library
124 North Indian River Drive   33450

201   **Florida**

ca. 100 linear feet of Floridiana, comprised of both a circulating collection of fiction and non-fiction and a reference collection of Florida materials, including a bound file of the **Florida Quarterly Magazine,** 1940-1977.

GAINESVILLE

Black, Crow, and Eidsness
7201 Northwest Eleventh Place   32602

202   **Library**

A technical collection of ca. 5,500 books and 180 journals relating to air pollution, wastewater, and solid waste disposal.   **R**

Santa Fe Regional Library
222 East University Avenue   32601

203   Gresham, Mary, Collection

A general genealogical collection of 275 volumes.

204   Local History

A small collection of varying formats, including local municipal documents, a picture file of local persons and architecture, microfilm copies and index of the Gainesville **Sun,** 1890's to date.

Coastal Engineering Archives
University of Florida   32601

205   Florida Coastal Engineering

A geographically arranged collection of 1,800 technical reports, 200 maps, 500 charts, and field data relating particularly to Florida and covering coastal protection, beach erosion, and documentation of changes in the Florida coastline.

206   General Coastal Engineering

4,200 technical reports, reprints, and journal articles on coastal engineering, including beach erosion, coastal geomorphology, tidal hydraulics, hurricanes, storm surge, ocean engineering, estuaries and related fields. Included are 770 reports of the Coastal Engineering Research Center and various hydraulics laboratories.

University Libraries
University of Florida   32611

207   Belknap Collection of the Performing Arts

Research collection, consisting of more than 500,000 items relating to the performing arts, with emphasis on American ephemeral material of the last 100 years. Included are posters, programs, and photographs concerning theatre, dance, opera, and film performances. Of special interest are the collections of popular sheet music and photographs of Ringling Circus performers.

208   Children's Literature

This library of ca. 70,000 volumes, which will open in 1978, consists of materials of interest to researchers, teachers, parents, and others concerned with the fields of children's study. The collection is particularly strong in 19th century British and American books for children.

209   **Price, Isser and Rae, Library of Judaica**

The Price Library, comprised of more than 55,000 volumes, provides research material concerning the political, social, economic, and intellectual history of the Jews in the ancient, medieval, and modern periods and in virtually all geographic areas.

210   **Latin America**

ca. 160,000 volumes of books, pamphlets, periodicals, and government documents in their origianl form and more than 9,000 units of microfilm relating to Latin America. The collection's greatest strength is in the material from and about the Caribbean, especially Cuba, Haiti, and the Dominican Republic.

211   **Yonge, P. K., Library of Florida History**

This collection of Floridiana, spanning 5 centuries, consists of ca. 22,000 books, 184 periodical subscriptions, 2,640 miscellaneous manuscript collections, 2,200 reels of microfilm, and 1,375 maps. In addition to the manuscript papers of Floridians who have been influential in the growth of the state, the collections of microfilms and photostats of documents relate to both the English period (1763-1784) and the two Spanish periods (1565-1763 and 1784-1821) of the state's history.

Department of Rare Books and Manuscripts

212   The Creative Writing Collection, with emphasis on Florida writers, contains 750 titles and occupies 172 linear feet and includes the papers of   (1) Alden Hatch,   (2) Zora Neale Hurston,   (3) John D. MacDonald,   (4) Marjorie Kinnan Rawlings,   (5) Edmund Skellings, and   (6) Lillian Smith.

213   The Poetry Collection, consisting of 5,000 first editions of modern British and American poets, has recently been expanded to include an archives of 137 tapes of recorded poetry to complement the printed collection.

214   The Rare Book Collection of 21,000 titles has significant concentrations in the fields of study relating to the Irish literary revival of the late 19th and early 20th centuries, Sir Walter Scott, the early English 18th century, and to the West Indies and Latin America.

215   The Manuscript Collection, occupying 150 linear feet, contains the Rochambeau Papers, the Raymond and Margaret Dreier Papers, and several small collections, including the papers of John Wilson Croker, William Perry Hay, and Frank R. Crumbie, Jr.

GULF BREEZE

United States Environmental Protection Agency
Sabine Island   32561

216   Library

ca. 1,600 volumes and 135 technical journals relating to pesticides, marine biology and ecology, fish pathology, and aquatic microbiology.   **R**

HALLANDALE

Hallandale Public Library
320 South Dixie Highway   33009

217   Floridiana

A collection of ca. 600 volumes relating to various aspects of the state of Florida. Included is local history materials on Broward County and Hallandale, coastal city and vegetable packing and shipping center.

HOMESTEAD

Reference Library
Everglades National Park   33030

218   Ornithology

In a collection of ca. 5,500 volumes relating to the plant and animal life of this vast swampland and wildlife refuge is a significant group, consisting of 800 books and bound journals, pertaining to bird life in this area and in many parts of the world.

JACKSONVILLE

Cummer Gallery of Art
829 Riverside Avenue   32204

219   Library

ca. 4,000 volumes and 75 periodical subscriptions relating to the fine arts, with emphasis on western and oriental art. Included are exhibition and auction catalogs. **R**

H. Y. Tookes Library
Edward Waters College   32209

220   **Afro-American Collection**

ca. 1,000 books and 25 journal subscriptions relating to Afro-Americans.

Church of Jesus Christ of the Latter-Day Saints
4087 Hendricks Avenue   32207

221   **Florida Genealogical Library**

A collection of 1,500 books and 6 journals, consisting of genealogical reference works and family histories along with state, county, and local histories.

Jacksonville Public Library
122 N. Ocean Street   32202

222   **Florida**

A varied collection of 13,000 books and pamphlets, 900 volumes of journals, 1,652 microfilm reels, and 325 maps relating to Florida, 1591 to date, with particular emphasis on the "Crown" area of Northeast Florida and Jacksonville. Included is the Merritt Collection of more than 500 rare maps, books, and documents.

223   **Delius, Frederick**

A collection consisting of musical scores, including Delius' first published composition, copies of letters, manuscript accounts of the rediscovery of his home at Solano Grove, monographs, and photographs relating to this English composer who lived in Florida, 1884-1885.

Carl S. Swisher Library
Jacksonville University   32211

224   **Delius, Frederick**

170 items of book-type materials, 38 phonorecords, and ca. 40 musical scores of Frederick Delius, including the manuscript score of the opera **Koanga,** which was inspired by memories of his sojourn in Florida.

225 Mathews, John E., Jr.

Legislative papers and correspondence of State Senator John E. Mathews, Jr., 1965-1970, occupying 30 vertical file drawers.

Bertha Smith Library
Luther Rice Seminary International   32207

226 Christian Ministry

A growing collection of more than 300 bound dissertations, including works in Old and New Testament exposition, New Testament Greek exegesis, Biblical theology, and Christian education.

Library
University of North Florida   32216

227 White, Eartha M.

Papers, consisting of more than 1,000 items, including letters, documents, photographs, and memorabilia pertaining to the life and activities of this noted Black humanitarian, 1875-1974.

Westinghouse Electric Corporation
8000 Arlington Expressway   32211

228 Library

A collection of 3,500 volumes and 90 journal subscriptions relating primarily to nuclear engineering and offshore power systems.

KENNEDY SPACE CENTER

John F. Kennedy Space Center
Kennedy Space Center   32899

229 Library

32,444 volumes, 567 journal subscriptions, 170,000 documents and technical reports, 125,000 specifications and standards, and 680,000 microform items relating to the aerospace sciences.   **R**

KEY WEST

Monroe County Public Library
700 Fleming Street   33040

230   **Florida**

>   Of particular interest in this collection of 8,000 volumes, 4,000
> photographs, 400 maps, 850 microfilm reels, and numerous clippings per-
> taining to state and local history are significant materials on local ar-
> chitecture and official papers of the Bahamas and a file of Bahama
> newspapers since 1784.

231   **Hemingway, Ernest**

>   A collection of 50 volumes along with clippings and other materials
> relating to Hemingway, who spent a great deal of time in Key West.

LAKE ALFRED

Institute of Food and Agriculture Science
University of Florida   33850

232   **Research Library**

>   An agricultural research collection, comprised of ca. 4,000 volumes, 142
> journal subscriptions and microform holdings relating chiefly to citrus fruits.

LAKE PARK

Professional Golfers Association of America
Lake Park   33403

233   **Library**

>   ca. 18,000 volumes on all aspects of golf, from turf care to tournaments.

LAKE PLACID

Archbold Biological Station
American Museum of Natural History   33852

234   Library

ca. 3,800 volumes and 235 periodical subscriptions relating to ecology, vertebrates, terrestrial arthropods, and Florida natural history. Included is a collection of 65 books and 1,200 reprints concerning the taxonomy of hymenopterans. **R**

LAKE WALES

Learning Resource Center
Warner Southern College   33853

235   Church of God Pioneer Books

ca. 1,000 books, pamphlets, periodicals, and song books, 1880-1960, written by early workers of the Church of God (Anderson, Indiana) and published by Warner Press. Also included are 30 tapes, which reveal the experiences of the pioneers of the Church of God in Florida.

LAKELAND

Roux Library
Florida Southern College   33802

236   Methodist Historical Collection

5,100 volumes, comprised of histories of United Methodist Churches in Florida, minutes of District conventions, denominational books and hymnals, and many old Bibles.

237   Haley, James A.

1,989 items, including correspondence, papers, and speeches of this United States Congressman from Florida's 8th District.

MADEIRA BEACH

Gulf Beaches Public Library
200 Municipal Drive   33708

238   Florida

ca. 500 items of Floridiana and local history, including nearby Treasure Island, where the Spanish explorer, Narvaez, is said to have anchored in 1528.

239 **Art**

ca. 600 items, consisting of theoretical and practical texts, art history, the philosophy of art, and reproductions.

MADISON

North Florida Junior College Library
Turner Davis Drive   32340

240 **American Indian**

ca. 1,000 items, including books and microforms relating to the history, ethnology, and anthropology of the American Indian.

241 **Black History**

600 items, consisting of books, bound journals, and filmstrips concerning Black authors and artists, social studies, and protest literature.

242 **Floridiana**

700 book and non-book items relating to Florida history, authors, and biography.

MAITLAND

Maitland Public Library
501 South Maitland Avenue   32751

243 **Smith, Andre, Art Collection**

ca. 600 volumes on art and artists, primarily pre-1945, from the private library of Andre Smith, local artist and founder of the Maitland Art Center.

244 **Natural History and Environment**

ca. 1,500 items, comprised of books and pamphlets relating to natural history, ecology, the environment and the Maitland area, the center of the campaign to eradicate the fruit fly in Florida, 1929-1930.

Bascom Palmer Eye Institute
Bates Leach Eye Hospital   33152

245 Library

6,500 books and 90 journal subscriptions relating to ophthamology, eye physiology, eye anatomy, and vision.

Central Agency for Jewish Education
4200 Biscayne Boulevard   33137

246 Educational Resource Center

Judaica collection, consisting of ca. 15,000 volumes and 70 periodicals, including materials in the Hebrew and Yiddish languages, relating to Jewish history, Jewish holidays, Hassidism, and other Semitic subjects.

Eastern Air Lines Corporation
Miami International Airport   33148

247 Library

ca. 1,000 volumes and 75 journal subscriptions relating to air traffic, airline and airport administration, and civil aeronautics. **R**

Fairchild Tropical Garden
10901 Old Cutler Road   33156

248 Library

ca. 4,000 volumes and 40 journals relating primarily to tropical botany and horticulture. **R**

Historical Association of Southern Florida
3280 South Miami Avenue   33129

249 Library

Emphasizing primary source materials on the history of Southern Florida, this collection consists of 3,000 volumes, 25,000 photographs, maps, periodicals, and ca. 80 cubic feet of manuscripts.

Miami-Dade Public Library
1 Biscayne Boulevard   33132

250   Florida

A collection of state and local history materials, consisting of 4,600 volumes, more than 30,000 documents, 2,300 maps, 246 scrapbooks, 86 serial subscriptions, 120 reels of microfilmed minutes of the Dade County Commission, pamphlets, and extensive files of news clippings. Also included are 22 tapes of local pioneer reminiscences, 11 of which have been transcribed.

251   Florida Authors

A collection of books by Florida writers along with 98 manuscripts in handwritten, typescript, and/or galley proof form. Included are the original manuscripts of Philip Wylie's **The Disappearance** and short stories by Marjorie Kinnan Rawlings.

252   Genealogy

2,900 genealogical works relating primarily to the Southern and Eastern United States, and 5,500 reels of microfilmed census records, covering all states through 1880.

253   Romer Photograph Collection

ca. 3,000 photographs and 10,000 negatives of photographs of the Miami area, 1910-1940's, made by Gleason Waite Romer.

Milgo Electronic Corporation
8600 Northwest 41st Street   33166

254   Library

ca. 2,500 volumes and 160 periodical subscriptions relating to data communications, voice communications, and similar engineering subfields. **R**

Southeast Fisheries Center
National Marine Fisheries Service
75 Virginia Beach Drive   33149

255   Library

A laboratory research collection of ca. 4,600 volumes and 350 journals relating to marine biology, fishes, and fisheries, along with materials on ecology and the environment.

Temple Israel Library
137 Northeast 19th Street   33132

256   Judaica

ca. 6,000 volumes and 400 pamphlets, with special strength in the Bible, archaeology, Jewish history and literature, Israel, and the Jews in the United States.

Vizcaya Museum
3251 South Miami Avenue   33129

257   Vizcaya Guides Library

1,130 volumes relating to the decorative arts, especially art history from the classical and Renaissance periods through the 19th century.   **R**

MIAMI SHORES

Barry Memorial Library
Barry College   33161

258   Catholic History

ca. 600 volumes relating to the history of the Catholic Church with emphasis on the development of the Catholic parochial system.

259   Early Florida History

A collection of 30 volumes pertaining to the history of the Catholic Church in the Floridas from ca. 1783.

MILTON

Fibers Division
American Cyanamid Company   32570

260   Library

ca. 1,700 volumes and 50 technical journals relating to textile chemistry, microscopy, spectroscopy, and allied fields.   **R**

NICEVILLE

Learning Resources Center
Okaloosa-Walton Junior College   32578

261   Florida

1,050 volumes of Floridiana, including history, literature, Florida statutes, city directories, and maps. Included are oral history tapes of interviews with "old-timers" in the two counties served by the college.

262   Holzhauer, Emil

A collection of 60 of his paintings donated by this well-known local artist along with 200 which are on loan to the college. Included are landscapes, seascapes, and portraits.

NORTH MIAMI

North Miami Public Library
835 Northeast 132nd Street   33161

263   Smik Memorial Collection

A collection of 109 volumes pertaining to art, including the Library of Great Painters series and the Panorama of World Art series, a file of the **Horizon Magazine,** and other works.

OCALA

Ocala Public Library
15 Southeast Osceola Avenue   32670

264   Wallace, John Haxton, Memorial

A collection of ca. 300 volumes on all aspects of horsemanship and equestrian skills, including materials on race horses, riding horses, and show horses.

ORLANDO

Florida Technological University Library
Alafaya Trail   32816

265   **Bryant West Indies Collection**

ca. 1,000 titles, consisting largely of monographs, serials, and periodicals relating to the history, geography, and economics of the West Indies and the Caribbean. Included are crafts, paintings, and other art items from the West Indies. Florida subjects are also represented.

266   **Wagar Space Collection**

ca. 2,000 news clippings covering every space launch from 1956 through 1973 along with 265 official NASA photographs of all moon shots.

John Young Museum and Planetarium
810 East Rollins Street   32803

267   **Library**

A collection of 2,500 volumes pertaining to astronomy, Biblical archaeology, natural history, and general science.   **R**

Orlando Public Library
10 North Rosalind Aveune   32801

268   **Walt Disney World**

Pamphlet collection, occupying 20 vertical file folders, providing news, facts, and descriptive information on Walt Disney World. Included are publicity releases, calendars of special activities, and other Disney World depository items.

269   **Genealogy**

Extensive collection of more than 6,000 volumes and 2,400 microfilm census records along with more than 500 individual family histories. Serving as the state DAR depository, this collection includes genealogical materials for all states east of the Mississippi River.

270   **Florida**

Along with books and pamphlets on Florida history and by state authors is a collection of 140 audiocassettes which recapture the reminiscences of local citizens on Central Florida history.

Horticultural Research Laboratory
U.S. Department of Agriculture
2120 Camden Road   32803

271   **Research File**

A collection of the printed results of ca. 60 research projects which have been conducted at the Horticultural Research Laboratory. Pertaining primarily to citrus fruits, some studies relate to subtropical fruits and vegetables.

ORMOND BEACH

Ormond Beach Public Library
30 South Beach Street   32074

272   **Automobiles**

Occupying 6 shelves, this collection consists of books relating to antique cars, automobile races, and automobile repair along with bound copies of **Automobile Quarterly.**

273   **Florida**

11 shelves of Floridiana, including history and travel, archaeology, natural history, biography, and fiction.

PALM BEACH

Historical Society of Palm Beach County
1 Whitehall Way   33480

274   **Library**
ca. 1,000 volumes, manuscripts, microforms, photographs, and other materials relating to the history of Palm Beach County and the State of Florida. Of special interest is the collection of first editions of Florida histories, dating back to the 1700's.   **R**

The Henry Morrison Flagler Museum
1 Whitehall Way   33480

275   **Archives**

Housed in the former Flagler residence among collections of furniture, silver, and costumes are extensive archival materials, including maps, letters, papers, and other items relating primarily to Flagler's Florida East Coast Railway Company.

276   Society of the Four Arts
Four Arts Plaza   33480

Library

25,634 volumes and 56 journal subscriptions relating to music, drama, literature, and art, with emphasis on painting.

PATRICK AIR FORCE BASE

Air Force Eastern Test Range
Patrick Air Force Base   32925

277   **Technical Library**

ca. 15,000 volumes and 169 periodicals pertaining primarily to aeronautical engineering, science, and business.   **R**

PENSACOLA

Lelia Abercrombie Historical Library
Pensacola Historical Society
405 South Adams Street   32501

278   **Local History**

ca. 2,000 volumes pertaining to Pensacola and Escambia County history and genealogy, 50 boxes of manuscripts, photographs, and 700 maps, charts, and architectural drawings.

279   **Carpenter, Cornelia, Collection**

More than 20,000 glass safety and nitrate negatives of Pensacola and West Florida scenes, including portraits, the downtown area, bridge construction, and rural and farm scenes.

280   **McEvers-Crowley Collection**

ca. 8,000 prints and negatives, 1914-1950, including ships, ships crews, and naval aviation in Pensacola and Escambia County.

Newport Division
Reichhold Chemicals, Incorporated   32596

281   Research Library

ca. 3,000 volumes pertaining primarily to naval stores as applied to adhesives, rubber, polymers, and chemical intermediates.

John C. Pace Library
University of West Florida   32504

282   West Florida

Most of the 5,000 titles in the Library's rare book collection relate to West Florida, the ten counties west of the Apalachicola River. Included are West Florida imprints; photographs of people and places in West Florida prior to 1930; and ca. 300 retrospective maps of Pensacola and surrounding area.

283   Florida Newspapers

Along with a varied collection of old Florida newspapers are issues of **Dat Moi,** the newspaper published by and for Vietnamese refugees at Eglin Air Force Base during the summer of 1975.

284   Fort Barrancas

Inventory of goods transferred at Fort Barrancas at the capitulation of Pensacola to Andrew Jackson in 1818. The collection consists of 5 pieces in a Spanish warehouseman's handwriting.

285   Mareno Library

The 100-volume library of Dr. Francisco Mareno, a Spanish physician who lived in Pensacola during the second Spanish period and, after 1821, became Spanish consul in Pensacola.

286   Peruvian Collection

A collection of books, pamphlets, reprints, and ephemera relating to Peruvian history and culture. Included among the 98 pieces other than books are notes of Ronald M. J. Gordon, a former British airlines agent in Lima.

287   **Pleas Photographic Plates**

      334 photographic glass plate negatives taken by C. W. Pleas and depicting country life in West Florida at the turn of the century.

POMPANO BEACH

Pompano Beach City Library
1213 East Atlantic Boulevard   33060

288   **Davidson Collection**

      ca. 5,000 musical recordings, 1912-1960's.

289   **Local History**

      Along with ca. 500 books by Florida authors are photographs, clippings, taped interviews, and other materials relating to South Florida and to Pompano, which was named for one of Florida's choicest food fish.

SAINT AUGUSTINE

Saint Augustine Historical Society
271 Charlotte Street   32084

290   **Library**

      ca. 500 linear feet of books, maps, photographs, artifacts, and reproductions of archival materials relating to the oldest city in the United States and to Florida history as it directly concerns Saint Augustine.

SAINT PETERSBURG

Electronic Communication, Incorporated
Saint Petersburg   33733

291   **Library**

      ca. 4,500 volumes and 150 journal subscriptions relating to electronics, communication, and technology.   **R**

Jim Walter Research Corporation
10301 Ninth Street, North   33702

292   Library

ca. 3,000 volumes and 125 periodicals relating to research and development in house construction, building standards, and building materials. **R**

Marine Research Laboratory
Florida State Department of Natural Resources
100 Eighth Avenue   33701

293   Library

ca. 1,600 volumes, 60 technical journals, 22,000 reprints pertaining to marine biology, oceanography, ichthyology, and ecology.

Museum of Fine Arts
255 Beach Drive, North   33701

294   Library

A reference collection of ca. 4,500 volumes and other resources relating to the history of art and architecture and to the decorative arts.

Saint Petersburg Public Library
3745 Ninth Avenue, North   33713

295   Florida History

A collection of 31,000 documents and publications relating to the history of Florida, including publications of non-governmental agencies in the state, brochures of various tourist attractions in Florida, and files of and indexes to local newspapers.

SARASOTA

Technical Information Center
EMR Telemetry Systems   33578

296   Library

ca. 2,200 volumes and 125 journal subscriptions in the field of aerospace technology and electronics, with emphasis on telemetry.   **R**

Mote Marine Laboratory
9501 Blind Pass Road   33581

297   Library

ca. 800 volumes and 50 technical journals relating to marine biology and estuarine ecology.   **R**

New College - University of South Florida Library
5700 North Tamiami Trail   33580

298   Hebraica

ca. 900 volumes, including the works of Jewish authors and books relating to Jewish religion and culture.

Ringling Museum of Art
Sarasota   33578

299   Library

An art research collection consisting of 7,000 books and 50 periodical subscriptions relating to art history and particularly to Baroque art and to Rubens.

SILVER SPRINGS

Ross Allen Research Library
Silver Springs   32688

300   Wilderness Survival

ca. 8,000 volumes pertaining primarily to snakes and to the science of wilderness survival.   **R**

STUART

Martin County Public Library
701 East Ocean Boulevard   33494

301   Sailing Ships

The nucleus of this continuing collection is the Salim Walker McArthur library of ca. 125 volumes published mainly in the 1920's and pertaining primarily to clipper ships and ship modeling.
Genealogy

TALLAHASSEE

Coleman Memorial Library
Florida Agricultural and Mechanical University   32307

302   Afro-American Collection

ca. 20,000 volumes along with microfilm, phonodiscs, pictures, and clippings concerning Blacks in the United States, Africa, and the Caribbean.

Florida Bureau of Coastal Zone Planning
115 Bloxham Street   32304

303   Library

ca. 7,500 books, monographs, and reports along with 50 journal subscriptions relating to coastal zone management, land-use planning, oceanography, marine ecology, and environmental planning in the coastal zone.

Robert Manning Strozier Library
Florida State University   32306

304   Authors' Manuscript Collection

87 titles, represented in various forms — holograph, typed, corrected drafts, and galley proofs. Among the 37 authors are manuscripts of one or more works of May McNeer, Louis Shores, and Philip Wylie.

305   Babylonian Clay Tablets

25 inscribed Babylonian tablets, 2100-2300 B. C., includes temple records, tax bills, business contracts, and a butcher's bill.

306   Florida Collection

8,867 items, 1591 to date, consisting of books about Florida, books by Florida authors, and books with a Florida setting. Included are cookbooks,

books on citrus-growing and tropical plants, waterskiing, treasure hunting, and the Seminole Indians. Augmenting the collection is an extensive vertical file of materials on Florida localities.

307 Herbal Collection

50 items, beginning with the **Herbarius** (1509) and including rare herbals, early books on botany, and several recent herbals, which reflect current interest in "natural" food and medicine.

308 Kelmscott Press Books

53 items, 1891-1898, containing a complete set of books printed by William Morris at the Kelmscott Press.

309 Lenski, Lois

867 items, 1925-1973, including various editions of books written, illustrated, and written and illustrated by Lois Lenski, along with versions of her manuscripts, early sketches, and finished illustrations for her books.

310 McGregor Collection

337 items, 1534-1936, comprised of scarce, rare, and uncommon books in American history, including works on discovery and exploration, the Colonial and Revolutionary periods, early travel, the American Indians, and early history of Florida.

311 Napoleon and the French Revolution

ca. 10,000 items comprising a research collection on Napoleon and the French Revolution, including letters and documents, published journals, memoirs, and diaries. Also included are materials relating to the Peninsular War, the Illyrian Provinces, and the diplomacy of the period, filmed for Florida State University by the Archives Nationales and other foreign records offices.

312 Ostraka Collection

32 items, consisting primarily of private or official letters to and from men serving in a unit of the Roman army on duty in Egypt in the 2nd century A.D. Of particular interest is a pass for a furlough for 10 days, written beforehand with a blank on which the name of the soldier was to be written.

313 **Papyrus Collection**

26 papyrus fragments from the 1st century B. C. They came from mummy cartonnage found at Abusir el-Melek, and the papyri in Greek text seem to be orders to a banker to pay a sum to a third person.

314 **Poetry of Sacred Song**

500 items, consisting of books of hymnology and gospel songs, ranging from early editions of Wesley's hymns and Watts' psalms to the private collection of Robert Lowry, hymn-writer of the late 19th century and the author of "Shall We Gather at the River."

315 **Richardson, Louise, Collection**

"The Night before Christmas," 1837-1976, 324 items, consisting of 150 editions of Clement C. Moore's famous poem, including 78 parodies, 4 musical versions, and 52 related items.

316 **Scottish Collection**

4,000 items, consisting of works relating to many aspects of Scotland. This collection has been provided largely by Northwest Floridians of Scottish descent, "In honor of the Scottish folk who conquered the wilderness of Northwest Florida."

317 **Shaw Poetry Collection**

20,000 items, consisting of English and American poetry, including original editions of the poets, manuscripts, letters, biography, criticism, and other materials. This collection is particularly strong in 19th century children's periodicals and annuals.

318 **State Photographic Archives**

70,727 items, consisting of photographs, maps, lithographs, portraits, and other illustrative materials covering all aspects of life in Florida from early explorers to the space programs of the 1960's.

Other Manuscript Collections

Among extensive manuscript holdings are the following collections:

319 Blue Ridge Institute for Southern Social Work Executives, Records, ca. 3,700 items, including minutes and other records from the first Institute in 1927 to the present.

320   Boyd, Mark Frederick, Collection, 1516-1965, 845 items, consisting primarily of translations and transcriptions of Spanish documents and research notes of this Florida historian and malariologist.

321   Campbell, Doak Sheridan, Papers, 1938-1972, relating to his work as educator, college president, and active Baptist layman.

322   Flagler Enterprises, Papers, 1884-1917, 2,927 items, relating to the Florida East Coast Railway Company and other Flagler enterprises.

323   Giono, Jean, Papers, 1924-1962, 255 items, comprised of books, essays, and other writings by this French author.

324   Warren, Fuller, Papers, 1927-1973, 60,900 items relating to the public life of this Florida Governor, 1949-1953.

325   Watkins, Richard Ellis, Papers, 1882-1931, 1,215 items, some of which relate to his experiences during the Spanish American War.

State Library of Florida
R. A. Gray Building   32304

326   Florida Collection

Consisting primarily of books, this collection of ca. 15,000 items of Floridiana also includes manuscripts, pictures, maps, broadsides, pamphlets, and ephemeral material.

327   Genealogy

ca. 3,500 genealogical works which are national in scope with emphasis on the Southeastern states. Printed and microform materials, dating from the 17th to the early 20th century, include heraldry, vital statistics, county and military histories, and census records.

328   Reference Collection

Among the reference sources of ca. 4,000 items are back files of several major Florida newspapers and current Florida city maps.

Tall Timbers Research Station
Highway 12   32303

329   Library

ca. 3,700 volumes and 1,000 periodical subscriptions pertaining primarily to fire, fire ecology, earthworms, snakes, conservation, and related fields.

Tallahassee Community College Library
444 Appleyard Drive   32304

Shaw, Beatrice, Collection

A Floridiana collection consisting of 1,036 titles, including Florida imprints, Florida authors, and books about Florida.

TAMPA

Hillsborough County Historical Museum
County Courthouse   33602

331   Library

ca. 1,700 volumes and 12 periodicals relating to Florida history and genealogy and particularly to that of Hillsborough County and Tampa.

Tampa-Hillsborough County Public Library
900 North Ashley Street   33602

332   Floridiana

3,823 volumes concerning Florida, including books, periodicals and other materials relating to history, ecology, government, education, natural history, Seminole Indians, Spanish territorial history, biography, and fiction.

333   Genealogy

3,241 volumes relating to genealogy of the Southeastern states, including family histories, early state papers, census records, Jewish genealogy, and Black genealogy.

Florida Historical Society
University of South Florida   33620

334 **Library**

ca. 20,000 volumes and other materials, including manuscripts, early diaries, photographs, maps, and long runs of historical journals as collected by the Society, which was founded in 1856.

University Library
University of South Florida   33620

335 **Special Collections**

Historical materials complementing the collection of the Florida Historical Society, which is housed here, including many pre-1900 maps of Florida and 19th century tourist pamphlets.

336 A collection of 50,000 volumes of 19th century American literature, including 8,000 American dime novels and 120 titles relating to Timothy Shay Arthur, popular author of **Ten Nights in a Barroom.**

Merl Kelece Library
University of Tampa   33606

337 **Booth, John Wilkes**

Legal-size file cabinet of materials assembled by Stanley P. Kimmel in writing **The Mad Booths of Maryland,** includes documents, letters, diaries, photographs, original portrait of Booth, and other materials relating to John Wilkes Booth and the assassination of Abraham Lincoln.

338 **Drama**

Extensive collection of theatre memorabilia, including 26 scrapbooks of playbills, photographs, clippings, and other materials relating to the career of Blanche Yurka.

339 **Florida Military Collection**

Established in 1973 to encourage research in military subjects for peaceful purposes, in military history, and in national security matters, this collection consists of ca. 6,000 volumes along with 6,822 journals, 254 newspapers, 718 pictures, 315 artifacts, and other materials.

TARPON SPRINGS

Anclote Psychiatric Center
Riverside Drive   33589

340   Library

ca. 5,000 volumes and 75 periodical subscriptions relating to psychiatry, psychotherapy, and neurology.

WEST PALM BEACH

Art Museum of the Palm Beaches
1451 South Olive Avenue   33401

341   Library

ca. 2,900 volumes and 20 periodicals relating to classical paintings, art history, and biographies of artists.

Central and Southern Florida Flood Control District
West Palm Beach   33402

342   Library

ca. 4,000 volumes and 100 journals relating to conservation, water in all phases, and the subtropical ecology of Florida.

E. C. Blomeyer Library
Palm Beach Atlantic College
1101 South Olive Avenue   33401

343   Theatre

1,500 volumes with emphasis on the American theatre of the 20th century.

WINTER PARK

Mills Memorial Library
Rollins College   32789

344   **Holt, Hamilton**

Papers, 93 manuscript boxes, 35 scrapbooks, 11,00 pamphlets and 7,000 letters relating to this president of Rollins College, 1925-1949.

345   **Rittenhouse, Jessie B., Collection**

Along with 1,200 volumes of the works of Byron, Shelley, Poe, and other poets is a unique collection of 1,280 letters from poets.

346   **Whitman, Walt**

A collection of 650 books by and about Walt Whitman, including 28 editions of the **Leaves of Grass.**

III

SPECIAL COLLECTIONS
IN
LIBRARIES OF GEORGIA

Compiled
By
David E. Estes

ALBANY

Albany-Dougherty Public Library
2215 Barnsdale Way   31707

347   **Local History**

In this collection of ca. 200 volumes are three histories of Dougherty County, including the **History and Reminiscences of Dougherty County,** compiled by the local chapter of the DAR in 1924, and the histories of neighboring counties. Of special interest are the only known manuscript diaries of Colonel Nelson Tift, who sailed up the Flint River in 1836 and began construction of the settlement which became the city of Albany.

Margaret Rood Hazard Library
Albany State College   31705

348   **Black Studies**

A collection of ca. 2,500 volumes covering the history and literature of Blacks in America.

AMERICUS

James Earl Carter Library
Georgia Southwestern College   31709

349   **Carter, Jimmy and Rosalynn**

On permanent display in the library, named in honor of the President's father, are pieces of family memorabilia on loan from the Carter family, several rarely seen photographs of the younger Jimmy Carter, and materials collected from recent and past Carter campaigns. The emphasis of the display is on the relationship of the Carters to Southwest Georgia College, which both the President (Freshman Class, 1941-1942) and the First Lady (Class of 1946) attended.

Lake Blackshear Regional Library
307 East Lamar Street   31709

350   **Georgia**

ca. 500 items, including nearly 400 county histories, along with ca. 650 works of Georgia authors and audio-slide sets, maps, paintings, and pictures of local historical sites.

351   Carter, Jimmy

A growing collection of materials about the President, including all published works about Carter and his family, genealogical information, vertical file of local and other clippings, minutes of the meetings of the library trustees during 1961-1962 when Carter served on the board, and memorabilia (bust of Jimmy Carter, original plates of 6 etchings by artist).

352   Civil War

ca. 500 books and other materials on the Civil War, with special emphasis on Andersonville. Included are items contributed by the headquarters staff of the Andersonville National Historic Site.

353   Genealogy

ca. 200 volumes, primarily relating to Georgia, but including the American Genealogical Biographical Index and Georgia census records, 1829-1890.

ATHENS

Athens Regional Library
120 West Dougherty Street   30601

354   Georgia

ca. 1,200 books about Georgia, including history, description and travel, biography, and miscellaneous items in government and literature. Among the items of local interest is an illustrated guide to the historic homes of Athens by Blanche Marsh entitled **Athens, Georgia's Columned City.**

355   Genealogy

ca. 400 items, including copies of typed materials and books relating primarily to Athens and Clarke County families, Georgia land lottery lists, census records, and a list of interments in two Athens cemeteries.

356   DAR

ca. 750 items, owned by the Elijah Clarke Chapter of the Daughters of the American Revolution but housed in the Athens Regional Library, including DAR lineage books, lineage indexes, the historical collections of the Georgia State Society of the DAR, the historical collections of the Elijah Clarke Chapter, and other materials.

The University of Georgia Libraries
Athens   30602

Manuscript Collections

357   ca. 1,500,000 pieces — chiefly manuscripts, including prints, photographs, oral history, maps, and other materials. Main strengths are in the history of Georgia and the Southeastern United States.

358   Notable are: 17th 18th, and 19th century Georgia family papers, including those of political figures, business records, and material relating to the counties, cities, and towns of Georgia. Many Southern literary, theatrical, and musical personages are also represented.

359   Georgia Literature

Over 125,000 pieces, including papers of Margaret Mitchell, Medora F. Perkerson, Corra Harris, Mildred L. Rutherford, Gertrude Hall, Marel Brown, and other Georgia authors.

360   Mitchell, Margaret

ca. 57,000 pieces, comprised of letters from literary figures and prominent Southerners of the period, family history, clippings, fan mail, and a large collection of materials concerning the publication of **Gone With the Wind.**

361   Perkerson, Medora Field

ca. 3,000 pieces covering writings, correspondence, and photographs of this Georgia journalist, the author **White Columns in Georgia.**

362   Reece, Byron Herbert

ca. 7,200 pieces, including letters, photographs, awards, scrapbooks, and lecture notes of this Georgia poet, novelist, farmer, and teacher.

Georgia Politics

As indicated, a number of these collections are housed in the Richard B. Russell Memorial Library of the University of Georgia Libraries.

Papers of Georgia Governors:

363   Brown, Joseph E., 1823-1918, ca. 2,600 pieces

364   Brown, Joseph Mackey, 1865-1930, ca. 3,500 pieces, along with Papers of the Brown family, 1837-1972, 925 pieces.

365   Colquitt, Alfred H., 1853-1894, 11 pieces

366   Russell, Richard B., 1920-1933, including some papers from Russell's service in the Georgia House of Representatives, 1 linear foot (In Russell Library)

367   Sanders, Carl, 1963-1967, 2,324 pieces

368   Stephens, Alexander H., 1841-1882, 29 pieces

Papers of Georgia Members of the United States Congress:

369   Blackburn, Benjamin Bentley, 1967-1974, 25 linear feet (In Russell Library)   **R**

370   Davis, John William, 1961-1974, 148 linear feet (In Russell Library)

371   Felton, Rebecca L., 1835-1930, ca. 5,500 pieces

372   Forrester, Elijah Lewis, 1951-1964, 1.5 linear feet (In Russell Library)

373   Harris, William Julius, 1905-1913 (Pre-Senatorial), 4 linear feet (In Russell Library)

374   Hughes, Dudley M., 1806-1972, ca. 15,750 pieces

375   Lanham, Henderson Lovelace, 1947-1957, 69 linear feet (In Russell Library)

376   Mitchell, Harlan Erwon, 1958-1960, 24 linear feet (In Russell Library)

377   O'Neal, Maston Emmett, Jr, 1965-1971, 93 linear feet (In Russell Library)

378   Pace, Stephen, 1939-1949, 1 linear foot (In Russell Library)

379   Pilcher, John Leonard, 1953-1964, 2.5 linear feet (In Russell Library)

380   Preston, Prince, 1946-1960, ca. 14,000 pieces

381   Russell, Richard B., 1933-1971, 1,708 linear feet (In Russell Library)

382   Stephens, Robert Grier, Jr., 1961-1976, 260 linear feet (In Russell Library)

383   Toombs, Robert, 1837-1880, 266 pieces

Papers of Other Political Figures:

384   Farrow, Henry P., 1855-1937, ca. 4,500 pieces

385   Howell, Clark, 1873-1946, 1,055 pieces

386   Lamar, Joseph Rucker, 1792-1936, 4,995 pieces

387   Lumpkin, Edwin King, 1859-1917, 45,555 pieces

388   Nix, Abit, 1940-1949, 2,189 pieces

389   **Southern History**

An extensive collection, comprised of many Civil War editorials from Northern newspapers; Confederate papers and diaries; Jefferson Davis materials, including a Davis whisker; and the Keith Read Manuscript Collection. Georgia social, economic, and religious history is depicted in such collections as the records of the Brumby Chair Company, the American Land Company, and the Georgia Railroad and Banking Company; the papers of Harden-Jackson-Carithers, Charles Colcock Jones (Presbyterian minister and planter), and Samuel Porter Jones (Methodist evangelist) and in the sermons of Bishop John W. Beckwith.

390   **Cuyler, Telamon**

ca. 62,000 pieces, containing letters, indentures, documents, records, pictures, and clippings of the Colonial, Revolutionary, and Civil War periods in the state of Georgia. Also included are some 20th century materials on Korea, the Treaty of Portsmouth, and early aircraft.

391   **Egmont Papers**

22 volumes kept by John Percival, First Earl of Egmont, Irish Peer, and first president of the trustees appointed by Royal Charter for establishing the colony of Georgia. Included are records of the trustees, letters to and from Georgia, journal of John Wesley, and a list of settlers.

392   **Hancock, Joy Bright**

Papers, comprised of more than 2,600 items concerning the career of this U.S. Navy captain, including correspondence, speeches, photographs, along with manuscripts of Hancock's book. **Lady in the Navy.**

393 De Renne Collection

Several thousand books, maps, engravings and newspapers pertaining to Georgia as colony and state, 1700-1929. The collection is particularly strong in its coverage of the Colonial Period in Georgia. The original permament Constitution of the Confederate States of America, with autograph signatures of all signers, is among the documents in this collection.

394 Hargrett Library

Extensive resource collection comprised of Georgia imprints and materials relating to Georgia with emphasis on pioneer Middle Georgia and sources of the Revolutionary and Federal periods in Georgia history.

395 Confederate Imprints

This collection of several thousand books, pamphlets, and newspapers printed in the Confederate States of America is one of the most extensive of its kind in existence. Although all areas of Confederate printing are well represented, state laws and military publications are thoroughly covered.

OTHER SPECIAL COLLECTIONS

396

Outstanding miscellaneous collections: **Theatre and Music,** including programs, records, collections of Charles Coburn and Guido Adler and playwright Ward Morehouse, Newcastle Playbills, and the Lucy Bates theatre and music collection; **Georgia Counties, Cities, and Towns,** including history of Athens; Jackson, Oglethorpe, Stephens, and Twiggs County records; and the Jefferson County School records. Of particular interest is the **Ladies Garden Club** (Athens) **Collection,** consisting of correspondence, documents, programs, scrapbooks and ribbons of the first garden club in America, organized in 1894.

ATLANTA

Atlanta College of Art
1280 Peachtree Street   30309

397 L. L. Haverty Memorial Library

ca. 14,000 volumes and 24,000 slides, including a special collection of contemporary art materials, comprised of books, exhibition catalogs, and video-tapes of interviews with visiting artists.

Atlanta Historical Society
3099 Andrews Drive   30305

398   ca. 3,500 volumes, pertaining primarily to Atlanta history with emphasis on biography, the Civil War period, and 19th century publications. Notable among extensive manuscript holdings are:

399   **Andrews' Raid Collection**

9 cubic feet of materials relating to the capture of the Confederate locomotive, **General,** by a band of Union soldiers in 1862 and the 86-mile chase which ensued. This collection was used by Walt Disney Studios in the production of "The Great Locomotive Chase."

400   **Frank, Leo Max**

2½ cubic feet of letters and other materials relating to the case in which Frank was convicted of the murder of Mary Phagen and subsequently lynched by a mob in Marietta in 1915.

401   **Lumpkin, Martha**

Papers, ½ cubic foot, relating to Martha Lumpkin (Mrs. T. H. Compton), for whom Marthasville was named in 1853. Marthasville was destined to become the city of Atlanta.

402   **U.S.S. ATLANTA**

½ cubic feet of materials relating primarily to the last two of the 4 ships known as the U.S.S. **Atlanta.** Christened by Margaret Mitchell, both served gallantly in World War II.

Atlanta Public Library
126 Carnegie Way, Northwest   30303

403   **Georgia**

A collection of ca. 5,000 volumes augmented by historical journals, rare documents, and maps relating to the history of Georgia and particularly to Atlanta. Included are literary works by Georgians and about Georgia and information on Indians in Georgia.

404   **High, Hattie Wilson, Memorial Collection**

ca. 7,500 printed or published genealogical works with primary emphasis on Georgia and secondarily on the other Southern states. Included are reference materials, periodicals, Georgia census records, 1820-1880, and basic works on heraldry and onomastics.

405   Mitchell, Margaret

Primarily an exhibit collection comprised of the original manuscript of **Gone With the Wind** and personal items of the celebrated author, including her private library of ca. 1,000 volumes, typewriter, and Red Cross uniform.

406   Williams, Samuel, Collection

Presenting a comprehensive history of Blacks in America, this collection consists of ca. 4,920 volumes, national and local newspapers, journals, information sheets on prominent Blacks, and a file of tapes on literary works of notable Blacks.

407   Oral History

The Atlanta Oral History Project, 1950-1970, resulted in 40 hours of tape and 500 pages of transcript of interviews with prominent civic and community leaders, covering urbanization, education, politics, civil rights, and the arts in Atlanta.

Foundation Library
Atlanta Public Library   30303

408   Foundations

This regional foundation depository is comprised of ca. 200 books, 30 directories, and 200 technical reports relating to philanthropy, fund-raising, and the techniques of proposal writing.

Atlanta Regional Commission
100 Peachtree Street   30303

409   Library

This regional planning library for the seven-county area surrounding Atlanta is comprised of ca. 850 volumes, 80 journals, maps, charts, and other materials relating to transportation, land use, health, housing, solid waste, and public administration.

Trevor Arnett Library
Atlanta University   30314

410   **Clarkson, Thomas**

42 items, 1785-1871, including correspondence, miscellaneous documents, and literary works of Thomas Clarkson, English abolitionist.

411   **Brown, John**

87 items, 1814-1859, comprised of correspondence and papers of this American abolitionist. Of special interest are two letters by a resident of Harper's Ferry, giving a detailed account of Brown's raid, and the military order signed by Robert E. Lee instructing a guard to escort Brown and his fellow prisoners to the Charleston (West Virginia) jail.

412   **Cullen, Countee, Collection**

This continuing collection of ca. 4,800 items, founded by New York teacher-musician Harold Jackman and named in honor of Countee Cullen, noted Black poet, includes books, journals, broadsides, photographs, theatre programs, and other materials which record the contributions of the Negro to the literary, graphic, and performing arts in 20th century America. Significant holdings, both in manuscript and printed forms, relate to (1) James Baldwin, (2) Arna W. Bontemps, (3) Countee Cullen, (4) W. E. B. DuBois, (5) Paul Laurence Dunbar, (6) William Christopher Handy, (7) Langston Hughes, (8) Georgia Douglas Johnson, (9) James Weldon Johnson, (10) Paul Robeson, and others.

413   **Slaughter, Henry P., Collection**

442 items, 1797-1890, comprising the nucleus of the Negro Collection, includes books, manuscripts, pamphlets, portraits, and sheet music. Emphasizing the early history of the Negro in the United States, the collection is composed primarily of slave papers and correspondence of Negro leaders, abolitionists, and outstanding political figures of the 19th century.

414   **Lincoln, C. Eric, Collection**

1,728 items, 1958-1965, consisting of correspondence, short stories, poetry and material relating to his research on Black Muslims in America. Included is a sizable amount of information on Malcolm X, and the typescript of Lincoln's study of Malcolm X, entitled **My Face is Black** (1964).

415   Towns, George Alexander

    1,340 items, 1894-1956, comprised of the correspondence, literary works, and notes of this poet, playwright, and author of **The Sharecropper.**

416   Interracial Cooperation Collection

    61,967 items, 1929-1943, records and papers of the Commission on Interracial Cooperation, an organization founded to reduce mounting racial tensions during the post-World War I period and later.

417   Southern Conference for Human Welfare

    15,478 items, 1946-1948, composed of a portion of the official records of this organization, including information on the presidential campaign of Henry A. Wallace.

Center for Disease Control
1600 Clifton Road, Northeast   30333

418   Library

    Research collection, consisting of 61,000 volumes, 750 journal subscriptions and a file of the Public Health Service publications relating to communicable diseases, microbiology, veterinary medicine, virology, and related subjects.

The Coca-Cola Company
310 North Avenue   30301

419   Archives

    Located in the Corporate Headquarters of the company, the archives is comprised of the company's publications, including a file of **The Coca-Cola Bottler,** 1909 to date, photographic material, and artifacts used in the promotion of the sales of Coca-Cola and its allied products. Much of the information relating to product development is restricted.   **R**

Robert W. Woodruff Library
Emory University   30322

Manuscript Collections

420   ca. 1,000,000 pieces, including manuscripts, photographs, and microfilm, relating primarily to Methodism, the Confederate States, and the economics, sociology, educational history, and literature of the South.

421   Notable among the collections are: (1) 19th century Georgia family papers; (2) Papers of Southern Methodist leaders from the late 17th to the 20th century; (3) Southern literary figures; (4) Southern political figures; and (5) Business records for the 19th and early 20th century.

422   **Southern Literature and Journalism**

ca. 50,000 pieces, including the following authors: (1) Julian LaRose and Julia Collier Harris, (2) Margaret Mitchell, (3) Henry W. Grady, (4) Corra Harris, (5) Minnie Hite Moody, (6) Larry Rubin, (7) Frank L. Stanton, and (8) Maurice Thompson.

423   **Harris, Joel Chandler**

ca. 20,000 items, including more than 6,000 manuscripts, a virtually complete file of family letters as well as correspondence of literary contemporaries and his publishers.

424   **Craddock, Charles Egbert** (Mary Noailles Murfree)

ca. 2,000 pieces, consisting of selections of literary manuscripts and correspondence of one of America's first local colorists. In the collection are chapters of published works, unrevised and unpublished stories, and letters to and from her publishers.

425   **McGill, Ralph E.**

ca. 40,000 pieces, including scrapbooks, personal papers, and souvenirs of this distinguished publisher and nationally syndicated columnist.

426   **Palmer, Charles Forrest**

ca. 50,000 items, including papers, photographs, and mementos, relating primarily to Palmer's duties in the administration of Franklin D. Roosevelt and his work with slum clearance and public affairs. This collection contains several hundred letters of Franklin and Eleanor Roosevelt.

427   **Methodism**

ca. 100,000 items, including the following major collections: (1) Papers of John and Charles Wesley and their family; (2) Papers of Methodist bishops and ministers in America; (3) Records of individual churches, conferences, and Indian missions; and (4) Other manuscripts on Methodism from its beginning to the present, including the papers of Young J. Allen, Warren A. Candler, A. G. Haygood, John McClintock, Arthur J. Moore, George G. Smith, Costen J. Harrell, A. J. and C. C. Jarrell.

428   Southern History

ca. 200,000 pieces relating to the history of the South during the 18th, 19th, and 20th centuries, including the Keith Read Confederate Collection; the papers of   (1) Alexander H. Stephens,   (2) Robert N. Gourdin,   (3) John H. Hewitt,   (4) Samuel H. Stout, Confederate physician,   (5) Robert Battey, and Southern women (6) Eleanor Raoul Greene,   (7) Mildred Seydell, and   (8) Emily B. Woodward.

429   Business, Economics, and Science

ca. 250,000 items, mainly of the 19th and 20th centuries, and comprised of the papers of a number of Southern leaders in these fields: (1) Asa Griggs Candler,   (2) Harrold Brothers,   (3) William Greene Raoul,   (4) Malcolm Bryan,   (5) Cason J. Callaway, and   (6) Charles Holmes Herty.

Rare Books

430   Some 15,000 volumes, pamphlets, broadsides, maps, and other printed items, the largest portion of which are devoted to English literature of the 18th and 19th centuries, and to American literature, 18th-20th centuries, with particular emphasis on Southern writers.

431   Candler, Charles Howard, Library

Over 300 volumes covering six centuries, consisting mainly of Bibles, English and Continental history, literature, and Georgiana.

432   Yellow-Backs

Consisting of more than 500 cheap editions of fiction, displayed for sale in railway bookstalls from the mid-19th century, this collection is one of the finest of its kind in existence.

433   Confederate Imprints

More than 3,000 books, magazines, pamphlets, newspapers, broadsides, and sheet music printed in the Confederate States of America.

434   Seydel, Paul Bernard, Memorial

A collection of Belgian books and manuscripts in the fields of history, literature, and the fine arts, including a number of volumes from the famous Plantin-Moretus Press in Antwerp.

Other Special Collections

435   Outstanding miscellaneous collections include: **The Stone Mountain Collection,** several thousand pieces, consisting of records, correspondence, publications, photographs, and other materials relating to both the mountain and the carving; The **Robert W. Woodruff Collection** of mementos, books, photographs and citations regarding his career and patronage to Emory; **Lucy Stanton Miniatures,** 36 paintings by one of America's most eminent minaturists; **Georgia Wildflower Paintings,** ca. 300 watercolors of Georgia wildflowers by Mary Motz Wills; **Ivan Allen Maps,** some 200 maps, particularly of Georgia and the Southeast; **Kemp Malone Library,** the working library of this specialist in Icelandic literature, with some rare and valuable items along with his personal papers; **Charles F. Palmer Housing Collection,** books and other printed materials on housing constitute one of the most extensive private collections in this field; **Southern Women,** a substantial group of papers relating to civic, social, professional, and political activities of Southern women; **Metropolitan Opera** and **Music,** major collections include papers of Charles H. and Flora Glenn Candler, Malcolm H. Dewey, Rebekah Cooledge, Mildred Seydell, and Geraldine Farrar; and **Southern Education,** including papers of Gustavus Orr, James S. Peters, John A. Sibley, Emily Woodward, Paul West, Dorothy Orr, and Mary C. Barker.

Federal Reserve Bank of Atlanta
104 Marietta Street   30303

436   Finance and Banking

ca. 40,000 volumes, 300 journal subscriptions, and other materials relating to finance, banking, and economics, including the publications of the Federal Reserve System and those of individual banks.

437   Caribbean Basin Collection

A research collection, comprised of 1,000 monographs, more than 200 periodicals, and 12 major newspapers relating to the economics of the Caribbean Basin, which includes the Caribbean Islands, Central America, and the northern countries of South America.

The Georgia Conservancy
3376 Peachtree Road, Suite 414   30326

438 Library

Consisting of ca. 600 volumes and 32 journal subscriptions, this collection deals exclusively with the environment and conservation. The library serves as a depository for the publications of the U. S. Environmental Protection Agency.

Division of Public Library Services
Georgia Department of Education
156 Trinity Avenue   30303

439 State and Local History

Extensive collection of books, pamphlets, and clippings relating to the history of Georgia from the Colonial period to the present, including microfilm copies of 522 doctoral dissertations pertaining to Georgia. A bibliography of the histories of Georgia counties represented in the collection was published by the Division in 1974.

Georgia Department of Archives and History
330 Capitol Avenue   30334

The Georgia Department of Archives and History is the official repository for the non-current files of state and county offices. The Department also collects and makes available for research the records and papers of individuals, families, churches and organizations. The total holdings of the Department now exceed 40,000 cubic feet.

440 Official State of Georgia Records, 1777 to the present, include:

(1) Records of the Executive Branch, consisting of the papers of most state agencies, including the minutes, reports, and correspondence of the governor; correspondence and other papers of the Military Department, which contain information on the Indian Wars, the Civil War, and later military action. Also included are the papers of the Colonial government of Georgia, 1733-1777. Holdings for the period after 1945 include extensive information on the state's programs in the field of human and natural resources. The gubernatorial papers of President Carter are complete.

(2) Records of the Legislative Branch include bills and resolutions, whether or not enacted into law.

(3) Records of the Judicial Branch, consisting largely of case files of the Supreme Court from 1847 and the Court of Appeals from 1907.

441 Official Records of Georgia Counties, 1777 to the present, includes deeds, tax records, marriage, probate, and other records.

442   Individual and Family Papers, 1780 to the present, include letters, diaries, plantation and business records, and other records of Georgia citizens and families, both famous and unknown.

443   Church Records, ca. 1800 to the present, of ca. 750 churches, including minutes, membership lists, birth and death records of both white and black Georgia churches of various denominations.

444   Organizational Records, 1860's to the present, include various social, political, educational, fraternal, cultural, and other Georgia organizations.

445   Georgia Genealogical Records, ca. 450 linear feet, include published and unpublished family histories, family Bible pages, cemetery lists, and other compilations.

446   Georgia Prints and Photographs, ca. 1850 to the present, ca. 3,100 items, including daguerreotypes, ambrotypes, tintypes, and photographs of Georgia scenes and citizens.

Price Gilbert Library
Georgia Institute of Technology   30303

447   Patents

One of the most complete of its kind in the Southeast, this collection consists of 1,627,000 patents.

448   Technical Reports

Currently comprised of 905,837 items, this collection includes the technical reports of the Energy Research and Development Administration, National Aeronautics and Space Administration, and the National Technical Information Service.

Georgia Mental Health Institute
1256 Briarcliff Road   30306

449   Addison M. Duvall Library

ca. 15,500 volumes and 330 journal subscriptions relating to psychology, psychiatry, and allied health subjects, including human genetics and biological psychiatry.

W. R. Pullen Library
Georgia State University   30303

450 **Southern Labor Archives**

A collection of documents relating to organized labor, particularly to those of the trade union movement in the South. These documents, which occupy ca. 425 linear feet, were received from local, national, and international unions, and they include papers of both labor leaders and union members.

Goethe Institute
400 Colony Square   30361

451 **Library**

ca. 6,000 volumes relating primarily to German geography and culture. Consisting mainly of works in German, the collection's particular strength is in German literature since 1945.

Home Mission Board
Southern Baptist Convention
1350 Spring Street   30309

452 **Resource Library**

ca. 4,500 volumes, including (1) the Home Mission Graded Series of books published each year since 1942 for each group in the church educational program; (2) collection of books, dating from 1912, on home missions or some area of the work of the Board; and (3) books on the development of Baptist work in individual states.

The Martin Luther King, Jr. Center
671 Beckwith Street   30314

Archives

Among the major holdings of the Civil Rights Archives are:

453   Coordinating Council of Community Organizations, Papers, 1965-1968, Office files of the Chicago Movement

454   Congress of Racial Equality, Papers, 1961-1968, Office files

455   King, Coretta Scott, Papers, 1968 to date, consisting of correspondence, photographs, clippings, and office files.

456   King, Martin Luther, Jr., Papers, 1950-1968, including correspondence, manuscripts, personal records, printed and materials, and office files.

457   Southern Christian Leadership Conference, Papers, 1957-1972, National office files

458   Student Nonviolent Coordinating Committee, Papers, 1960-1968, comprised of files from the Washington, D.C., New York, and Alabama offices

Oglethorpe University Library
4484 Peachtree Road   30319

459   **Georgia Collection**

More than 300 volumes relating to the state of Georgia, including a signed copy of DeBrahm's **History of the Province of Georgia** (1849), first editions of other early histories of Georgia, and the manuscript of Corra Harris' **In Search of a Husband.**

460   **Japanese Collection**

Over 500 volumes along with pamphlets, prints, lithographs, and pictures relating primarily to Japanese history and culture, in the English language.

461   **Lanier, Sidney**

75 volumes, including first editions of the works of this famed Georgia poet and Oglethorpe alumnus as well as books and materials about him.

462   **Oglethorpe, General Edward**

A collection of 70 volumes along with oil paintings, etchings, articles, and clippings dealing exclusively or principally with the founder of the colony of Georgia.

463   **Whitman, Walt**

In this collection of 291 volumes are first editions of Whitman's works and biographical and critical materials pertaining to him. Of the original ten editions of **Leaves of Grass,** the collection contains the 3rd (1860), 5th (1872), 6th (1876), 7th (1881-1882), 8th (188-1889), and 10th (1897).

U.S. Department of Housing and Urban Development
1371-1375 Peachtree Street   30309

464   Region IV Library

A branch of the HUD Library System throughout the United States, this library is composed of 11,000 volumes on housing and urban development, community planning, economics, poverty, statistics, and urban law.

U.S. Environmental Protection Agency
1421 Peachtree Street   30309

465   Region IV Library

A collection of ca. 1,000 volumes, 140 journal subscriptions, 4,000 technical reports, and 80,000 microform items relating to water, air, and noise pollution, radiation, pesticides, and solid waste.

AUGUSTA

Reese Library
Augusta College   30904

466   Genealogy and Local History

ca. 1,000 volumes, including the papers of the local chapter, Daughters of the American Revolution; an index to wills and burial records of Augusta and Richmond County; and significant source materials on the history of both the city and county, including Berry Fleming's **Autobiography of a Colony; the First Half-Century of Augusta, Georgia,** and **Guide to the Study of Augusta and Richmond County** by A. Ray Rowland.

Augusta Regional Library
902 Greene Street   30902

467   Local History and Genealogy

Along with the correspondence, papers, and photographs of the Augusta Arsenal, 1918-1945, are 34 oral history tapes relating to Augusta and ca. 100 genealogical works and Georgia census records, 1820-1880, on microfilm.

Warren A. Candler Library
Paine College   30901

468   King, Martin Luther, Jr., Collection

>A collection of 125 volumes, including books and reprints on Blacks in American culture.

469   Yerby, Frank

>ca. 30 items, comprised of correspondence, manuscripts, and poems donated by the author.

BAINBRIDGE

Southwest Georgia Regional Library
Shotwell and Monroe Streets   31717

470   Genealogy and Local History

>A general genealogical collection along with specific local history items relating to Decatur, Miller, and Seminole Counties. In addition to ca. 500 volumes, the collection includes material collected by Frank Jones for his **History of Decatur County.**

BRUNSWICK

Gould Memorial Library
Brunswick Junior College   31520

471   Coastal Georgia History

>ca. 300 volumes relating to the history of Brunswick, Glynn County, and the Golden Isles, especially Fort Frederica. Emphasizing the Colonial, Revolution, and Post-Revolutionary War periods, the collection includes **Early Days of Coastal Georgia** by Orrin Sage Wightman and Frances Anne Kemble's **Journal of a Residence on a Georgia Plantation in 1838-1839.**

CAIRO

Roddenbery Memorial Library
North Broad Street   31728

472   Cairo-Grady County

>A collection of documents, journals, photographs, clippings, and loose-leaf materials relating to all aspects of Grady County, including such unique

annual events as Rattlesnake Roundup in Whigham and Mule Day in Calvary. Along with tapes and cassettes pertaining to the history of Cairo, founded in 1870, is documentation on the organization of Grady County in 1906. The genealogical collection is comprised of a number of family histories in printed and manuscript form.

473   **Gardening**

Enhancing an extensive collection of materials on gardening, including books, brochures, journals, and slides of local gardens, is an impressive herbarium of the wild flowers of Grady County, collected by Dr. Wayne R. Faircloth of Valdosta State College.

CANTON

Sequoyah Regional Library
400 East Main Street   30114

474   **Genealogy**

A collection of manuscript and printed materials relating to a number of families in Canton, Cherokee County and North Georgia.

CARROLLTON

Library
West Georgia College   30117

475   **A & M School Collection**

ca. 200 items, including bulletins, diplomas, and photographs of the Fourth District Agricultural and Mechanical School, founded in 1907 and made a junior college in 1933.

476   **Local History**

ca. 600 pieces, relating to the West Georgia Region, including county histories, local and church histories, club minutes, and city and county plat maps.

477   **Sacred Harp**

A collection of 125 pieces, including annual minutes of Sacred Harp conventions, hymnals, and two recordings from the songbook most often found in the homes of rural Southerners after 1844.

CLEVELAND

Cofer Library
Truett McConnell College   30528

478   **Truett, George W., Collection**

354 volumes from the personal library of Dr. George W. Truett.

COCHRAN

Roberts Memorial Library
Middle Georgia College   31014

479   **County Histories**

Capitalizing on its location in the center of the largest Southern state, the library supplemented its holdings of the published histories of Georgia counties with scrapbooks students prepare on the history of their home counties. The project has resulted in a varied and valuable historical collection.

COLUMBUS

Chattahoochee Valley Regional Library
1200 Bradley Drive   31906

480   **Georgia**

Showboats to Soft Shoes; a Century of Musical Development in Columbus, Georgia, 1828-1928, by Katherine Hines Mahan, and Etta Worsley's **Columbus on the Chattahoochee** are among the titles of local interest in this collection of 1,900 volumes covering all aspects of Georgia history.

481   **Genealogy**

Many forms of material, including tax digests, military records, and abstracts of wills, combine to make this collection of more than 2,000 genealogical works outstanding, and one which will eventually cover all 50 states.

482   **Books for the Blind**

The majority of the 5,000 recorded books and magazines was supplied by the Library of Congress, but some books of local interest, including Augusta Evans Wilson's **St. Elmo,** were recorded by Columbus volunteers and are unique to this collection.

Simon Schwob Memorial Library
Columbus College   31907

483   The Chattahoochee Valley Local and Oral History Archives serves as the repository for a number of collections of historical importance in the area. Notable among these are:

484   **Chappell, Absalom Harris**

Papers and Library, ca. 700 items, including letters and speeches of this Georgia legislator and U.S. Congressman; and his personal library of 600 volumes, all of which were collected prior to 1860.

485   **Dubose, Louise Gunby Jones**

82 items, relating to this teacher, journalist, and author, whose pseudonym was Nancy Telfair.

486   **Jones-Benning**

675 items, including letters, financial records, and legal papers of Seaborn Jones, lawyer, businessman, and one of the founders of Columbus, and papers relating to the law practice and military career of his son-in-law, Henry L. Benning, jurist, statesman, and Confederate Major-General, for whom Fort Benning was named.

487   **Mahan, Joseph B., Jr.**

6 storage boxes, comprising the research collection of this historian, who served as director of the Westville Village Project, the re-creation of a Georgia town of the 1850's in Lumpkin, Georgia, including extracted notes from Colonial and early Federal primary sources relating to the history of Indian tribes of Eastern North America and early 19th century archaeology; and materials relating to American pre-history, particularly discoveries of inscriptions, coins, and metal artifacts indicating pre-Colombian trans-Atlantic culture contacts.

488   **Columbus Collections**

Other collections include 8 letter boxes of letters, diaries, and other materials relating to the history of the city; the Transaction Book, 1858-1863, of Allan C. McGehee, a Columbus slave dealer; and 35 transcribed oral history interviews pertaining to the history of Columbus, Phenix City and its reformation in the 1950's, and Fort Benning.

Columbus Museum of Arts and Crafts
1251 Wynnton Road   31906

489   **Research Library**

> 1,330 volumes, largely reference works in the arts, graphic arts, and crafts. Also included are archaeological studies and artifacts of the Yuchi Indians, which had once settled along the Chattahoochee River.

DALTON

Dalton Regional Library
101 South Selvidge Street   30720

490   **Georgia**

> A collection of ca. 400 volumes, comprised of books and other materials written by and about Georgians and Georgia, including the histories of two adjoining North Georgia counties — the **Official History of Whitfield County, Georgia,** compiled by the County History Commission in 1936, and Susie Blalock McDaniel's **Official History of Catoosa County, Georgia, 1853-1953.**

Whitfield-Murray Historical Society and Archives
Dalton   30720

491   **Loveman, Robert**

> A collection of books, manuscripts, and papers relating to this Georgia poet, who is best known for his delicate and rhythmic "Rain Song."

DAWSON

Kinchafoonee Regional Library
Main Street   31742

492   **Mims, Floyd C.**

> Papers of Lieutenant Colonel Floyd C. Mims, including photographs and correspondence from General Pershing and other notables of World War I, citations, news clippings, and material on prisoners of war.

DECATUR

Maud Burrus Library
215 Sycamore Street   30030

493   **Historical Collection**

 Miscellaneous collection, including microfilm files of South Carolina newspapers, 1732-1873; Georgia county histories and the Macon **Telegraph,** 1860-1866, on microfilm; and Willard Neal's **Story of Stone Mountain: Geology, History, Memorial** and other materials on nearby Stone Mountain.

McCain Library
Agnes Scott College   30030

494   **Frost, Robert**

 A collection of 737 items relating to Frost, who for years was a regular visitor on the Agnes Scott campus. Included are letters, manuscripts, poems, prose works, etchings, poems set to music, recordings, tapes, and transcriptions of his talks.

495   **Arp, Bill**

 29 letters along with a number of issues of **Home and Farm** with columns by this noted American humorist (1826-1903) and native Georgian, whose real name was Charles Henry Smith.

496   **Posey, Walter, Brownlow, Collection**

 ca. 900 volumes along with 100 magazine articles relating to religion on the American frontier, including Dr. Posey's own regional histories of religion.

497   **"Gone With the Wind"**

 99 volumes, consisting of 50 editions of this famous novel as translated into different languages, including that of Iran and Vietnam, along with three foreign biographies of Margaret Mitchell.

DOUGLAS

Satilla Regional Library
617 East Ward Street   31533

A collection of Colonial records, Revolutionary War records, and other general genealogical materials as well as histories of 40 Georgia counties, including **Ward's History of Coffee County,** compiled by Warren Preston Ward in 1930.

EAST POINT

James A Burns Memorial Library
Atlanta Christian College   30344

499   Church History

Historical materials, occupying ca. 1,200 linear feet, relating to the history of the Christian Church (Disciples of Christ) and to the Restoration Movement in the United States.

FORT VALLEY

H. A. Hunt Memorial Library
Fort Valley State College   31030

500   Dobson, Jessie Emma Jefferson, Collection

Papers, 1928-1975, 21 items of materials concerning Fort Valley Normal and Industrial School, which was chartered in 1896 and known as Light of the Valley, and the Ushers Temple C.M.E. Church.

501   Miller, Mary E., Collection

Papers, 1900-1969, comprised of 485 items, including correspondence, reports, speeches, and memorabilia relating to G. B. Miller, long-time principal of Voorhees Industrial School.

502   O'Neal, Otis Samuel, Collection

Papers, 1916-1949, 30 items of photographs, papers, and memorabilia depicting the highlights of the annual Fort Valley Ham and Egg Show, including autographed pictures of Booker T. Washington and other dignitaries in attendance.

FRANKLIN SPRINGS

Library
Emmanuel College   30639

503   **Pentecostal Holiness Church**

ca. 500 items relating to the history of the Pentecostal Holiness Church, including books, pamphlets, minutes of church conferences, and a complete file of the **Pentecostal Holiness Advocate,** from its beginning in 1917 to date.

GAINESVILLE

Lessie Southgate Simmons Memorial Library
Brenau College   30501

504   **Watson, Thomas, Collection**

The private library of this Populist statesman from Georgia (1856-1922), consisting of ca. 700 volumes, several of which were written by Watson.

GRACEWOOD

Hospital Library
Gracewood State School and Hospital   30812

505   **Mental Retardation**

ca. 500 items, including books, journal files, and audio-visual materials relating to the mentally handicapped. Included are two classics in the field — **The Jukes** by Robert L. Dugdale (1877) and Henry Herbert Goddard's **The Kallikak Family** (1914), early studies of the relationships of heredity and mental retardation and mental disease and crime.

GRIFFIN

Flint River Regional Library
800 Memorial Drive   30223

506   **Georgia Room**

The works of the noted juvenile writer, Robert Burch from neighboring Fayetteville, are featured in this collection of 1,500 books relating to the history and literature of Georgia.

LAFAYETTE

Cherokee Regional Library
305 South Duke Street   30728

507   **Local History**

This collection is comprised of local history materials for Chattooga, Dade, and Walker Counties, and it includes histories of Walker County and the towns of Holland, New England, and Chickamauga; Cherokee claims, 1836-1838; census records of the 3 counties, 1840-1880; the Walker County **Messenger,** 1883 to date; and miscellaneous county and other records from the mid-1800's.

LAGRANGE

Coleman Library
Lincoln Street   30240

508   **Local Newspapers**

A file of local newspapers, including the LaGrange **Daily News,** is complete from 1868 to date, providing primary source material for more than a century in the history of LaGrange and Troup County.

William and Evelyn Banks Library
LaGrange College   20340

509   **Grogan, Florence, Collection**

Papers, including original manuscripts of short stories, poems, and miscellaneous writings of Elmira Farnham Grogan.

510   **LaGrange College Collection**

Along with first editions of works by LaGrange College authors are personal papers and a number of paintings by Lamar Dodd, noted Georgia artist. It is appropriate that this collection also contains an original manuscript relating to the Marquis de Lafayette as the city was named for Lafayette's estate, La Grange, in France.

Troup Harris Coweta Regional Library
500 Broome Street   30240

Along with Louise G. Barfield's **History of Harris County, Georgia** (1961), Mary G. Jones' **Coweta County Chronicle** (1928) the **History of Troup County** (1935) by Clifford Lewis Smith, and other county histories, the collection is comprised of a number of histories of local families, and census records for Troup, Harris, and Coweta Counties, 1830-1880.

LOUISVILLE

Jefferson County Library
East Broad Street   30434

512   Southern Literature

Along with 150 works by Georgia and other Southern authors are those of two local writers, poet Louise McMillan and Louise Abbott, short fiction writer.

513   Little, A. P.

A collection of ca. 150 historical works relating to Georgia and the South.

LUMPKIN

Westville Historic Handicrafts, Inc.
Trotman Road   31815

514   Library

The history of Southwest Georgia prior to 1850 is the subject of this collection of ca. 1,000 books, periodicals, maps, and original art. Westville is a re-created Georgia town of the 1850's.

MACON

Stetson Memorial Library
Mercer University   31207

515   Georgia Baptist History

As the archives of the Georgia Baptist Historical Society, this collection consists of ca. 11,000 sets of minutes of Georgia Baptist associations and churches; Georgia Baptist Convention Annuals; a complete file of **The Christian Index,** Georgia Baptist newspaper, 1840 to date; and photographs and miscellaneous books and pamphlets relating to Baptist history.

516   **Kilpatrick, William Heard**

54 boxes of correspondence, 1937-1958, and the transcript of tape recordings made for the biographer of this noted American educator.

Willet Memorial Library
Wesleyan College   31201

517   **Caudill, Rebecca**

The manuscripts of **Time for Lisa** and **Up and Down the River** are included in the collection of juvenile books by this Wesleyan graduate.

518   **Lanier, Sidney**

Along with ca. 600 items, which Eugenia Dorothy Blount Lamar used in securing a place for this Georgia poet in the Hall of Fame, are two flutes and several music scores which belonged to Sidney Lanier.

519   **Soong Sisters**

150 items, including original photographs of these famous sisters, Madame H. H. Kung, Madame Sun Yat-sen, and Madame Chiang Kai-shek, and their families; a manuscript by Madame Sun Yat-sen; and clippings and other materials relating to these Wesleyan alumnae.

520   **Park, Orville, Collection**

ca. 3,500 significant items of Georgiana, including the early and rare histories of the state.

MARIETTA

Cobb County Public Library System
30 Atlanta Street   30060

521   **Georgia Room**

A collection of ca. 1,800 books about Cobb County and Georgia, and/or by Cobb County and Georgia authors. Also included are extensive vertical files of information relating to the county and to the state, and the histories of 25 local families.

Lockheed-Aircraft Corporation
86 South Cobb Drive   30063

522   Library

ca. 45,000 volumes, 800 journal subscriptions, 200,000 technical reports, and large holdings in microforms and other materials relating to aeronautics, aerospace, electronics, meteorology, and related fields, including the Government-Industry Data Exchange Program reports.

MILLEDGEVILLE

Ina Dillard Russell Library
Georgia College   31061

523   O'Connor, Flannery

A collection of 267 folders of manuscripts, letters, various editions and translations of her works, photographs, recordings and other materials relating to this noted local author, along with 594 volumes from Miss O'Connor's personal library.

524   Thompson, William Tappan

20 items, including 3 manuscripts, photographs, and published works of this 19th century master of Georgia rustic dialect.

525   Bonner, James C., Collection

Consisting of 18th and 19th century Federal and state documents, books and periodicals of the 19th century, and 446 pages of letters written between 1840 and 1880, this collection contains the research material used by Dr. Bonner for his publications on the history of Southern agriculture, early Georgia history, and the Civil War.

526   Branham Cookbook Collection

More than 600 cookbooks, including both foreign and domestic cuisine but particularly strong in regional cookery.

MOULTRIE

Colquitt-Thomas Regional Library
204 Fifth Street   31768

527   Local History and Genealogy

ca. 1,500 items along with periodical files on Georgia history with
concentration on area genealogy and local history, including William Alonzo
Covington's **History of Colquitt County** (1937), and William Warren Rogers'
three volumes covering the history of Thomas County from 1825 to 1900.

MOUNT BERRY

Memorial Library
Berry College   30149

528   Berry, Martha

This collection is comprised of multiple copies of 25 titles relating to the
history of the Berry Schools, including both Berry Academy and Berry
College, and to the life of Martha Berry, who developed these institutions
from a boarding school she opened for 5 boys in 1902.

NORCROSS

Bell Laboratories
2000 Northeast Expressway   30071

529   Library

An industrial collection, consisting of ca. 6,000 volumes, 275 periodical
subscriptions, 2,400 technical reports, and 4,500 microforms relating to
materials science, polymer chemistry, metallurgy, management, and
telecommunications.   **R**

OXFORD

Library
Oxford College of Emory University   30267

530   Special Collections

Correspondence, largely 19th century, and newspaper clippings concerning Robert Emmett Dixon; ca. 20 printed family histories; and 45 oral history tapes relating to the history of Emory College, now Oxford College of Emory University.

ROME

Carnegie Library
607 Broad Street   30161

531   **Brooks, J. F., Collection**

511 items relating to the Cherokee Indians, including books, Congressional documents, maps, and a complete file of the **Cherokee Phoenix.**

532   **Genealogy and Local History**

Along with 755 volumes relating to genealogy of the Southern states are cemetery lists, early maps of Rome, and the papers of George M. Battey and Dr. Robert Battey, who performed the first oophorectomy in Rome in 1872.

Tri-County Regional Library
606 West First Street   30161

533   **Business**

ca. 3,000 volumes and 140 periodical subscriptions pertaining to business, economics, investments, estate planning, and consumer information.

SAVANNAH

Georgia Historical Society
501 Whitaker Street   31401

534   **Berrien, John Macpherson**

Papers, 1779-1942, 1,392 items, including personal, political, and legal papers of this Georgian who was elected as U. S. Senator in 1825, along with records of members of his family.

535   **Bevan, Joseph Vallence**

Papers, 1733-1826, 134 items, including several official papers of the

Colony and State of Georgia and letters and depositions of famous men of the time.

536 Bragg, Lillian Chaplin

Papers, 1858-1967, 911 items, relating chiefly to the Bethesda Orphanage in Savannah.

537 Chatham Artillery

Papers, 1786 to date, 21 linear feet, consisting of accounts, minutes, rosters, correspondence, and other materials, including information on participation in the War of 1812.

538 Confederate States of America

Papers, 1861-1865, 3,301 items, consisting primarily of financial records signed by the Assistant Quartermaster of the Army, and 632 items of financial records of the Wilmington, North Carolina, Naval station.

539 Dugas Collection

Papers, 1787-1846, 153 items, consisting of personal and financial papers of the Dugas Family, including information on the Dahlonega mint.

540 Gordon Family

Papers, 1802-ca. 1936, ca. 10,000 items, consisting of the personal and financial papers of William Washington Gordon, first president of the Central Railroad and Banking Company, and members of his family. Included are the papers of his granddaughter, Juliette Gordon Low, who founded the Girl Scouts of America in 1912.

541 Granger, Mary Lois

Papers, 1918-1935, 290 items, including first scripts of her historical-religious novels, **Wife to Pilate** and others.

Management Services Bureau
City of Savannah 31402

542 Research Library

ca. 600 volumes, 63 journal subscriptions, and 400 technical reports relating to urban management, land use and development, and public works.

Savannah Public Library
2002 Bull Street 31401

543 Gamble, Thomas

More than 200 items, including books, pictures, maps, and original observations relating to Savannah and early Georgia history, collected by a former mayor and noted local historian. Included is information concerning the naval stores industry in Georgia.

544 Georgia Collection

Over 1,000 books and pamphlets relating to the history of Savannah, birthplace of the Georgia colony, and the state which rapidly grew from this original settlement. Among numerous histories of Savannah and Chatham County are William Harden's **History of Savannah and South Georgia** (1913) and **Historic Savannah,** published by the Georgia Historical Society in 1968. A name and subject index has been compiled for Savannah newspapers, 1763-1888, 1891, and 1929-1976.

Asa H. Gordon Library
Savannah State College 31406

545 Negro History

A collection of 5,400 volumes and other materials by and about the Negro, along with 12 subscriptions to Black newspapers.

Ships of the Sea Museum
503 East River Street 31401

546 Library

Historical and modern nautical works, occupying ca. 75 linear feet, devoted to ships, ship art, sea captains, and pirates. Featured is a first edition of Captain James Cook's account of his voyage to the Pacific Ocean, **Troisieme Voyage de Cook,** published in Paris in 1785.

Skidaway Institute of Oceanography
University of Georgia 31406

547 Library

ca. 10,000 volumes, 350 journal subscriptions, and other materials relating to biological, chemical, geological, and physical marine science.

STATESBORO

Statesboro Regional Library
124 South Main Street   30458

548   Genealogy and Local History

ca. 1,000 volumes, consisting of general genealogical works, a file of local family histories, Leodel Coleman's **Statesboro: 1866-1966,** and the works of Denark Dekle, local author.

TIFTON

Coastal Plain Regional Library
Tifton   31794

549   Genealogy and Local History

ca. 200 volumes, comprised of general genealogical works, several histories of area families, and local history items, including Ida Belle Williams' **History of Tift County** (1948).

550   Black Studies

This Black Heritage Collection is comprised of ca. 500 volumes relating to the history and culture of the Negro in America.

Coastal Plain Experiment Station
University of Georgia   31794

551   Library

ca. 14,000 volumes, 280 journal subcriptions, and extensive vertical file holdings relating to agriculture, entomology, and plants, especially peanuts and tobacco. Included is a collection of theses on the peanut.

VALDOSTA

Valdosta State College Library
1500 North Patterson Street   31601

552   Bass, Emory Pate

Papers, 1940-1966, 2,100 items, including correspondence relating to

Bass' efforts in establishing and reactivating Moody Air Force Base along with maps, photographs, and clippings concerning the Base.

553   **Georgia**

A collection of ca. 300 volumes relating to state, county, and local history, including the **History of Lowndes County, Georgia, 1825-1941,** published by the local chapter of the Daughters of the American Revolution in 1942.

WASHINGTON

Mary Willis Library
Liberty and Jefferson Streets   30673

554   **Wilkes County**

A collection of 34 volumes and files of local newspapers dating from 1816, relating to the history of Washington and of Wilkes County, including **Early Records of Georgia: Wilkes County** by Grace Gilliam Davidson (1932) and the manuscript of Willis C. Lindsey's **History of Washington-Wilkes County,** Georgia (1955); 53 genealogical items relating to Wilkes County families; and 80 works, representing 31 authors, who were born or who have spent a significant part of their lives in Wilkes County.

WATKINSVILLE

Oconee County Branch
Athens Regional Library

555   **Ivy Genealogical Collection**

ca. 2,000 items, collected by Mrs. J. Swanton Ivy, Sr., and consisting of published genealogies, census reports for 30 states, state and county histories, and reprints of research works which trace migration into Georgia and the other Southeastern states.

WAYCROSS

Okefenokee Regional Library
401 Lee Avenue   31501

Alexander Stephens McQueen's **History of the Okefenokee Swamp** and other materials relating to this vast wilderness area, and Laura S. Walker's **History of Ware County, Georgia** (1934) are among the 300 volumes in this collection, which includes 20 family histories and 7 volumes of **Pioneers of Wiregrass Georgia.**

YOUNG HARRIS

The Duckworth Libraries
Young Harris College   30582

557   **Reece, Byron Herbert**

A representative collection of novels, collected poetry, clippings, and memorabilia of this native of nearby Blairsville.

IV

SPECIAL COLLECTIONS
IN
LIBRARIES OF KENTUCKY

Compiled
By
Michael H. Harris

ASHLAND

Ashland Public Library
1740 Central Avenue   41101

558   Boyd County

Historical materials relating to Ashland, the industrial center of Eastern Kentucky, and Boyd County include early newspapers, photographs, voter lists, pictorial and biographical county histories of the area, and a collection of reminiscences of local people.

559   Winder, Minnie C., Collection

2,257 items of genealogical interest, including published sources of births, deaths, and marriages; cemetery, land, and court records, individual family histories; Mormon genealogical records on microfilm for five counties in this area; and census records, 1790-1880, for Kentucky and surrounding states.

AUGUSTA

Knoedler Memorial Library
315 Main Street   41002

560   Local History

Highlights of the long history of Augusta, first settled in 1792; are recorded in small but significant collection, which includes manuscript materials dating back to 1797; history of Augusta College, 1822-1849; a published account of an important Civil War battle, **Morgan's Cavalry and the Home Guard at Augusta, Kentucky** (1862); the history of Bracken County towns and the burley tobacco area of Kentucky, 1839-1939; and an oral history collection prepared for the National Register of Historic Places.

BARDSTOWN

Nelson County Public Library
90 Court Square   40004

561   Fitch, John

A compilation of 150 pages, including letters, pictures, and letters concerning the man now acknowledged as the inventor of the steamboat. Records indicate that Fitch's first successful experiment with a boat propelled by steam was made on the Delaware River in 1787, predating Fulton's **Clermont** by 20 years.

562   Foster, Stephen

A small collection relating to Foster, who supposedly wrote "My Old Kentucky Home" while visiting a cousin at Federal Hill here in 1852, includes one of the few existing copies of the **Biography, Songs & Musical Compositions of Stephen C. Foster,** written by his brother, Morrison Foster.

BENTON

Marshall County Public Library
1003 Poplar Street   42025

563   Coins History

Supporting a small collection of books on numismatics is an extensive display of coins from around the world.

564   Oral History

Along with census records for Marshall and surrounding counties and local genealogical source materials, there are 35 tapes relating to Benton and Marshall County.

BEREA

Hutchins Library
Berea College   40403

565   Southern Appalachian Region

Housed in the library of the oldest and largest of the mountain schools in Kentucky are 8,000 volumes and 250 linear feet of archival and manuscript materials relating to the history and culture of the Southern highlands. Assembled over a period of 50 years, this collection is comprised of books, pamphlets, manuscripts, photographs, tapes, and films.

566   Lincoln Collection

ca. 1,500 volumes, including books and pamphlets on the life and career of Abraham Lincoln, who was president of the United States during the early years of Berea College.

567   Rare Books

A collection of ca. 8,000 volumes, including centuries-old rare Bibles, English literature and ballads of the 18th century, and first editions of American literary works.

BOWLING GREEN

Helm-Cravens Library
Western Kentucky University   42101

568   Folklore

Comprising the Folk-lore, Folk-life, and Oral History Archives are the materials collected in the field by faculty and students of the Department of Intercultural and Folk Studies: (1) Information on the life styles, beliefs, customs and material culture of South Central Kentucky; (2) ca. 900 tapes of oral history, primarily consisting of songs and music of the region, including an extensive collection of fiddle tunes from Kentucky; (3) Transcribed versions of songs and ballads collected in Kentucky; and (4) the Gordon Wilson Collection of beliefs and folk speech from the Mammoth Cave area.

Kentucky Library and Museum
Western Kentucky University   42101

569   Clusky, Michael W.

Correspondence, 1854-1871, 1 box, 10 folders, relating to Clusky's position as Postmaster of the U.S. House of Representatives, 1851-1859, his service in the Confederate Army, and his editorship of the Louisville **Daily Ledger.**

570   **Cobb, Irvin Shrewsbury**

    5 folders, containing the manuscripts of 5 short stories written prior to 1940.

571   **Ellis, Courtney M., Collection**

    454 items of photographs and informational material relating to steamboats which operated in the Ohio and Mississippi River Valleys, including correspondence with steamboatmen and with other collectors.

572   **Giles, Janice Holt**

    174 items, 1948-1969, including manuscripts and galley proofs of her literary works, background research material and notes.

573   **Knott Collection**

    Papers, 1776-1953, 745 items, including correspondence, business papers, speeches, and drawings of J. Proctor Knott, lawyer, Congressman, and Governor of Kentucky; the Civil War diaries of Knott's mother; and letters, clippings, and photographs relating to other members of the family.

574   **Underwood, Joseph Rogers**

    Papers, 1791-1912, 869 items, including correspondence, legislative papers, and genealogical material relating to this U.S. Senator and to members of his family.

Other Collections

    Notable among other collections in the extensive manuscript holdings:

575   Bardstown and Nelson County Papers, 1819-1885, 14 folders, comprised of deeds, licenses, and business papers; slavery items, Bardstown-Louisville turnpike papers; and horse pedigree items.

576   Brashear, William Helm, Papers, 1880-1940, 12 folders and 35 notebooks, including manuscripts of the poems, essays, and plays of this poet and writer from Bowling Green.

577   Clagett, John Henry, 2 folders containing the typed manuscript of his novel, **Cradle of the Sun,** published in 1952.

578   Hays, William Shakespeare, Papers, ca. 1856-1907, comprised of 29 folders of correspondence, poems, lyrics for songs and other materials relating to this poet, composer, and newspaper columnist of Louisville.

579   McHenry Coal Company Collection, 1886-1905, 6 volumes of production ledgers of the mines and business records of the company stores in Ohio County, Kentucky.

580   Rice Collection, 1898-1965, ca. 1,765 items, including manuscripts of poems, short stories, and books along with letters, photographs and business papers of Cale Young Rice, poet and author, 1872-1943, and of Alice Hegan Rice, author, 1870-1942.

581   Rowan Family Papers, 1784-1923, 113 items, including correspondence, business papers, and other materials relating to John Rowan, Sr., 1773-1843, lawyer, judge, U.S. Representative and Senator, and owner of "Federal Hill" in Bardstown; and of John Rowan, Jr., 1807-1855, master of "Federal Hill" and charge d' affaires to the Kingdom of the Two Sicilies, 1848-1850.

582   Shakers, South Union, Kentucky, 4 collections, 1800-1916, including account books, other business records, journals, and the dairy of Shaker eldress Nancy Moore, covering the Civil War years in South Union.

CAMPBELLSVILLE

Library
Campbellsville College   42718

583   **Kentuckiana**

ca. 1,000 volumes, consisting of books by Kentucky writers and about the state, and 10 tapes which orally recall the early days at Campbellsville College, which was founded in 1907.

COLUMBIA

Katie Murrell Library
Lindsey Wilson College   42728

584   **Methodist Collection**

An extensive collection of materials on the history of Methodism in Kentucky, including Conference Records from 1773 to date.

COVINGTON

Kenton County Public Library
Fifth and Scott Streets   41011

585   **Duveneck Collection**

12 oil paintings by Frank Duveneck, 1848-1919, as well as a large collection of newspaper clippings, photographs, and other materials relating to this Covington native.

586   **State and local History**

ca. 1,000 volumes, including history, biography, and fiction; city directories for Covington and Newport, 1834 to date; 2,000 reels of Covington-based newspapers, 1835 to date; and Kentucky census records, 1810-1890.

CYNTHIANA

Cynthiana Public Library
103 South Church Street   41031

587   **Gregg Cook Book Collection**

700 volumes of recipes and compilations concerning cuisine from around the world, collected by Cissy Gregg, Home Consultant for the Louisville **Courier-Journal,** 1942-1962.

588   **Historical Collections**

In addition to a collection of more than 100 volumes of Civil War history and photography, including some very rare works, are ca. 75 volumes relating to the history of Harrison County and Cynthiana, the scene of one of the bloodiest battles of the Civil War.

DANVILLE

Grace Doherty Library
Centre College of Kentucky   40422

589   **Rare Books Collection**

ca. 1,000 volumes, including 40 Paris imprints of the 16th century and an extensive collection of Presbyterian literature of the 19th century.

EDDYVILLE

Lyon County Public Library
East Main Street   42038

590   **Hodge, Shelby, Collection**

Adding special interest to the materials on the history of Lyon County is this outstanding collection of artifacts from Western Kentucky. Included are thousands of arrowheads and other Indian items, including weapons, utensils, and pottery.

EDMONTON

Metcalfe County Public Library
Main Street   42129

591   **Kentuckiana**

ca. 500 books relating to Kentucky, including a microfilm file of local newspapers, census records, 1860-1880, and other materials on the history of Edmonton and Metcalfe County.

FORT CAMPBELL

R. F. Sink Memorial Library
Building 38   42223

592   **Military**

A comprehensive collection of ca. 6,000 volumes of military history, including histories of units. Particularly strong in its coverage of World War II, it includes the official records of the Civil War, World War I, and the Korean War.

FORT KNOX

Library System
U.S. Army Armor Center   40121

593   Defense

ca. 115,000 volumes, the composite holdings of three libraries at the Fort, which emphasize military history, armor equipment and weapons, and armed warfare.

FORT MITCHELL

Library
Thomas More College   41017

594   More, Thomas

A collection, occupying 2 linear feet, relating to this revered Tudor statesman and author, including his own writings.

595   Kentuckiana

ca. 36 linear feet of materials relating to various aspects of Kentucky, including the works of Kentucky authors, early histories of the state, church history, and local history.

FRANKFORT

Division of Public Services
Kentucky Department of Library and Archives

596   The Kentucky Thousand

ca. 1,000 items of the Lost Cause Press microfiche collection of a basic library of out-of-print, scarce, and rare Kentuckiana, compiled for the Bicentennial. An accompanying booklet lists items in this collection in alphabetical order by author.

597   Geology and Anthropology

ca. 350 items of the Kentucky Geological Survey and other studies, many by Willard Rouse Jillson, dating from the 1920's; and ca. 50 items concerning the anthropology of Kentucky by William S. Webb and William D. Funkhouser.

598 County Histories

A substantial collection of historical materials relating to 93 of Kentucky's 120 counties. A list of these histories was published as **Kentucky History; Secondary Sources for Secondary Schools** in 1973 (now o.p.).

599 Oral History

This continuing collection consists of 225 taped interviews with Kentuckians on subjects of social, cultural, and historical interest. The variety of topics includes the flood of 1937, impact of TVA, christening of the **Belle of Louisville,** and the last hanging in Kentucky.

Kentucky Historical Society
Broadway   40601

600   As an official repository, the Society's files contain the public records of the State of Kentucky, including the Acts of the General Assembly, 1792 to date; Journals of the House of Representatives, 1792 to date; Journals of the State Senate, 1792 to date; Papers of the Governors, 1792-1923; Reports from State agencies, 1834-1958; Maps prepared by the Kentucky Geological Survey; Muster Rolls and Pension Records of the Civil War period; and vital records, 1852-1862, 1874-1878, and irregularly until 1911; and tax lists by counties, 1787-1875 on microfilm.

Notable among many other manuscript holdings are the papers of the following:

601   Allen, James Lane, 1890-1924, 71 items, including letters of this Kentucky novelist and short story writer.

602   Clay, Henry, 1800-1848, 32 items, along with other materials relating to Clay as outstanding member of the U.S. House of Representatives, Senator, and Secretary of State.

603   Harrison, William Henry, 1811-1824, 15 letters along with copies of other letters of this War of 1812 officer and U.S. Senator from Ohio, who would become the 9th President of the U.S.

604   Johnson, George M., 300 items relating to this Confederate Governor of Kentucky.

605   Letcher, Robert P., 1844-1850, 46 items of correspondence of this U.S. Representative and Kentucky Governor.

606   Taylor, Zachary, 1809-1850, 17 items relating to this Kentuckian, who became the 12th president of the United States.

607   Also included are a number of Civil War letters and diaries; Cemetery records of Kentucky soldiers buried in Kentucky from the Revolutionary War through World War I; Kentucky River Lock #10, 75 volumes, including survey of the Lock and other reports, 1905-1946; and a Bible collection of 165 original family Bibles.

Blazer Library
Kentucky State University   40601

608   **Black Studies**

   3,546 books and 155 file folders relating to African and African/American history and culture.

609   **Young, Whitney M., Sr.**

   Papers, artifacts, and other memorabilia of the late Whitney M. Young, Sr., former president of Lincoln Institute.

GEORGETOWN

Cooke Memorial Library
Georgetown University   40324

610   **Thompson, J. W., Collection**

   Assembled in honor of a Bible scholar and teacher, this collection is comprised of ca. 2,000 volumes of Biblical literature, including a number of rare Bibles.

GRAYSON

Lusby Memorial Library
Kentucky Christian College   41143

611   **Restoration Movement**

    ca. 500 volumes relating to the founding and early development of the Christian Church (Disciples of Christ) in America.

GREENUP

Greenup County Public Libraries
203 Harrison Street   41144

612   **Kentuckiana**

    Local history of the area so colorfully pictured in the stories and autobiography of Jesse Stuart add interest to this fine collection of Kentucky materials, consisting of 1,548 volumes, 2,930 vertical file pieces, 21 prints, and 13 recordings.

HARDINSBURG

Breckinridge County Public Library
Main Street   40143

613   **County History**

    ca. 200 items, including books and folders on Breckinridge countians who became famous; 55 books and 19 folders on the cities and towns of the county; 20 books on the early history of the county; the histories of 80 county churches; and local newspapers on microfilm, 1878-1957.

614   **Genealogy**

    Extensive files of genealogical materials, including 80 printed volumes and 187 folders of individual family histories; cemetery records of Breckinridge and surrounding counties; county census records, 1790-1880; deeds, wills, and marriage records, 1852-1915; and 20 volumes of military records.

HARLAN

Harlan County Public Library
Third and Central   40831

615   Caudill, Rebecca

ca. 100 items, including signed editions of all of Miss Caudill's books, including foreign editions, along with personal scrapbooks and memorabilia. This collection is maintained in the Rebecca Caudill Branch Library in Cumberland.

616   Coal Mining

Supporting ca. 90 volumes on the subject is a collection of artifacts depicting the history of coal mining. Included in cases and in a wall display is a 5' x 10' professional model of an underground mine.

Harrodsburg

Harrodsburg Historical Society Library
220 South Chiles Street   40330

617   Shaker Collection

Comprised of 10 handwritten journals covering various periods between 1842 and 1911 with most dating from the mid-1800's, this collection also includes a few miscellaneous business papers of the Society at Pleasant Hill and several printed volumes, a few of which were published locally.

618   Genealogy

Numerous files of primarily local family histories; cemetery, marriage, and census records for Mercer County; original issues of various county newspapers, 1849-1968; and standard volumes of Kentucky genealogical records.

HAWESVILLE

Hancock County Library
Hawesville   42348

619   Oral History

Beginning collection consisting of 10 tapes, recording information on topics of local interest, including history of the Hancock County Court House, the Old Catholic Church, and the Squire Pate House.

HAZARD

Perry County Public Library
Hazard   41701

620   Kentucky Shelf

Ranging from James Lane Allen's **Kentucky Cardinal** to the recent works of Kentucky writers, this collection is comprised of ca. 1,500 volumes by a variety of state authors and others who have written about Kentucky or Kentuckians.

621   Genealogy

A growing collection of materials relating to specific families along with court, marriage, and cemetery records of Perry County and DAR publications, including a list of Kentucky soldiers in the American Revolution.

622   Oral History

In addition to the tapes made from interviews with old-timers, this collection includes a recording of the tales of John Creason Hill. A mountain heritage preservation project is now underway.

HOPKINSVILLE

Hopkinsville-Christian County Public Library
1101 Bethel Street   42240

623   McCarroll Genealogical Collection

Purchased from the proceeds of the McCarroll Trust Fund, this collection, currently consisting of ca. 300 volumes, emphasizes local history and genealogy and, secondarily, regional and state sources of history and genealogy.

LEXINGTON

Council of State Governments
Iron Works Pike   40511

624   Interstate Loan Library

ca. 15,000 items, consisting of 250 current journals, state blue books, almanacs, statistical compendia, state document checklists, state budgets, and the publications of university bureaus of government, interstate organizations, and related federal agencies. Subject areas include state government organization, state legislative procedures, inter-governmental relations, and public administration.

Office Products Division
IBM Corporation   40507

625   Technical Library

Varied collection including 1,250 IBM computer science manuals, describing products, programs, and equipment; 535 OPD product manuals; the OPD archival collection of 900 booklets, brochures, and articles; manufacturer's catalogs on 1,250 reels of microfilm; 125 books, reports, and reprints pertaining to typewriters; and 450 books and tapes for use in personal development.

Keeneland Association
Keeneland Race Course   40501

626   Library

Unique collection of ca. 5,500 volumes relating to the breeding and racing of thoroughbred horses and horse sports. Included is a collection of photograph negatives, covering horse racing in America.

Lexington Public Library
251 West Second Street   40507

627   Battaile, Barton, Collection

ca. 400 8″ x 10″ views of old Lexington, including houses, businesses, and other buildings.

628   Old Library

A collection of ca. 125 works published prior to 1830, including travel books, early almanacs and an 1818 Lexington City Directory; and 350 volumes of newspapers, including the **Kentucky Gazette,** 1787-1910.

629   Genealogy

ca. 900 volumes, consisting of genealogical sources for Kentucky and Virginia with limited materials on North Carolina and Pennsylvania, 1790 census records, and family histories.

Spindletop Research, Inc.
Iron Works Pike   40511

630   Library

A research collection of ca. 3,000 volumes, relating primarily to area and urban development, commerce, communications, environment, natural resources, and transportation.

Frances Carrick Thomas Library
Transylvania University   40508

631   Medical History

A collection of ca. 7,000 volumes relating to the history of medicine, including rare, historical works published during the 16th and 17th centuries but consisting largely of medical books published between 1800 and 1840. The manuscript collection includes a number of Jefferson Davis Family papers and those of Robert Peter, Kentucky chemist.

Margaret I. King Library
University of Kentucky   40506

632   In addition to the Kentuckiana Collection, which occupies ca. 5,000 cubic feet, the Library has extensive special holdings in French and Spanish drama, 1600-1900; the history of books and printing; and western travel.

633   Allen, James Lane

Correspondence, 1888-1899, consisting of 48 letters to John Fox.

634   Barkley, Alben William

Papers, 1900-1956, ca. 65,000 items relating to him as lawyer, judge, and statesman, who served in both Houses of Congress and as Vice President of the United States, 1949-1953.

635 Buckner, Benjamin Forsythe

Papers, 1785-1918, 6,616 pieces, including his service to the Union Army during the Civil War and in various judicial positions in Kentucky.

636 Clay, Henry

Papers, 1801-1843, 73 pieces, with the exception of court decree, this collection consists of letters, the majority of which were written to Francis Taliaferro Brooke of Fredericksburg, Virginia, and dealt mainly with political affairs.

In addition, 411 pieces in various small collections relate to Henry Clay.

637 Fox Family •

Papers, 1852-1920, 12 boxes, consisting of the papers of John W. Fox, Sr., a school teacher, and his son, John Fox, Jr., Kentucky author.

638 Hunt-Morgan Family

Papers, 1784-1949, 4,500 pieces, consisting primarily of the business and personal correspondence of 4 generations of a Kentucky family, including the letters of Dr. Thomas Hunt Morgan, who received the Nobel Prize in 1933 for his discoveries concerning the laws and mechanisms of heredity.

639 Merton, Thomas

Papers, 1947-1968, 1,208 pieces, consisting of poems, articles, and correspondence of this theologian, poet, and social critic.

640 Stanley, Augustus Owsley

Papers, 1844-1958, ca. 10,000 items relating to this Kentucky statesman and political leader, who served in both Houses of Congress and as Governor of Kentucky.

641 Vinson, Frederick Moore

Papers, 1907-1953, 302,462 items, including files on Vinson's career as Congressman, his participation in the Bretton Woods Conference, and his service as Secretary of the Treasury and as Chief Justice of the United States.

Other Collections

Notable among many other manuscript collections are:

642 Burley Tobacco Cooperatives, Records, 1904-1923, 430 pieces, including records of the Burley Tobacco Society, the Burley Tobacco Company, and the Strater Tobacco Company.

643 Chandler, Albert B., Papers, 1920-1973, 319,500 items relating to this Kentucky governor.

644 Clay, Cassius Marcellus, Correspondence, 1871-1913, 2,120 pieces, relating to Clay as farmer, stockbreeder, and member of the Kentucky State Legislature.

645 Clay, Laura, Papers, 1882-1941, ca. 7,000 items concerning this Kentucky leader in the woman suffrage movement.

646 Clements, Earle C., Papers, 1940-1960, 294,000 pieces, regarding this Kentucky governor and U. S. Senator.

647 Democratic Party, Papers, 1896-1952, ca. 4,000 pieces, the political papers of Samuel Mackay Wilson and Mary Shelby Wilson cover more than 50 years of activity in the Democratic Party at local, state, and national levels.

648 Flanery, Mary Elliott, Papers, 1883-1972, 4 boxes, pertaining to Mrs. Flanery, the first woman to serve in a Southern legislature. She was elected to the Kentucky House of Representatives from Boyd County in 1921.

649 Hines, Thomas Henry, Papers, ca. 1860-1869, covering the period of the Civil War, consists of diaries, scrapbooks, notebooks, maps, letters, and military orders. Later additions to this collection include material through 1890.

650 Kentucky Association for the Improvement of the Breed of Stock, Records, 1828-1869, 736 items, including association business matters, nominations for races, race meet schedules and purses, and rules and regulations for the operation of the track.

651 Lindsay Family, Papers, 1867-1932, ca. 14,000 pieces, relating to William Lindsay, prominent Kentucky lawyer and U. S. Senator, and to his wife, Eleanor Holmes Lindsay.

652 Morton, Thruston Ballard, Papers, consisting of the files and records of this U. S. Senator, 1957-1969.

653 Neville, Linda, Papers, 1848-1959, ca. 35,500 items concerning this Lexington native, who devoted her life to the eradication of trachoma in the mountains of Kentucky.

654 Shouse, Jouett, Collection, 1911-1959, ca. 3,000 items, relating to this lawyer and political leader, who served in the U. S. House of Representatives from Kansas.

655   Spence, Brent, Papers, 1930-1962, ca. 37,500 items, including office files, correspondence, and other materials relating to this Kentucky lawyer and Congressman, 1931-1962.

656   Stewart, Cora Wilson, Papers, 1900-1940, ca. 40,000 pieces, relating to this founder of Moonlight Schools, a pioneer attempt to eradicate adult illiteracy.

657   Underwood, Thomas Rust, Papers, ca. 1923-1935, ca. 8,000 items, concerning this Lexington newspaper editor, Congressman, and U.S. Senator.

658   Watts, John Clarence, Papers, 1951-1971, ca. 177,496 pieces, covering the Congressional career of Watts, who served in the U.S. House of Representatives from 1951 until his death in 1971.

659   Willis, Simeon Slavens, Papers, ca. 1915-1959, 10 boxes, relating to his public life as Judge of the Kentucky Court of Appeals and as Governor of Kentucky, 1943-1947.

660   Wilson, Judge Samuel M., Papers, 1743-1959, ca. 70,000 manuscript items, primarily concerning Kentucky history, collected by this Lexington attorney, writer, civic leader, and collector of books and manuscripts.

Medical Center Library
University of Kentucky   40506

661   Harvey, William

553 titles, including works by and about William Harvey, contemporary criticism, orations by Harvey, portraits, and publications of Harvey societies, and materials concerning the political and literary age of Harvey.

662   Servetus, Michael

68 volumes, including works by Servetus, biographical and critical materials concerning Servetus, and information on the age of Servetus.

Waveland State Shrine
Higbee Mill Road   40503

663   Library

Historical collection of ca. 1,000 items, including Civil War letters and books, early diaries, bills of sale for land and slaves, and other materials relating to the settlement and development of Kentucky. Current volumes deal largely with costumes and antiques.

LOUISVILLE

Bellarmine College Library
Newburg Road   40205

664   Louisville Archdiocesan Collection

Interviews and programs, 34 to date, concerning the Catholic Church in Louisville and in Kentucky.

665   Louisville Historical League

A collection of interviews and programs, 48 to date, sponsored by and recorded by the Louisville Historical League. Subjects cover the history of both Louisville and Kentucky.

Brown & Williamson Tobacco Corporation
1600 West Hill SXtreet   40201

666   Library

Research collection, consisting of 2,700 volumes, 153 periodical subscriptions, and extensive vertical file materials relating to agriculture, chemistry, tobacco, and tobacco products.

Data Courier, Incorporated
620 South Fifth Street   40202

667   Library and Information Center

Marine life, environment, and pollution are covered in this technical collection of ca. 800 volumes, 1,000 journal titles, and 44,000 documents. Included are special materials for ocean research.

The Filson Club
118 West Breckinridge Street   40203

The Filson Club, organized in 1884, collects, preserves, and publishes historical material, especially that which pertains to Kentucky. As such, it has assembled an extensive collection of manuscripts. Notable among these are:

668   Allen, James Lane, 1893-1924, 45 items, pertaining to this Kentucky novelist and short story writer.

669   Anderson, Richard Clough, 1777-1887, 2 boxes, relating to this Revolutionary War officer and surveyor-general.

670   Brown Family Papers, 1799-1846, 1 box of letters written by members of the John Brown family, mostly by Margaretta Brown, wife of John Brown, Kentucky's first Senator.

671   Cawein, Madison Julius, 1888-1912, 3 boxes, relating to this Kentucky poet.

672   Clark, Jonathan, 1734-1812, 12 boxes, concerning this Revolutionary War officer and his family.

673   Clay, Henry, 1810-1852, 32 items relating to this outstanding Kentuckian, who served in both Houses of Congress and as U. S. Secretary of State.

674   Durrett, Rueben Thomas, 1849-1913, 23 boxes concerning this lawyer, newspaper editor and historian

675   Guthrie, James, 1820-1869, 49 boxes relating to this Kentucky lawyer, U. S. Senator, and Secretary of the Treasury of the United States

676   Harlan, John Marshall, 1888-1911, 114 items pertaining to Harlan as Justice of the U. S. Supreme Court

677   Johnson, Richard Mentor, 1824-1841, 2 boxes, relating to his service in both Houses of Congress and as Vice President of the United States

678   Johnston Family Papers, 1798-1943, 8 boxes, consisting chiefly of the correspondence of General Albert Sidney Johnston and William Preston Johnston. Also includes pamphlets, newspaper clippings, and genealogical information

679   McAfee, Robert Breckinridge, 1813-1845, 565 pages referring to his service as War of 1812 officer, lawyer, State legislator, and historian

678   Johnston Family Papers, 1798-1943, 8 boxes, consisting chiefly of the correspondence of General Albert Sidney Johnston and William Preston Johnston. Also includes pamphlets, newspaper clippings, and genealogical information

679   McAfee, Robert Breckinridge, 1813-1845, 565 pages referring to his service as War of 1812 officer, lawyer, State legislator, and historian

680   Pope, John, 1808-1843, 2 volumes and 9 items, concerning his service in both Houses of Congress and as Territorial Governor of Arkansas

681   Shelby, Isaac, 1760-1839, 2 boxes of materials relating to this officer in b the Revolutionary War and the War of 1812 and Governor of Kentucky

682   Short, Charles Wilkins, 1811-1869, 15 boxes comprised of the papers of this Kentucky physician and botanist and the correspondence of William Short, diplomat

683   Thruston, Clark Ballard, 1873-1946, 21 volumes and 51 boxes, comprised of materials relating to this distinguished Kentucky geologist

684   Todd, Charles Henry, Papers, 1848-1917, 6 boxes, consisting of the papers of this doctor, Confederate Army surgeon, historian, and author

685   Willson, Augustus Everett, 1873-1921, 13 boxes and other materials relating this lawyer, who served as Governor of Kentucky

686   Yandell, Papers, 1823-1887, 8 boxes, consisting chiefly of letters, diaries, and autobiographical material concerning Lunsford Pitts Yandell, prominent Kentucky paleontologist and physician.

Other Manuscript Collections

687   Included are: (1) Temple Bodley Collection, 1614-1940, 41 volumes and 5 boxes, including material on the history of the West during the American Revolution and the career of George Rogers Clark; (2) Papers relating to the genealogy of the Signers of the Declaration of Independence, 53 volumes; (3) Journals and other papers of the Shakers of Mercer County, 1815-1905, 24 volumes; (4) Military records of Kentuckians who served in the armed forces of the United States during World War I, 144 volumes; and (5) Numerous files of account books and other records of Louisville business firms, 1800-1900, including the John F. Jefferson Papers, 1849-1925, 50 volumes and 5 boxes, consisting largely of the diary, 1857-1906, of this Louisville merchant.

General Electric Company
Appliance Park   40225

688   Library

This technical collection, serving the company's Major Appliance

Laboratory, consists of ca. 14,000 volumes in the fields of chemical, electrical, and mechanical engineering, chemistry, mathematics, and physics.

Girdler Chemical, Incorporated
4900 Crittenden Drive   40219

689   Library

ca. 4,500 volumes, 50 journal subscriptions, and extensive vertical file materials pertaining to catalysis, chemistry, engineering, physics, and management.

Kentucky Railway Museum
1837 River Road   40201

690   Library

A collection of ca. 250 items, including railroad directories from the 1860's to modern times, a file of the Louisville and Nashville Railway's monthly magazines, beginning ca. 1912, and other historical materials relating to American railroads.

Louisville Academy of Music Library
2740 Frankfort Avenue   40206

691   Harris, Roy

Published and unpublished music and literary items of this American composer, including his biography by Nicholas Slonimsky, programs, brochures, tapes, recordings, letters, photographs, and clippings, prior to 1960.

692   Speed, Hattie Bishop

The collection of this Louisville pianist and patron of the arts contains programs of her performances, 1870's-1920's, and other programs, 1870-1942. Also included are several hundred books, many of which are first editions of 19th and early 20th century works.

693   Biographical Files

Complete biographical and some genealogical information on 110 Louisville musicians, and incomplete files on ca. 600 other local musicians.

Louisville Free Public Library
Fourth and York Streets   40203

694   Phonograph/Tape Archives

ca. 30,000 discs, primarily for use by the library's noncommercial educational FM radio station. In addition, there are 200,000 titles on tape recordings.

695   Rice Collection

60 volumes, scrapbooks, and photograph albums, including books from the private library as well as works by Cale Young Rice, Kentucky poet, and his wife, Alice Hegan Rice, author of **Mrs. Wiggs of the Cabbage Patch.**

696   Kentucky Authors

ca. 5,000 volumes of works by native and adopted Kentuckians with emphasis on Louisville writers.

697   Kentucky History and Genealogy

10,000 volumes, strongest in mid-19th history and in the history of Louisville, including early Louisville newspapers on microfilm and a subject index to the Louisville **Courier-Journal,** 1917 to date. Of the 2,711 genealogical works, many pertain to Kentucky families and subjects.

698   Negro Collection

4,500 volumes with emphasis on Negro authorship. Included are manuscripts of Joseph Seamon Cotter, Kentucky educator and the author of **Negro Tales** (1912).

699   Cook Books

Extensive collection of materials relating to the art of cooking, consisting of ca. 1,800 volumes.

700   Watterson, Henry, Collection

6,000 volumes from the private library of Henry Watterson, including many relating to the history of the Confederacy.

Louisville Presbyterian Seminary Library
1044 Alta Vista Road

701   **McKowen, Emmet C., Collection**

        20 volumes, consisting of photographic copies of all the important manuscripts of the New Testament.

702   **Presbyterian History**

        A collection of 300 volumes in addition to manuscripts relating to Presbyterian Church with emphasis on the Presbyterian Church in Kentucky. Included are the original manuscripts of the Minutes of the Synod of Kentucky from its organization in 1802, of the Presbytery of Transylvania from its founding in 1786, and of other presbyteries in Kentucky.

703   **Rare Bibles**

        A collection of 700 Bibles in all languages, ranging from the very old to the most recent versions.

Preservation Alliance of Louisville
712 West Main Street   40202

704   **Library**

        ca. 250 items, including volumes relating to Louisville history, historical architecture, and preservation techniques.

Joseph E. Seagram & Sons
Seventh Street Road   40201

705   **Library**

        ca. 3,500 volumes and journals relating to alcoholic beverage production, including works in chemistry, biology, and the fermentation of whiskey.

James P. Boyce Centennial Library
Southern Baptist Theological Seminary   40206

706   **Graham, Billy, Collection**

        A significant collection of newspaper clippings, photographs, and other materials relating to this distinguished evangelist along with display copies of all of Dr. Graham's books and books about him.

707   Southern Baptist Collection

Extensive collection, consisting of more than 90,000 volumes of minutes of Baptist associations and state Baptist conventions. As the repository for the Kentucky Baptist Historical Society, the collection includes the association minutes, Kentucky Baptist Convention Annuals, and a file of Kentucky Baptist newspapers.

708   Biblical Archaeology

28 vertical file drawers of off-prints of periodical articles concerning Biblical archaeology and related fields. These materials supplement the valuable collection of bound volumes on the archaeology of Bible lands, which was presented to the library by Dr. William F. Albright and placed in the circulating collection.

Spalding College Library
853 Library Lane   40203

709   Theology-History

2,000 volumes culled from the books gathered by Bishop Benedict Joseph Flaget for the seminary of the Bardstown Diocese, covering ecclesiatical, devotional, and scriptural commentaries. Most of the 16th-18th century writings are in French and Latin, and they indicate the development of binding, typography, and illustration.

J. B. Speed Art Museum Library
2035 South Third Street   40208

710   Weygold Collection

A collection of 126 books on the American Indian along with paintings and many artifacts.

D. Lane Tynes Library
9901 Linn Station Road   40223

711   Insurance

This library, which serves the Research Department of the Blue Cross-Blue Shield Insurance Company, consists of 700 books relating to management, sales, motivation, computer science, and other allied fields as well as insurance.

University of Louisville
Belknap Campus   40208

712   **Baum, L. Frank**

ca. 130 items, including all of Baum's books and other Oziana, consisting of books, periodicals, and toys.

713   **Burroughs, Edgar Rice**

ca. 3,300 items, consisting of a virtually complete collection of first editions and first appearances in print of the "Tarzan" books and other Burroughs novels. Also included are periodicals, comics, movie stills, recordings, and posters relating Burroughs and his works.

714   **Bullitt, William Marshall, Collection**

100 rare first editions of important works in astronomy and mathematics by Euclid, Diophantus, Archimedes, Galileo, Newton, Einstein, and others. Included is a first edition of Nicolaus Copernicus' **De Revolutionibus** (1543).

715   **DiPrima, Diane**

75 items, comprised of business and personal correspondence, literary manuscripts, notebooks, and diary. Included are manuscripts of unpublished works.

716   **Great War Collection**

The Lafon Allen collection of 2,500 items relating to World War I, including books, official documents, and tracts, augmented by prints, etchings, paintings, posters, and maps.

717   **Greene, Graham**

A collection of ca. 250 items, consisting of literary first editions, critical works, periodicals, and other materials relating to Graham Greene.

718   **Hearn, Lafcadio**

ca. 150 items, including first editions, clippings, manuscript facsimiles, and a print relating to this Anglo-American author who became an authority on Japan.

719   Mencken, H. L.

Correspondence, scrapbooks, signed first editions and memorabilia are among the ca. 500 items in this collection, assembled by Victor Reno.

720   Rackham, Arthur

ca. 500 items, comprised of first editions, original paintings and drawings, manuscripts, photographs, notebooks, and other materials relating to Rackham.

721   Dime Novels

ca. 1,000 items, including partial runs of **Nick Carter, Deadwood Dick, Wild West Weekley, Pluck and Luck,** and others of this genre.

722   Pulp Magazines

Over 150 titles of science fiction, detective stories, westerns, super heroes, adventure, and romance.

MAYFIELD

Graves County Library
Sixth and College Streets   42066

723   Holifield, M. B., Collection

A collection of 1,254 volumes, consisting of ca. 300 books in the field of religion and more than 800 historical works, relating particularly to the Civil War and to the writings of political and military leaders.

MAYSVILLE

Maysville Community College Library
Route 2   41056

724   Local History

Early histories of Kentucky, Records of the United Baptist Church of Mayslick, 1788-1947, and Minutes of the Bracken Association of Baptists in Kentucky, 1799-1871 are among the 70 volumes in this historical collection.

MIDWAY

Midway College Library
Midway 40347

725   **Brotherhood Collection**

ca. 2,000 volumes on the history and personnel of the Christian Church (Disciples of Christ) in America.

726   **Kentucky Collection**

ca. 400 volumes relating to Kentucky history, literature, and biography from the early 19th century to the present, including materials on Midway itself, which is said to have furnished local color for Mary J. Holmes' **Tempest and Sunshine.**

MOREHEAD

Johnson Camden Library
Morehead State University 40351

727   **Doran, Adron**

Papers, 1920-1976, more than 2,000 items, consisting of correspondence, periodicals, photographs, memorabilia, and 400 tapes of speeches and conferences of the Doran years at Morehead State University.

728   **Still, James**

Over 300 items of correspondence, diaries, journals, typewritten manuscripts, photographs, and memorabilia, relating chiefly to the Appalachian region.

MURRAY

Calloway County Public Library
710 Main Street 42071

729   **Kentucky**

Genealogical records of Calloway County and materials on the first families of Kentucky are among the 1,000 volumes in this collection of Kentuckiana.

730   Oral History

35 tapes/recordings, recalling the customs, folklore, and local history of Murray. This project of recording historical material is being extended to cover Calloway County.

Murray State University Library
Murray   42071

731   Stuart, Jesse

ca. 100,000 items, consisting of letters, manuscripts, scrapbooks, first editions, anthologies, and personal memorabilia of this noted Kentucky writer.

732   Jackson Purchase

150 books and periodicals and 8 linear feet of manuscripts and files relating to the history and genealogy of the eight counties of Western Kentucky.

733   Breathitt, Edward T., Jr.

Personal and offical records and correspondence, 40 linear feet, of this Governor of Kentucky, 1963-1967.

734   Everett, Robert A.

330 linear feet of personal and official records and correspondence of "Fats" Everett, U. S. Congressman, 1958-1969, from Tennessee.

735   Gregory, Noble J.

Correspondence and personal and official records, 33 linear feet, of this U. S. Congressman, 1936-1959.

736   Stubblefield, Frank Albert

80 linear feet of correspondence and records of this U. S. Congressman, 1959-1975.

737   Waterfield, Harry Lee

Official records and correspondence of this Lieutenant Governor of Kentucky, 1959-1967, occupy 65 linear feet.

738   History and Genealogy

A collection of ca. 3,500 books and periodicals, 7,000 reels of microfilm, and 8 linear feet of files and manuscripts relating principally to the history and genealogy of Kentucky, Tennessee, the Carolinas, and Virginia.

OWENSBORO

Kentucky Wesleyan College Library
3000 Frederica Street   42301

739   United Methodist Heritage Center

As the official archives of the Louisville Conference of the United Methodist Church, this collection of ca. 1,000 volumes consists of the official records and manuscripts of the Church in Kentucky from ca. 1800 to date. Included are items on the general history of the Church, with emphasis on the Methodist Episocpal Church, South, 1845-1939.

740   Kentuckiana

2,300 items on the history and literary development of the Commonwealth along with materials on the geography of the area.

741   Orrahood, Dr. and Mrs. M. David, Collection

240 first editions, including presentation signed copies, of the works of American and English authors, 1820's through the 1930's.

Owensboro-Daviess County Public Library
450 Griffith Avenue   42301

742   State/Local History and Genealogy

ca. 1,000 volumes of genealogical works and instructional materials on genealogy, along with ca. 1,500 volumes covering all aspects of Kentucky history, literature, and biography. Also included is a beginning collection of oral history tapes relating to Owensboro and Daviess County.

PADUCAH

Paducah Public Library
555 Washington Street   42001

743   **Cobb, Irvin S.**

Representing this native writer and creator of the Judge Priest stories is this collection of ca. 300 volumes, manuscripts of **Exit Laughing,** correspondence from friends, pictures of family, newspaper clippings, and a mask made during his lifetime.

PAINTSVILLE

Research Historians
Johnson Central High School   41240

744   **Library**

A Kentucky Room collection of ca. 750 items relating to the history of the 40 counties of Eastern Kentucky, but broadly covering the Central Appalachian region, including Western Virginia and West Virginia. Bound photocopies of articles from early newspapers of the area include accounts of the Hatfields and McCoys.

PARIS

John Fox, Jr., Memorial Library
Duncan Tavern   40361

745   **Fox, John, Jr.**

An outstanding collection of manuscripts and first editions of his works, along with pictures and memorabilia relating to the author of **The Trail of the Lonesome Pine** and other popular novels of the early 20th century.

746   **DAR Collection**

As the library serves as the state headquarters of the Daughters of the American Revolution, this collection consists of state and national DAR records, extensive files of family histories, and many unpublished family records.

PIPPA PASSES

Ethel Mueller Barrat Library
Alice Lloyd College   41844

747   Appalachian Collection

Currently consisting of ca. 1,700 items, this growing collection includes material relating to the whole area of Appalachia and the entire state of Kentucky. Emphasis is on the works of the writers of the region.

PRESTONSBURG

Prestonsburg Community College Library
Bert Combs Drive   41653

748   Kentucky

ca. 600 volumes relating to state and local history, which includes the Civil War battle of Middle Creek, the first substantial victory of the Union Army (1862). A clipping file is comprised of more than 3,000 items on Kentucky-related topics.

PRINCETON

George Coon Public Library
114 South Harrison Street   42445

749   Rare Books and Manuscripts

The nucleus of this collection was transferred from the Old Princeton Collegiate Institute and included a complete set of George Bancroft's **Histories of the United States** in 39 volumes, beginning in 1834. Among the manuscripts are scrap books of World Wars I and II, Civil War letters, and materials relating to the early schools and colleges of Caldwell County.

750   Genealogy

Started with funds in memory of Ira Fears, this collection is comprised of books relating to the states from which early Kentuckians migrated, state and county histories, court records, and family histories. An incomplete file of Caldwell County newspapers dates back to the early 1870's.

RICHMOND

John Grant Crabbe Library
Eastern Kentucky University   40475

751   Kentucky Collection

Of special interest in this collection of 15,000 items of Kentuckiana is the John Wilson Townsend Collection of 1,700 first editions signed by Kentucky authors and 2,500 letters written to Townsend by Kentucky authors and other notables prior to 1930. Also included are 100 genealogical items, relating primarily to Boonesborough from the early dates to the present.

TRAPPIST

Gethsemani
Trappist   40073

752   Abbey Library

A monastery library collection of 26,000 volumes with a concentration on monasticism, patristics, philosophy, and religion with special emphasis on Cistercian Monastery history and liturgy. Included is a special collection relating to the priest-poet, Thomas Merton.

VANCLEVE

Gibson Library
Kentucky Mountain Bible Institute   41385

753   Holiness

Collection of literature, occupying 30 linear feet, which promotes sanctification as an instantaneous work of grace, wrought in the believer through faith, subsequent to regeneration and witnessed by the Holy Ghost.

754   Missions and Biography

33 linear feet of materials relating to missionary work in many parts of the world, and 65 feet devoted to the biography of famous Christians, past and present.

WILMORE

B. L. Fisher Library
Asbury Theological Seminary   40390

755   **Day, Albert Edward**

Papers, 1916-1957, occupying 4 linear feet, comprised of manuscripts of sermons, addresses, and lectures of this Methodist minister, lecturer, and radio preacher.

756   **Christian and Social Service Organizations**

Brochures, conference programs, form letters, and other materials collected by these various organizations, 1967 to date.

WINCHESTER

Public Library
109-111 South Main Street   40391

757   **Historical Reference Collection**

ca. 450 books, booklets, and manuscripts relating to Kentucky life and history, many of which were collected by Dr. George F. Doyle. Included are Clarke County family histories, court records, and histories of 3 early churches of Clark County.

V

SPECIAL COLLECTIONS
IN
LIBRARIES OF MISSISSIPPI

Compiled
By
Rush G. Miller

ABERDEEN

Evans Memorial Library
Aberdeen   39730

758   Local History

ca. 85,000 items, comprised of both published and manuscript sources (letters, dairies, account books, legal papers), including:

759   Old South Collection, comprised of books on Southern history and maintained by the local chapter of the United Daughters of the Confederacy.

760   Reuben Davis Collection, composed of books from the Davis family library, including **Recollections of Mississippi and Mississippians** and poetry written by Davis' first wife, whose pen name was Hinda.

761   Parson Gladney Collection of books from the library of Richard S. Gladney, early president of Aberdeen Female College, which was founded in 1838.

762   An extensive genealogy collection relating to area families.

BAY ST. LOUIS

Divine Word Seminary of St. Augustine
Bay St. Louis   39520

763   Negro in America

A collection of ca. 500 volumes relating to the American Negro in a library used by novices at this Catholic seminary.   **R**

NASA/NSTL Research Library
National Space Technology Laboratory

764   Research Collection

ca. 10,000 volumes, 3,000 technical publications, and 150 periodical subscriptions covering a broad scope of technical and scientific fields, with special emphasis on cryogenic engineering, low temperature physics, and environmental sciences. **R**

BILOXI

Biloxi Public Library
Biloxi   39533

765   Genealogy Collection

ca. 750 items, covering the eastern half of the U.S., Gulf Coast States (Alabama, Mississippi, Louisiana and Texas) and some Canadian records. Census, marriage, and court records for Harrison County, and local family histories in printed and manuscript form.

766   Mississippi Collection

ca. 750 books and other materials relating to Mississippi history, including county histories, local histories, and particularly Gulf Coast history.

767   Oral History

74 tapes, including French and Yugoslavian languages, customs, and foods; dialects of the area, descriptions of Biloxi as an old resort city, the seafood industry, and experiences of coastal residents during hurricanes.

McBride Library
Keesler Air Force Base   39543

768   Technical Collection

12,000 volumes with an emphasis on electronics and avionics. **R**

769   World War II

1,500 volumes on World War II with emphasis upon the role of the U.S. Air Force in this global conflict. **R**

BLUE MOUNTAIN

Guyton Library
Blue Mountain College   38610

770   Lowrey Family

Genealogy of the Lowrey family and its contributions to Blue Mountain College, including unnumbered scrapbooks, autobiographies, reminiscences, family ledgers and records, and newspaper clippings.

BOONEVILLE

Eula Dees Memorial Library
Northeast Mississippi Junior College   38829

771   Genealogy

ca. 200 items of printed material and census records on microfilm for the 5-county area served by the college.

BROOKHAVEN

Lincoln County Public Library
Brookhaven   39601

772   Genealogy

A collection of ca. 40 histories of local families, cemetery lists of Lincoln County, and 38 microfilm reels of area census records.

CLARKSDALE

Carnegie Public Library
114 Delta Avenue   38614

773   Archaeology Collection

ca. 80 books and journal articles along with interesting artifacts relating particularly to prehistoric Mississippi, the Mississippi Valley, and Indians of the Southeast.

774   Mississippi Collection

Books, vertical file, pictures, and maps on Mississippi, Coahoma County, and Clarksdale. ca. 600 books, 1900 to date, along with pamphlets, clippings and maps of Mississippi, and 670 volumes of genealogy with emphasis on Clarksdale and Coahoma County.

CLEVELAND

Bolivar County Library
104 South Leflore Street   38732

775   Local History

ca. 700 volumes, including an extremely rare copy of **Bilbo, Brewer, and Bribery in Mississippi Politics** by Gambrell Austin Hobbs and 25 oral history tapes of interviews with residents regarding Bolivar County history.

W. B. Roberts Library
Delta State University   38733

776   Hand, James and Theresa Moore, Collection

Papers, 1792-1975, 3 linear feet of plantation day books, letters, slave bills of sales, deeds, wills, clippings, and pamphlets. James Hand, Jr. of Rolling Fork is a prominent cotton planter and the first farmer in the lower Delta to mechanize a plantation.

777   Miscellaneous Manuscript Collections

Included are "The Dairy of Philip H. Sherman, 1873-1879"; original manuscripts of Wirt Williams' **The Enemy** and Evelyn Hammett's **I Priscilla;** a Civil War manuscript in diary form written by an anonymous confederate solider; Annie E. Jacobs' unpublished manuscript entitled "The Master of Doro Plantation: An Epic of the Old South," which deals with Charles Clark and His family (Charles Clark was a lawyer, planter, and Civil War governor of Mississippi); and "Judge J. C. Burrus and His Family" by Ethel Burrus Sutherland.

778   Mississippi Collection

ca. 10,000 items including books, pamphlets, clippings, and other material relating to Mississippi, and a collection of art works representing Walter Anderson, Theora Hamblett, Marie Hull, Marshal Bouldin, Lee McCarty, Malcolm Norwood, and other Mississippi artists of note.

779   Oral History Collection

40 interviews dealing with the history of Delta State University and the Delta, including flood experiences of Delta residents.

CLINTON

Leland Speed Library
Mississippi College   39056

780   **Mississippi Baptist Historical Collection**

ca. 1,200 volumes and ca. 2,500 other items, consisting of church records, minutes of Baptist Associations, early newspapers and periodicals published by the denomination, and a number of rare books which tell the Baptist story in Mississippi. Outstanding source materials include **Annuals** of the Mississippi Baptist Convention from its organization in 1836 to date; **The Baptist Record** from its first issue in 1877 to date; and **Religious Luminary,** the state's first Baptist newspaper published in Natchez, 1836-1837.

COLUMBUS

Base Library
Columbus Air Force Base   39701

781   **Military**

A collection of ca. 2,000 items, including United States Air Force materials with emphasis on military history and different types of aircraft.   **R**

John Clayton Fant Memorial Library
Mississippi University for Woman   39701

782   **Williams, Blanche Colton, Collection**

A collection of ca. 100 volumes by and about the Victorian novelist, George Eliot (Mary Ann or Marian Evans).

CORINTH

Northeast Regional Library
1023 Fillmore Street   38834

783   **Oral History**

An on-going project of interviewing 60 residents of Corinth and Alcorn County regarding various aspects of local history. Transcripts of these tapes are to be compiled for publication.

ELLISVILLE

Memorial Library
Jones County Junior College   39437

784   **"Free State of Jones"**

A collection of ca. 20 books, clippings and manuscripts relating to Jones County, the area of Mississippi which seceded from the Confederate state of Mississippi during the Civil War.

GREENVILLE

Washington County Library System
341 Main Street   38701

785   **Greenville Cotton Exchange Papers**

Papers, 1888-1969, over 300 items in addition to one minute book, mainly concerning membership in the Greenville Cotton Exchange — important records for economic history of the Mississippi Delta.

786   **Keating, Bern**

Papers, 1959-1975, over 6,000 items including correspondence, source materials, galley proofs, and original manuscripts of 48 articles and 15 published and unpublished books.

GREENWOOD

Greenwood-Leflore Public Library
408 West Washington Street   38930

787   **Genealogy**

ca. 3,000 volumes, including the genealogical collections of May Wilson McBee, Maybelle Smith Garrard, and Judge Zelma Price, is not restricted to local families.

788   **Local History**

A varied collection including the **History of Greenwood Leflore and the Choctaw Indians** by Florence Rebecca Ray, a great granddaughter of Leflore, a typescript of William Franklin Hamilton's **History of Carroll County;** movie

152

typescripts of both **The Reivers** and **Ode to Billy Joe** along with photographs taken during the filming of these movies in the Greenwood area.

GRENADA

Elizabeth Jones Library
Grenada   38901

789   Genealogy and Local History

ca. 300 volumes along with pamphlets and clippings relating to the history of Grenada and Grenada County from 1836 to the present, with emphasis upon the 19th century and the architecture of the region. Genealogical materials of the Southland are in both printed and manuscript form.

GULFPORT

Gulfport-Harrison County Library
Gulfport   39501

790   Genealogy

ca. 1,500 items including books, periodicals, and manuscripts regarding family histories with the emphasis on the Southeast.

791   Mississippiana

4,000 items relating to all aspects of the state including reports of regional and local agencies and substantial material on Jefferson Davis.

Naval Construction Battalion Center
Gulfport   39501

792   Library

A collection of 18,000 volumes and 50 journals, including technical reference materials, battalion yearbooks, and construction guides, which are used in training 10,000 Seabees each year.   **R**

Southern Forest Experiment Station
U. S. Forest Service   39503

793 **Library**

ca. 1,200 volumes and 3,000 reprints relating to plant genetics, plant diseases, and destructive insects, primarily termites. **R**

Medical Library
Veteran's Hospital   39501

794 **Neuropsychiatry**

As this is a neuropsychiatric hospital, the entire collection of ca. 2,050 volumes is slanted toward this medical specialty, with particular strength in areas of rehabilitative medicine and audiology. **R**

HATTIESBURG

Hattiesburg Public Library
723 Main Street   39401

795 **Local History**

A collection of 1,782 volumes relating to state and local history, 740 genealogical sources, and census records and the Hattiesburg **American** since 1915 on microfilm.

William David McCain Library
University of Southern Mississippi   39401

796 **The Association of American Editorial Cartoonists Collection**

Editorial cartoons, 1968 to date, 3,400 items by more than 200 artists, including Gene Basset, Charles Brooks, Bill Daniels, Syd Hoff, Bob Howie, Jim Ivey, Jack Jurden, Jon Kennedy, Reg Manning, John Milt Morris, John Pierotti, Eldon Pletcher, Arthur Poinier, John Piedell, Robbie Robinson, John Shevchik, John Stampone, Ed Valtman, L. D. Warren, and Richard Yardley.

797 **Bilbo, Theodore G.**

Papers, 1915-1947, ca. 1,200 linear feet, including correspondence, financial records, clippings, photographs, and memorabilia relating to Bilbo who served two terms as Governor of Mississippi (1916-1920, 1928-1932) and was a United States Senator from 1934 until his death in 1947.

798   Colmer, William M.

Papers, 1933-1973, 424 linear feet, including correspondence, legislative files, newsletter, and speeches of Colmer who served as a United States Representative from Mississippi from 1933 to 1973.

799   de Grummond, Lena Y., Collection of Children's Literature

Literary manuscripts, correspondence, and original illustrations for children's books, original editions of children's books and magazines, 1750 to date, ca. 1,000 linear feet. Includes contributions from over 800 authors and illustrators, among them Kate Greenaway, Maude and Miska Petersham, Merrit Mauzey, Marguerite de Angeli, Scott O'Dell, Lois Lenski, Roger Duvoisin, Lynd Ward, Taro Yashima, Marcia Brown, Adrienne Adams, and Madeleine L'Engle.

800   Mississippiana

10,500 volumes, 1832 to date. A collection of publications on Mississippi or by Mississippians, including state documents, works on genealogy, geography, history and fiction, and Indexes to the Jackson **Clarion Ledger** and the Hattiesburg **American,** 1960 to date.

801   Walen, Ernest A., Collection

Books, documents, pamphlets, newspapers, and journal articles on the history of the Confederate States of America, 500 linear feet, including 524 original Confederate imprints.

802   Woods, Sam, Collection

1,150 volumes, 1532 to 1950. Sam Woods was a Mississippian who served in various diplomatic posts in Europe from 1929 to 1952. His collection consists in large part of books published before 1800, with principal concentrations in religion, classics, geography, and history, the earliest being an edition of speeches from Livy (1532)

HOLLY SPRINGS

Leontyne Price Library
Rust College

803   Negro

ca. 1,000 paperback books by and about Negroes, and a small collection of recordings by Leontyne Price, former Metropolitan Opera soprano from Mississippi.

JACKSON

Hood Library
Belhaven College

804   **Presbyterian**

This collection, occupying ca. 55 linear feet, consists of records and archives of the Presbyterian church in the southeast.

Jackson Metropolitan Library
301 North State Street   39201

805   **Mississippi Collection**

ca. 4,000 books on Mississippi, local history, and Mississippi authors; and a loose-leaf file of biographical data on Mississippi artists. A bibliographic guide to genealogical sources is available.

Henry T. Sampson Library
Jackson State University   39217

806   **Afro-American Collection**

ca. 15,460 volumes plus manuscripts, clippings, programs and other material, occupying 17 linear feet, on the Negro in Africa and America. Included are the galley sheets of Margaret Walker's **Jubilee** and uncorrected copy of **Poetic Equations,** conversations between Margaret Walker and Nikki Giovanni.

Millsaps-Wilson Library
Millsaps College   39210

807   **Lehman Engle Collection**

ca. 2,000 volumes relating to the fine arts, 400 recordings, musical scores, and manuscripts of original compositions of contemporary composers, especially Charles Ives.

808   **Methodist Collection**

Archival material for North Mississippi and Mississippi Annual Conferences of the United Methodist Church, occupying ca. 600 cubic feet, includes manuscript collections of prominent Methodist figures, such as B. M. Drake, William Winans, Bishop Charles Galloway; minutes of the annual conferences; denominational periodicals and newspapers; a complete file of the **New Orleans Christian Advocate,** 1850-1946 and **Mississippi United Methodist Advocate,** 1947 to date. Access to the Methodist Collection is by appointment with Mrs. Loyce McKenzie of Jackson.

Mississippi Department of Archives and History
100 South State Street   39205

Library Collection

809   Mississippiana

ca. 32,000 volumes by and about Mississippians and Mississippi history, including the Research and Development Center Clipping File, 1970-1976 and the Works Progress Administration collection of material compiled by W.P.A. workers on Mississippi history and culture.

810   Genealogy

ca. 8,000 volumes relating directly to genealogy, including county records on microfilm. Emphasis on eastern and Southeastern states. A guide to use of the collection, entitled **Research in the Department of Archives and History,** is available upon request.

Official Records

811   Official Records of the State of Mississippi

1729-present, including the non-current records of all state agencies and commissions and the governor's office. Of special interest are the records of governors from 1817 to the present and the French, English, and Spanish provincial records. **An Official Guide to the Historical Materials in the Mississippi Department of Archives and History** was compiled by Dunbar Rowland in 1914. A revision of Rowland's guide was compiled by Thomas W. Henderson and Ronald E. Tomlin in 1974.

Manuscript Collections

The Mississippi Department of Archives and History, the largest repository of manuscript collections in the state, contains literally hundreds of manuscript collections, varying in size from one page to many linear feet.

The following list includes a brief description of those collections which are most likely to be of interest to researchers outside the state.

Authors

812   Buck, Charles W.

Papers, 1852-1922, 607 items including letters, legal papers, diary, pictures, miscellaneous papers, and the original manuscript of **Uncle Bob.**

813   Carter, Hodding

1942-1950, Manuscripts of **Lower Mississippi, The Winds of Fear, Flood Crest, Southern Legacy,** and **Where Main Street Meets the River.**

814   Claiborne, John F. H.

Papers, 1807-1881, 1,700 items comprised of historical letters collected by Claiborne, as well as political papers and manuscripts.

815   Creekmore, Hubert

Papers, 1924-1948, 372 items including notes, notebooks, manuscripts and typescripts of **The Fingers of Night,** and miscellaneous papers.

816   Faulkner, William

Uncorrected proof from Random House of William Faulkner's **The Hamlet** (1940).

817   McLemore, Richard Aubrey

Papers, 1910-1971, 37 boxes of correspondence, papers, and other materials relating to McLemore's career as an educator and director of the Mississippi Department of Archives and History.

818   Monette, John W.

Papers, 1841-1851, 145 items, including letters, material relating to his **History of the Discovery and Settlement of the Valley of the Mississippi,** and manuscripts of two poems.

819   Percy, William Alexander

1917-1941, 6 items, including letters to reviewers of his book and others, original (typed) manuscript of **Lanterns on the Levee: Recollections of a Planter's Son.**

820   **Rowland, Dunbar**

Papers, 1885-1937, over 5,000 items consisting primarily of Rowland's correspondence from 1890 to 1937, pertaining to the Department of Archives and History and the Mississippi Historical Society, business papers, and legal papers. Included is a typescript of **Military History of Mississippi.**

821   **Street, James H.**

1939-1945, manuscripts of 19 short stories, five novels, and one volume of short stories, and typewritten printers copies of **Oh, Promised Land, In My Father's House, Tap Roots, By Valour and Arms,** and **The Gauntlet.**

822   **Welty, Eudora**

Papers, 1930-1975, 1,127 items including letters from noted writers, letters by Miss Welty to friends, photographs, manuscripts of **The Ponder Heart, The Shoe Bird, Losing Battles,** and 12 short stories.

BUSINESS

823   **Bank of Mississippi Collection**

Papers, 1819-1882, 3 manuscript boxes containing correspondence, charter, reports, receipts, and miscellaneous papers of the Bank of Mississippi.

824   **Drake, Winbourne Magruder**

Papers, 1901-1966, 58 boxes of correspondence, royalty deeds, oil and gas leases, ledgers, cattle books, and other material relating to Drake's career as cattleman, farmer, and president of the Board of Trustees of Jefferson Military College.

825   **Leverich, Charles P.**

Papers, 1833-1854, 966 items including correspondence from Natchez merchants to Leverich, a New York merchant.

826   **Little and Griffin Collection**

Papers, 1787-1921, 364 items including business papers, lease agreements, letters, promissory notes, land records pertaining to Peter Little, 1784-1857, and Alonzo Mercer Griffin, 1811-1872, of Natchez. Little brought the first steam engine to Natchez in operating a sawmill, and Griffin was Natchez postmaster.

827 McNutt Plantation Collection

Papers, 1835-1845, 8 items including papers concerning business arrangements of George Rust of Virginia and Alexander B. McNutt of Warren County concerning the purchase of slaves.

828 Trask-Ventress Family Collection

Papers, 1791-1921, 332 folders of items of an economic nature regarding the production, shipment, and sale of cotton in Wilkinson County.

Civil War

829 Civil War Patriotic Envelopes Collection

292 patriotic envelopes published in 1861 by firms in New York, Boston, Philadelphia, and Cincinnati which were sold to soldiers by camp vendors and sent home to families.

830 Davis, Jefferson

Papers, 1847-1910, 168 items of correspondence between Jefferson and Varina Davis, Mrs. Margaret Davis Hayes, and Lucy Hayes collected by Fred A. Rosenstock of Denver, Colorado. Of particular interest are a letter dated November 30, 1847, from Davis to Secretary of War W. L. March recommending rifles made by Eli Whitney; 8 confederate bonds; a letter from Robert E. Lee to Davis dated September 14, 1863 concerning troop movements; and an autograph album containing the signatures of the Confederate cabinet and U. S. officials.

831 McCardle Photograph Collection

66 photographs of prominent men of the Confederacy collected by William H. McCardle for his **History of Mississippi.** Included are photographs of P. G. T. Beauregard, Braxton Bragg, Jefferson Davis, Wade Hampton, Robert E. Lee, Joseph E. Johnston, John B. Hood, Stonewall Jackson, J. E. B. Stuart, and others.

832 McKean, Thomas J.

96 items of manuscripts and clippings on the Battle of Corinth; 89

manuscripts comprise the offical papers of Brigadier General McKean, temporary commander of Corinth in 1862 and commander of the 6th Division of the Army of Tennessee in the Battle of Corinth.

833   Nugent, William L.

Papers, 1860-1896, 103 items of correspondence of William Nugent to his wife, Eleanor Fulkerson Smith Nugent.

834   Ruggles, Daniel

Papers, 1862-1865, 315 items including military papers, correspondence, and telegrams of Brigadier General Daniel Ruggles.

835   Sessions, J. F.

Papers, 1862-1865, 166 items including letters, orders, reports, and other military papers of J. F. Sessions, who served as a captain in the Regiment of Mississippi Infantry, C.S.A.

836   Stuart, Oscar J. E.

Papers, 1848-1909, 200 items of letters, diaries, and broadsides concerning the family and connections of Colonel Stuart, over half of which relate to the period of the Civil War.

837   U.S.S. Mississippi Collection

Log books, 1847-1848, of the U.S.S. **Mississippi,** which was sunk during the Civil War.

Education

838   Jefferson College Collection

Papers, 1803-1965, 8,867 items including correspondence, receipts, financial papers, journals and minutes of the Board of Trustees, student and miscellaneous records of Jefferson College at Washington. Also included is a set of 88 boxes of additional papers of Jefferson Military College with emphasis on the period 1947-1964.

Plantations

839 James Allen Plantation Collection

1860-1865, 1 plantation book, 1860-1865, of James Allen of Warren County with information on land, slaves, and family history.

840 John C. Burrus Collection

Papers, 1831-1918, 2,152 items of family, business, and legal correspondence of John Crawford Burrus, owner of a plantation at Benoit.

Politics

841 Alcorn Family

Papers, 1839-1906, 52 items including letters and papers of the family of James L. Alcorn, the second largest planter in Mississippi in the 1840's who served as state legislator, Brigadier General in Confederate Army, governor, and U.S. Senator.

842 Ames, Adelbert

Papers, 1874-1929, 36 items of correspondence dealing with Governor Ames' Reconstruction administration. A letter to the President of Brown University describes the financial affairs of Mississippi during reconstruction; another letter gives "secret" information on the Vicksburg riots.

843 Association of Citizens' Councils of Mississippi

Papers, 1942-1973, 742 items from the files of the Association of Citizens' Councils of Mississippi headquarters at Greenwood, including articles, court cases, correspondence, educational materials, and photographs.

844 Bilbo, Theodore G.

Papers, 1915-1941, 65 items of correspondence and personal papers of Bilbo concerning his career as State Senator, Lieutenant Governor, Governor, and U. S. Senator.

845 Bruce, Blanche K.

Papers, 1877-1878, 7 items of memorabilia and letters of Bruce, the second Negro U. S. Senator from Mississippi.

846   Calhoun, Solomon S.

Papers, 1851-1908, 263 items including petitions and letters of Judge Solomon S. Calhoun, president of the Constitutional Convention of 1890.

847   Clark, Charles

Papers, 1810-1892, 416 items of personal, business, and military papers and family photographs of Charles Clark, who served in the Confederate Army and was Governor of Mississippi, 1863-1865.

848   George, James Z.

Papers, 1845-1888, 168 items of correspondence and papers of James Zachariah George, who served as Confederate officer, Chief Justice of the Mississippi Supreme Court, and U. S. Senator. Most are letters to his wife which detail the social life of Jackson in the 1850's and his life as a prisoner of war on Johnson's Island.

849   Holmes, David

Papers, 1796-1825, 21 items including letters, certificates, and commissions of Holmes, governor of both the Mississippi Territory and the state of Mississippi and U. S. Senator.

850   Quitman, John A.

Papers, 1812-1860, 2,530 items including correspondence, papers, and records of John Anthony Quitman of Natchez, who served in the state legislature, as a judge of the Mississippi Superior Court of Chancery, a member of the Constitutional Convention of 1832, state senator, governor, military governor of Mexico City, and Congressman.

851   Lamar, L. Q. C.

Papers, 1854-1918, 242 items including letters, speeches, and documents relating to Lamar's career as Congressman and Special Commissioner from C.S.A. to Russia.

852   Lowry, Robert

Papers, 1861-1908, 37 items of correspondence received by Lowry while a general in the Confederate Army and as governor of Mississippi, including letters from Jefferson Davis.

RELIGION

853   Drake, Benjamin M.

Papers, 1805-1950, ca. 7,900 items of letters to and from the Reverend Benjamin Michael Drake, a Methodist minister in Mississippi, and the Drake family papers.

854   Ford, John

Papers, 1818-1944, 145 items including documents, letters, and business papers of the Reverend John Ford, a pioneer Methodist minister in Mississippi, and his descendants.

Mississippi Geological Survey
2525 North West Street   39216

855   Library

A collection of ca. 30,000 volumes relating to the geology of Mississippi and other states, petroleum exploration, water resources, and paleontology, including most publications of the U. S. Geological Survey and the U. S. Bureau of Mines. Of special interest to rock hounds and others is a display collection of ca. 300 minerals from around the world.

Mississippi Research and Development Center
3828 Ridgewood Road   39205

856   Information Service Division

A collection of ca. 6,000 volumes and 500 journals in technical, business, and economic fields, along with manufacturer's directories and other reference aids for Mississippi businessmen.

KOSCIUSKO

Mid-Mississippi Regional Library
201 South Huntington Street   39090

857   Local History and Genealogy

A collection of ca. 300 items, including census records back to 1800, the **Star-Herald** and its predecessors, 1854-1910, a file of a Holmes County newspaper, beginning in 1838, and 15 items relating to Thaddeus Kosciusko, the Polish patriot who came to America and became a brigadier general in the Continental Army.

LAUREL

Lauren Rogers Library and Museum of Art
Fifth Avenue and Seventh Street   39440

858   Library

ca. 1,000 volumes of genealogical works with emphasis on the New England states, books on the history of Laurel and Jones County, and publications which complement the Museum's art collection with its concentration on American painting of the 19th and early 20th centuries.

MACON

Noxubee County Library
501 South Jefferson   39341

859   Local History

ca. 200 volumes of Mississippi materials relating primarily to the history and genealogy of Macon and Noxubee County, including the works of two local writers — William Ward, a 19th century poet, and Zona Idella Marshall, author of **Certain Women,** a biographical sketch of several women in the Bible.

MERIDIAN

Meridian Public Library
2517 Seventh Street   39301

860   Local History

ca. 2,000 volumes, along with clipping, picture, and genealogical files covering the Southern states but emphasizing Meridian and Lauderdale County. Included are census records, **The Meridian Star** from 1898 to date, and George Kline Shank's **Meridian,** a history of the city, published in 1961.

MISSISSIPPI STATE

Mitchell Memorial Library
Mississippi State University   39762

861 **Mississippiana**

Housed in the Special Collections Department are 11,000 cataloged volumes relating primarily to the history and literature of Mississippi, including first editions of the works of William Faulkner, Eudora Welty, Tennessee Williams, and other Mississippi writers.

862 **Brougher, William Edward**

Papers, 1906-1964, 800 items consisting of diaries, correspondence, poems, reports, speeches, and scrapbooks of Brougher, a U. S. Army officer, including diaries of his years as a prisoner-of-war in a Japanese camp during World War II.

863 **Catledge, Turner**

Papers, 1936-1975, 140 linear feet, partly on microfilm, consisting chiefly of Catledge's office files during his tenure as managing and executive editor of the **New York Times,** 1945-1970. Also included are speeches, memorabilia, photographs, and research material for his autobiography, **My Life and the Times.**

864 **Cox, Allen Eugene**

Papers, 1934-1975, 30 linear feet, consisting of correspondence, clippings, published material, and other papers, chiefly pertaining to racial problems in the South, the Citizens' Council, National Council of Churches, farm labor unions, and cooperative farms.

865 **Dantzler Lumber Company**

Records, 1888-1968, 75 linear feet, consisting of ledgers, journals, correspondence, maps, aerial photographs, land books of this south Mississippi company.

866 **Delta Ministry**

Papers, 1965-1970, 18 linear feet, including memoranda, minutes, budgets, newsletters, and clippings, relating to the involvement of the Delta Ministry, a project of the National Council of Churches, with race relations, church affairs, and political and social issues in the Mississippi Delta.

867 **Fontaine, Edward**

Papers, 1818-1923, 19 reels of microfilm (ca. 2,000 items), including correspondence, daily journals, church records, legal papers, and lectures of Edward Fontaine, an Episcopal minister and Confederate officer.

868   Griffin, Charles H.

Papers, 1964-1973, 70 linear feet, consisting of correspondence, speeches, newsletters, and reports concerning Griffin's service as U. S. Representative from Mississippi, including material relating to the Mississippi Freedom Democratic Party and Representative John Bell Williams.

869   Hobbs Family

Papers, 1835-1935, ca. 25,000 items consisting of correspondence, statements of account, and other material concerning B. T. Hobbs, Brookhaven newspaper editor; Mississippi politics; the prohibition movement in Mississippi; and the Anti-Whitecap Movement in Lincoln County.

870   Rice, Nannie Herndon

Papers, 1824-1963, 7,500 items including correspondence, diaries, bills of sale of slaves, rent and labor contracts, and school reports of Miss Rice and her family.

871   Ross, Emmett Lloyd

Papers, 1825-1955, 835 items including correspondence, legal papers, short story manuscripts, and the diary of a Union soldier, and the Civil War letters of Ross, a Confederate officer and journalist.

872   Ross, Isaac

Estate Papers, 1845-1889, 276 items concerning the estate settlement of Isaac Ross, who provided for the manumission of his slaves and their return to Liberia if they so desired. Also included are correspondence, business papers, and legal papers of Isaac Ross Wade, in part concerning the American Colonization Society.

873   Sheldon, George

Papers, 1928-1961, 5,512 items, including correspondence, legal papers, speeches, poetry, and clippings, concerning primarily the "Lily White" Republican Party of Mississippi.

874   Stennis, John C.

Papers, 1927-1977, 1,100 linear feet, consisting of the official correspondence, books, pamphlets, newspaper clippings, photographs, tapes, and memorabilia of Senator Stennis.

875   Ward, Rufus

Collection, 1837-1900, ca. 1,500 items consisting of correspondence, business papers, military orders, and other papers of the James Sykes family of Columbus during the antebellum, Civil War, and Reconstruction periods.

876   Other Manuscript Collections

1784-1977, Approximately 600 linear feet pertaining primarily to Mississippi political, agricultural, social, and literary history.

NATCHEZ

Judge George W. Armstrong Library
South Commerce and Washington Streets   39120

877   Natchez Collection

A complete file of Natchez Pilgrimage folders and programs, 1932 to date, are among a collection of local historical materials and works of Natchez authors, including the manuscript of Alice Walworth Graham's historical novel, **Cibola;** galley proofs of **Natchez Under the Hill** by Edith Wyatt Moore; and a typescript of Elizabeth Brandon Stanton's **Burr** and **Fata Morgana.**

NEW ALBANY

Jennie Stephens Smith Library
Court Avenue   38652

878   Genealogy

ca. 2,400 items, including printed material from most of the Eastern and Southeastern states; census, pension, and enlistment records; church and local histories with genealogical material; immigration records, and heraldry.

OCEAN SPRINGS

The Laboratory Library
Gulf Coast Research Laboratory   39564

879 Marine Sciences

Representing 15 fields of marine science, this collection of ca. 10,000 volumes, 280 journals and 25,000 reprints, supports a research program which is restricted to the 369-mile tidal shoreline of Mississippi.

PHILADELPHIA

Choctaw Central High School
Pearl River Community   39350

880 American Indians

A collection of ca. 300 volumes on North American Indians with emphasis on the Choctaw tribe of central Mississippi and Alabama along with textbooks in the Choctaw language.

PICAYUNE

Pearl River County Library System
Goodyear Boulevard   39466

881 Zeltner, W. A., Collection

ca. 450 items of printed and manuscript material about and/or by Mississippians, old Hancock County, and Pearl River County, along with a tape collection of historical recollections.

PONTOTOC

Dixie Regional Library
114 North Main Street   38863

882 State and Local History

ca. 1,000 items, including books, pictures, clippings, and a file of local newspapers, **The Pontotoc Progress** and its predecessors, from 1836 to date.

PORT GIBSON

Harriette Person Memorial Library
Port Gibson   39150

883   **Russell, Irwin**

A collection of Russell memorabilia, including a portrait of Russell, his parents, and his intended bride; paintings by his mother; and photographs, and letters, is appropriately maintained in a handsome historic building, which was erected 14 years before the poet's birth in 1853.

STONEVILLE

Delta Branch Experiment Station
Stoneville   38776

884   **Library**

Agricultural research materials, including 17,000 volumes and extensive files of federal and state agricultural publications, comprise the library of the Delta Branch of Mississippi State University, the world's largest cotton experiment station.

TOUGALOO

Coleman Library
Tougaloo College   39174

885   **Black Collection**

3,400 volumes of books and periodicals by and about blacks, including first and rare editions, and supplemented by 250 recordings by black recording artists.

886   **Bruhland, Michael, Memorial Collection**

ca. 150 linear feet of newspapers, periodicals, underground and radical publications dealing with civil rights, civil liberties, socialism, marxism, and the Vietnam War.

887   **Delta Ministry**

Papers, 1964-1974, ca. 40 linear feet of material including the organizational files of the Delta Ministry in Mississippi. Voter registration, civil rights, civil liberties, and economic ills in the black communities of Mississippi are key areas covered in this collection.

888   Horowitz, Charles, Collection

Papers, 1960-1971, ca. 5 linear feet of papers collected by Horowitz during the Civil Rights era, including some items on the Delta Ministry, Mississippi Freedom Democratic Party, and other civil rights activists and groups in Mississippi.

889   King, B. B.

Memorabilia, 1950-present, 150 items including plaques, certificates, recordings and other materials relating to this famous blues recording artist.

890   Kudzu File of Radical News

ca. 6 linear feet including original copies of articles and photographs published in the Jackson (Miss.) underground KUDZU paper, 1969-1972.

891   The Civil Rights Movement in Mississippi

Papers, 1950-1974, ca. 300 linear feet of papers of the NAACP Legal Defense Fund, Inc., the Lawyers Constitutional Defense Committee, and the Lawyers Committee for Civil Rights Under Law. Consists of legal briefs, transcripts of civil rights trials and lawsuits, during the Civil Rights Era.

892   James A. Loewen, et. al. Collection

Papers, 12 linear feet, including papers and manuscripts of research done on Mound Bayou and other parts of Mississippi; the original notes and manuscripts for Loewen's book. **The Mississippi Chinese;** and Loewen and Charles Sallis' **Mississippi: Conflict and Change.** (Some of the Mound Bayou papers are restricted until 1980.)

893   Ross, Emery, Collection

Papers, 1890-1965, over 150,000 items, including clippings, books, and pamphlets dealing with black and white persons in Africa and America. Most of the materials on Africa deals with the Schweitzer years.

894   Schutt, Jane, Collection

Papers, 1962-1976, concerning the U.S. Commission on Civil Rights, the local committee in Jackson, correspondence and minutes for local meetings, and correspondence between persons in the Washington, D. C. office and the Jackson office.

895   Staples, Robert

Papers, 1957-1977, 18 items of original manuscripts of this eminent black sociologist, covering black sociological thought and research on/by black sociologists in America.

896   Sugarman, Tracy

Drawings, 83 framed original drawings by Sugarman during the summer of 1964 for his book, **Stranger at the Gates,** which depicts the civil rights movement of that period.

897   Ward, Jerry

Papers, 1972 to date, copies of correspondence to/from Jerry Ward, Mississippi poet and critic, from contemporary black writers and critics. Some of the most eminent writers included are George Kent, Houston A. Baker, Jr., Julius Thompson, and Etheridge Knight.

898   Wilson, Hilda C.

Papers, 1960-1974, 6 linear feet of papers and a journal kept by Mrs. Wilson in her travels across the state as a civil rights worker.

TUPELO

Lee County Library
219 Madison Street   38801

899   Mississippi Room

From the 1852-1902 diary of S. A. Agnew, who established one of the early schools in the Tupelo area, to a linear foot of materials relating to Tupelo-born Elvis Presley, this collection of ca. 3,000 volumes covers a wide range of Mississippiana with emphasis on Lee County and Tupelo. Also included are early Pontotoc deeds and records as sections of Pontotoc County were once a part of Lee County.

Visitor Center and Headquarters
Natchez Trace Parkway   38801

900   Library

In addition to ca. 2,600 volumes and other materials relating to the history and natural history of the Natchez Trace, an Indian trail which has become one of the most popular parkways in the nation, the collection includes files of prints, slides and transparencies; archaeological and geological specimen and authentic reproductions of historical items used along the 450-mile Trace.

UNIVERSITY

University of Mississippi Library
University   38677

901   The Mississippi Collection

Currently occupying six rooms, this collection of Mississippiana is comprised of 20,000 cataloged volumes along with thousands of uncataloged items of historical and cultural importance to the state. In addition to the distinctive William Faulkner collection, the works of David Cohn, Elizabeth Spencer, James Street, Eudora Welty, Richard Wright, Stark Young, and many other Mississippi writers are well represented. The major manuscript holdings and other collections in the Mississippi Room are described separately.

902   Abernathy, Thomas Gerstle, Collection

Papers, 1940-1970, 217 linear feet, correspondence, bulletins, clippings, Defense Department study on Southeast Asia, correspondence and documents related to 1965 seating challenge, and African trip briefing documents.

903   Agnew, Reverend Samuel

Papers, 1853-1902, 9 linear feet, Diaries, primarily recording Agnew's youthful experiences at the Battle of Brice's Cross Roads.

904   Barrett, Russell H. Collection

Papers, 1959-1970, 12 linear feet, material concerning James Meredith's admission to Ole Miss, race in Mississippi, speeches, correspondence, clippings regarding integration at the University of Mississippi.

905   Bellamann, Henry, Collection

Papers, 1920-1948, 500 items including correspondence from friends in literary and musical world, manuscripts of 300 published and unpublished poems, and original and publishers' manuscripts of **King's Row** and seven other novels.

906   **Byrnes, Roane Fleming Collection**

Papers, 1860-1950, 24 linear feet, correspondence, clippings, family history, material dealing with Natchez Trace.

907   **Canzoneri, Robert W.**

Papers, 1962-1970, 5 linear feet, various drafts: the novel **Men with Little Hammers,** poems entitled **Watch Us Pass** and **Barbed Wire and Other Stories.**

908   **Cohn, David L.**

Papers, 1927-1960, 10 1/2 linear feet, including correspondence with artists, writers, and political figures, rough drafts of published works, other manuscripts, typescripts, notebooks, and business correspondence.

909   **Collins, Ross, Collection**

Papers, 1912-1950, 3 linear feet, including scrapbook of 134 photographs of Churchill, Eisenhower, Truman, Roosevelt, U. S. Army Generals, Chiefs of Staff, and others of World War II era and photographs of war, cartoons, and copies of speeches.

910   **Deavours, Judge Stone, Collection**

Book collection, ca. 1900, includes 400 volumes of Mississippiana — religious works, fiction, history, biography, and poetry — from Judge Deavours' private library.

911   **The Douglas Collection**

Papers, 1899-1935, 9 linear feet, comprised of over 400 White House photographs and other memorabilia, presidential photographs, White House invitations, newspapers, and McKinley memorial items.

912   **Eastland, James Oliver**

The papers of Senator Eastland, recently placed in the University Library, have not been accessioned.

913   **Faulkner, William**

ca. 690 volumes of criticism — books, dissertations, theses, pamphlets, and off-prints; 1,190 copies of editions of Faulkner's works, original Faulkner letters, related manuscripts collections, pictures, films, tapes, and clippings.

914   **Garner, James Wilford**

Papers, ca. 1900-1939, 80 linear feet, includes correspondence, typescripts of lectures, manuscripts and published articles, and personal financial records.

915   **Gartin, Carroll**

Papers, 1953-1966, 67 linear feet, including correspondence arranged by counties, autograph letters from colleagues, clippings, reports, bills, and statements in typescript form.

916   **Hamblett, Theora**

Papers, 1913-1972, 6 linear feet, including 29 original drawings, oil paintings, photographs of Miss Hamblett, and catalogs of her work.

917   **Harrison, Byron Patton**

Papers, 1913-1941, 51 linear feet, of correspondence from colleagues and constituents, clippings, speeches, framed political cartoons and photographs and campaign buttons.

918   **Hudson, Arthur Palmer**

Papers, 1910-1966, 5 linear feet, collection of Mississippi folklore — versions of Mississippi ballads, lyrics, and tape recordings of bird calls, ballads, and reminiscences.

919   **Huxley, Julian**

Papers, ca. 1910-1950, 1 linear foot, comprised of letters from Stark Young to Julian Huxley and to Lady Huxley.

920   **Johnson, Felton M.**

Papers, 1950-1968, 20 linear feet, Memoranda, photographs, and letters from public figures.

921   **Lumber Archives**

Records, 1833-1958, 268 linear feet, comprised of extensive material concerning five major lumber companies, business correspondence, magazines, and over 50 letter books.

922   Miller, William M. "Fishbait"

Papers, 1941-1974, 180 linear feet, includes office memoranda, menus, souvenirs, large photograph collection, autographed letters, baseball, and 12 restricted boxes.

923   Robinson, David M.

Papers, 1907-1955, 23 1/2 linear feet, consisting of correspondence and drawings of objects, buildings, and cities unearthed in course of Robinson's archaeological career, and daily reports and book orders.

924   Rowland, Dunbar

Papers, ca. 1900-1960, 3 linear feet, of correspondence, manuscripts, and photographs pertaining to Mississippi during this period.

925   Silver, James W.

Papers, 1951-1975, 1 1/2 linear feet, including articles, newspaper clippings, and a series of articles under title of "Report from Britain," 1950.

926   Whittington, Will M.

Papers, 1939-1950, 164 linear feet, correspondence with colleagues and constituents, clippings, slip laws, and other records of Congressman Whittington.

927   Williams, John Sharp

Papers, 1910-1932, 5 linear feet, Copies of letters from colleagues and constituents, autographic letters (notably from James K. Vardaman) and a few photographs.

928   Other Manuscript Collections

ca. 72 collections, including the papers of Byron D. Beckwith, John Faulkner, Bobbie Gentry, L. Q. C. Lamar, and Winthrop Sargent; Ku Klux Klan materials; the playscript of Tennessee Williams' **Cat on a Hot Tin Roof** and **Orpheus Descending**; and an extensive collection of musical recordings by Mississippians.

VICKSBURG

Technical Information Center
U. S. Army Engineer Waterways Experiment Station   39180

929   Library

>   ca. 225,000 items in fields of hydraulics, soil dynamics and mechanics, trafficability of vehicles, dredged material, flexible pavements, effects of nuclear weapons, explosive evacuation, expedient surfacing and related subjects. Serving as a central reference library for the U. S. Army Engineer Waterways Experiment Station and the entire Corps of Engineers in assigned subject fields, the library maintains a catalog of 12 other technical collections throughout the country.

Vicksburg and Warren County Historical Museum
Old Court House   39180

930   Library

>   Featured in a collection which includes ca. 7,000 volumes relating primarily to the Confederacy, the Siege of Vicksburg, and Warren County genealogy is a complete file of J. Mack Moore's glass negatives of the most famous steamboats ever to ply the Mississippi River. As a Bicentennial project, selected prints from these negatives were published by the Museum in an attractive paperback, entitled **Vicksburg Under Glass.**

YAZOO CITY

Ricks Memorial Library
310 North Main Street   39194

931   Local History

>   ca. 300 volumes which relate to the history of Yazoo City and Yazoo County, including the source materials for the history of Yazoo County prepared by the Works Progress Administration and the manuscript of Harriet DeCell's Bicentennial history, entitled **Yazoo, Its Legends and Legacies.**

VI

SPECIAL COLLECTIONS
IN
LIBRARIES OF NORTH CAROLINA

Compiled
By
J. Isaac Copeland

ALBEMARLE

Learning Resource Center
Stanly Technical Institute
Route 4, Box 5   28001

932   **Respiration**

A respiratory therapy collection of ca. 100 volumes and 25 sound filmstrips and programmed sets on this subject and the related fields of physiology, pharmacology, and nursing.

ASHEBORO

Randolph Public Library
201 Worth Street   27203

933   **Local History**

Randolph County history, 1779 to date: 1,000 volumes including histories of the county and North Carolina histories which cover this county along with microfilm copies of county census records, 1790-1880, wills, deeds, estates, etc., 1779-1900, and the **Encyclopedia of Quaker Genealogy.**

934   **Genealogy**

250 books covering Randolph County families and a card index by name of tax lists and census records prior to 1820.

ASHEVILLE

Pack Memorial Public Library
Asheville   28801

935   **North Carolina Collection**

Over 15,000 items relating to the state with emphasis on Asheville and Western North Carolina, including a large collection of North Carolina fiction, poetry, and biography; 30 file drawers of newspaper clippings dating from the 1920's; over 1,000 photographs of Asheville and vicinity; and 400 volumes of genealogy and regional history.

936   **Wolfe, Thomas**

More than 3,000 items concerning the author, including 500 books, 1,000 periodical articles, 40 notebooks of newspaper clippings, 8 notebooks of photographs, 25 original letters of Wolfe, many family letters and memorabilia. The emphasis of the collection is on Wolfe's connection with Asheville.

937   **Sondley Reference Library**

Now a part of the Library's Reference Department, this collection of 35,000 volumes was donated by Foster A. Sondley in 1930. Major areas of the collection include literature, Indians of the Southeast, the Civil War, and natural history.

BANNER ELK

Carson Library
Lees-McRae College   28604

938   **Stirling Collection**

ca. 5,000 items, including books, pamphlets, maps and clippings on the Southern Appalachian Region with emphasis on Western North Carolina, East Tennessee, Southwest Virginia, and North Georgia.

BEAUFORT

Atlantic Estuarine Fisheries Center Library
National Marine Fisheries Service   28557

939   **Special Library**

Serving the second oldest fisheries laboratory sponsored by the federal government (established in 1899) the collection is composed of ca. 10,000 volumes and ca. 15,000 reprints dealing with marine biology and ecology, fish and fisheries, oceanography, and the radioecology of aquatic organisms as affected by radiation.

BELMONT

Abbot Vincent Taylor Library
Belmont Abbey College   28012

940   Benedictine

ca. 3,500 items, including books and periodicals written and published by Benedictine monks and nuns. A number of these works were published in the 17th and 18th centuries; several rare Benedictine journals were issued by European abbeys in the 19th and early 20th centuries.

941   North Carolina

ca. 1,000 volumes on the history of North Carolina from Colonial times to the present, including several county histories and a significant section on the history of religion and especially the Roman Catholic Church in the state.

942   Valuable Books

Over 10,000 rare books with particular emphasis on patristical writings and the works of important historical figures in the Catholic Church. Included are several incunabula, the earliest being a 1471 edition of the works of St. Albertus Magnus.

McCarthy Library
Sacred Heart College   28012

943   Reid, Christian

A collection of 19 books written by Frances Christian Fischer Tierman, a native of Salisbury, North Carolina, who wrote under the pseudonym of Christian Reid along with the original Laetare Award presented to Mrs. Tierman by Notre Dame University.

BOILING SPRINGS

Dover Library
Gardner-Webb College   28017

944   Dixon, Thomas

The author's personal library of 1,112 items, including copies of most of his works, published items about him, the manuscript of his play, "The Traitor," and the outline of his autobiography, **The Story of a Minister's Son.**

945   **Gardner, Oliver Max**

65 folders, binders and boxes of scrapbooks, diaries and holographs of the families of Oliver Max Gardner and his wife, Fay Lamar Webb. Her diaries and scrapbooks cover the period, 1929-1933, when Gardner was governor of North Carolina.

946   **North Carolina Baptist History**

ca. 500 items, consisting largely of the associational minutes, particularly of the Old Tryon County (roughly Lincoln, Gaston, Rutherford, and Cleveland counties and three counties in upper South Carolina).

BOONE

Carol Grotnes Belk Library
Appalachian State University   28608

947   **William Leonard Eury Appalachian Collection**

Relating to the Southern Appalachian Mountains, this collection is comprised of over 10,000 volumes, clippings, slides, oral history tapes, and original manuscripts of John Foster West's **Time Was, This Proud Land,** and **Ballad of Tom Dula,** Vera and Bill Cleaver's **Where the Lilies Bloom,** and John and Ina Van Noppen's **History of Western North Carolina Since the Civil War.**

Also included are four extensive collections of ballads — the Amos Abrams, the I. G. Gree, the James York, and the Virgil Sturgill Collections, along with the Tatum Collection of the tools and houseware items of Appalachia and the Fry Collection of knotted bedspreads, illustrating 20 different patterns.

BUIES CREEK

Carrie Rich Memorial Library
Campbell College   27506

948   **Campbell Collection**

ca. 500 items, including letters, pictures and other materials relating to Dr. James Archibald Campbell, who founded Buies Creek Academy which became Campbell College in 1926, and the correspondence and personal files of Dr. L. H. Campbell, which occupy more than 30 file folders and cover the years 1931-1967.

BURGAW

Pender County Library
Box 487   28425

949   **Mattie Bloodworth Collection**

History and genealogy of Pender County and the lower Cape Fear Region of North Carolina.

CHAPEL HILL

Louis Round Wilson Library
University of North Carolina   27514

Rare Book Collection

950   **Burton, Emmett, Collection**

1,000 volumes of first and special editions of 19th and 20th century English and American authors.

951   **Confederate Imprints**

More than 1,000 books, pamphlets, periodicals, and newspapers printed in the Confederate States of America, 1861-1865, covering a wide range of subjects. Excluded are North Carolina imprints.

952   **Davie, Preston, Collection**

50 volumes of early Americana, consisting of works relating to the Americas, beginning in the 16th century.

953   **Detective-Mystery Collection**

Over 6,000 titles, including first editions of many works of noted British and American mystery writers.

954   **Eton College**

A collection of 169 volumes of reminiscences, histories, poetry, and fiction relating to Eton College in England.

955   **Gray, Bowman, Collection**

4,000 World War I posters and broadsides from America, Britain, France, Germany, Russia, Italy, and other European countries. These posters, some designed by such renowed artists as Joseph Pennell, display a wide variety of mood, intent, and artistic style, as well as providing useful information on conditions and attitudes during the First World War.

956   **Hanes Collection of the History of the Book**

Comprised of books and their antecedents: Sumerian and Babylonian clay tablets, papyri (Egyptian and Greek writings), stone inscriptions, manuscripts, and 600 items of 16th, and 17th, and 18th century printing, including many outstanding landmarks in the history of printing.

957   **Hanes Collection of Incunabula**

778 specimens of incunabula, ranging in length from one page to complete volumes, including examples of early printing from the countries of Western Europe.

958   **Hebraica and Judaica**

Books, periodicals, and articles, beginning in 1523, chiefly in Hebrew and English, with many volumes from the 17th and 18th centuries.

959   **Henderson, Archibald, Collection of Shaviana**

ca. 4,000 books and pamphlets, 1,000 playbills, programs, cartoons, and pictures of play productions written by or relating to George Bernard Shaw. Included are first editions of Shaw's plays, novels, and essays, along with later and foreign editions.

960   **Holt, Roland, Collection**

A collection relating to the American theatre, 1881-1931, consisting of 15,000 clippings, programs, pictures, photographs, and articles, supplemented by 13 scrapbooks, 250 photographs in albums, 100 opera libretti, and 60 miscellaneous books on drama.

961   **Hoyt, William Henry, Collection**

More than 850 volumes relating to French history, primarily of the French Revolution and Napoleonic eras, including personal correspondence of Napoleon.

962   **Jente Collection of Proverbs**

2,000 items relating to the proverb from the 15th century to 1952, including volumes of critical and bibliographical material.

963   **Mazarinades**

Over 800 Mazarinades including Scarron, Cyrano de Bergerac, the Cardinal de Retz, and the Prince de Conti. Also included are **La Mazarinade** and Moreau's **Bibliographie des Mazarinades.**

964   **Medieval and Renaissance Manuscripts**

A collection of 506 manuscripts, from the 12th to the 16th century, chiefly Italian and Latin, including documents, Books of Hours, and literary works.

965   **Sanskirt (Indic) Manuscripts**

24 Olas (palm leaf manuscripts) dealing with medicine, astrology, and sermons on Buddha.

966   **Shedd Collection of Aphorisms**

229 books relating to aphorism, from the 17th century to 1920, primarily English but including French, German, Spanish, and Latin works.

967   **Southern Pamphlets Collection**

Over 8,300 pamphlets, 1820 to the present, from the South, exclusive of North Carolina. This collection covers a wide range of subjects.

968   **Tannenbaum Collection**

Over 300 volumes of the works of Shakespeare, including the 2nd (1632), 3rd (1663-1664), and 4th (1658) folios, along with the 1954 facsimile of the 1st folio.

969   **Wilmer Collection**

Over 825 novels, 1861 to the present, concerning the Civil War. Bibliographical material is also included.

The Whitaker Collections:

970   Costume Plates in color: 50 books and portfolios, in both historical and geographical vein.

971   Cruikshank, George: More than 100 first and special editions containing illustrations of this 19th century English illustrator.

972   Dickens, Charles: All but 3 of Dickens' novels published in monthly numbers, along with first and rare editions of the complete works of Dickens.

973   Johnson, Samuel: Over 500 first and rare editions of the writings of Johnson and his friends, including important works of James Boswell, Chesterfield, Goldsmith, and Fanny Furney.

974   Thackeray, William Makepeace: 125 volumes, including all of Thackeray's major works, many of his less-known works, and installments of the journals in which his writings were published.

975   **Maps Collection**

ca. 75,500 maps and 1,800 volumes, comprised of sheet maps, atlases, gazateers, and other cartographical reference works.

976   **The North Carolina Collection**

A comprehensive collection of North Caroliniana, including more than 130,000 books and pamphlets, 120,000 mounted newspaper clippings, 23,000 photographs and negatives, 6,300 reels of microfilm, 3,500 maps, and 500 recordings.

Although manuscripts are now added to the Southern Historical Collection, the North Carolina Collection maintains some manuscript materials, including the Thomas Wolfe Collection, 1894-1957, of 1,400 pieces **(R)** and more than 70 linear feet of manuscripts of books by other state authors.

MANUSCRIPTS DEPARTMENT

977   **Southern Historical Collection**

A collection of 7,000,000 items, dating from 1588, and organized in more than 4,000 groups, including private papers of individuals, families, organizations, and institutions from every Southern state; primarily letters, diaries, account books, business and legal documents, and literary manuscripts, pertaining to all aspects of the history of the Southern states. Transcripts produced by the Southern Oral History Program are included.

Most of the holdings are described in Blosser and Wilson's **The Southern Historical Collection: A Guide to Manuscripts** (1970) and Smith's **The Southern Historical Collection: Supplementary Guide to Manuscripts, 1970-1975.**

978   General and Literary Manuscripts

17,000 items, from non-Southern states of the United States, several groups of European manuscripts, and a large group of private papers from Popayan, Colombia.

CHARLOTTE

Mint Museum of Art Library
501 Hempstead Place   28207

979   Delhom-Gambrell Reference Library

ca. 2,000 volumes along with auction and museum catalogs and slides specializing in historical pottery and porcelain, particularly English and Oriental, and in the applied arts.

Public Library of Charlotte and Mecklenburg County
301 N. Tryon Street   28202

980   Genealogy and Local History

ca. 14,000 volumes of local history with concentration on Charlotte and Mecklenburg County, but including North Carolina and, to a limited extent, the Southeast, along with representative works by North Carolinians. Standard genealogical sources with some family histories, DAR and census records.

981   Golden, Harry

Deposit collection of manuscripts, galley, page and autographed copies of most of Golden's works, assorted working papers, resource materials, and interviews. 129 boxes of manuscript materials, including **Only in America, For 2¢ Plain,** and other writings.

982   Textiles

Extensive collection of printed materials on the textile industry, since 1940 with some earlier, with emphasis on spinning, weaving and dyeing. Some international publications, including directories.

Everett Library
Queens College   28274

983   **North and South Carolina History**

ca. 1,200 volumes, all related to the history of the two Carolinas, with no particular area of interest.

984   **Women's Studies**

Queens College collection of women's studies, 1771 to date, 48 linear feet of materials, including manuscripts, correspondence, photographs, and scrapbooks.

J. Murrey Atkins Library
University of North Carolina at Charlotte   28223

985   **Caroliniana**

ca. 50 linear feet of papers of individuals and organizations and ca. 2,000 titles which document the history and culture of North and South Carolina with emphasis on the Piedmont section in general and Mecklenburg County in particular. Represented in the collection are papers by Harry Golden, Carl Sandburg, Bruce and Nancy Roberts, Eugene Payne, and Marian Sims.

986   **Historical Maps**

Collection of 53 maps, mostly pre-1900 maps of North and South Carolina, including Collet's **Compleat Map of North Carolina,** 1770, and Mouzon's **An Accurate Map of North and South Carolina,** 1775.

987   **English Drama**

842 English plays, 1620-1826, originally collected by Princess Augusta Sophia, daughter of King George III, including works by Henry Fielding, David Garrick, and John Gay.

988   **Erotica**

86 volumes, ca. 1890-1930, including scholarly works on sex as well as scatological novels.

989   **Oral History**

ca. 70 tapes, variety of interviews with such outstanding North Carolinians as Sam Ervin, Jr. Harry Golden, and Luther Hodges along with P.O.W.'s of World War II.

CLINTON

Sampson-Clinton Public Library
Connestee Street   28328

990   **Local History**

83 reels of microfilm covering vital statistics and other information on Sampson and surrounding counties along with a number of published and unpublished histories of North Carolina counties, and local genealogies.

DAVIDSON

Davidson College Library
Davidson   28036

991   **Wilson, Woodrow**

ca. 200 books by and about Woodrow Wilson, 4 signed letters, Wilson's personal notebook kept while a freshman at Davidson, 4 scrapbooks of clippings and other materials.

992   **Ney Collection**

30 books and pamphlets on Peter Stuart Ney and Marshal Michel Ney; photographs of Peter S. Ney, holograph poems, a mathematics notebook in his handwriting, several books with his marginalia, and a scrapbook of clippings on the Neys.

993   **Rogers, Bruce**

150 volumes and printed ephemera designed by Bruce Rogers, many inscribed by him, in a collection containing most of the works which are considered Rogers' finest.

994   **Burns, Robert**

35 early editions of the works of Robert Burns, including the 1787 "First Edinburgh Edition."

DOBSON

Surry Community College Library
Box 304   27017

995   Surry County

Collection comprised of two locally-produced histories of the county from earliest settlement to ca. 1935; material on Eng and Chang Bunker, the original Siamese twins; and genealogies of ten local families.

DURHAM

William R. Perkins Library
Duke University   27706

Manuscript Department

996   The Manuscript Collections, from 1500 to date, are comprised of ca. 7,000,000 items constituting more than 6,700 collections of correspondence, business and labor records, organizational archives, scrapbooks, diaries, and other original materials. The collections focus on the history and culture of the American South, but numerous items relate to the literature and to the political, social, military, religious, and economic history of the United States. Substantial holdings concern Peru and the British Empire. Also included is a limited amount of audiovisual material on a variety of topics, including North Carolina folklore and 20th century American diplomacy.

A revision of the **Guide to the Manuscript Collections in the Duke University Library,** compiled in 1947, is currently in preparation.

Rare Books and Manuscripts

Notable among extensive holdings are the following special collections:

997   **American Writers**

Collections of the papers of American writers include those of Thomas Nelson Page, E.D.E.N. Southworth, and Thomas H. Chivers, and, more recently, those of Fred Chappell, Frank G. Slaughter, William Styron, and Ovid W. Pierce.

998   **Bellamann Collection**

More than 300 volumes relating to Dante Aligheri, 14th century Italian poet, were presented by the widow of Henry Bellamann, author and musician.

999   **British Writers**

Sizable collections of the papers of Joseph Conrad, Thomas Carlyle, the

Rossetti family, and Sir Edmund W. Gosse represent literary activity during the 19th and early 20th centuries.

1000 Frank C. Brown Folklore Collection

54,000 items consisting of correspondence, 230 recordings, 60 wax cylinders, 50 aluminum discs, and transcriptions of poems, stories, anecdotes, and folk songs collected by Professor Brown during his research on the folklore of the Southeast.

1001 Confederate Imprints

3,300 works published in the Confederate States of America, 1861-1865.

1002 Emblem Books

ca. 350 volumes relating to the art of illustrating literary works with symbolic engravings, which was employed in Western European countries in the 16th and 17th centuries.

1003 Flowers Collection of Southern Americana

An endowed collection consisting of 2,500,000 items relating to many aspects of the history, literature, and life in the Southern states. Although all periods are covered, the collection has notable strength in the Civil War and Reconstruction eras.

1004 Greek and Latin Manuscripts

A collection of 69 Greek manuscripts, primarily consisting of religious texts, and 145 Latin manuscripts, including a 10th century codex of Saint Augustine's commentary on the Psalms and 6 manuscript works of Cicero.

1005 Hayne, Paul Hamilton

More than 1,800 books, pamphlets, and other materials from the library of this South Carolina poet. Many of these works include interesting marginalia penned by Hayne.

1006 History of Medicine

The private library of Josiah C. Trent formed the nucleus of this collection of ca. 18,000 volumes covering six centuries of the history of medicine. This collection is housed in the Duke Medical Center Library.

1007   Italian Literature

Enhanced by the private library of Guido Mazzoni, a Florentine scholar, this collection is the most significant one relating to Italian literature in the Southeast. The Mazzoni library, purchased in 1948, consists of 23,000 books and 67,000 pamphlets and reprints, with emphasis on the 19th century.

1008   Moses, Montrose J., Collection

This collection of correspondence from and about many prominent authors, playwrights, and actors, along with photographs, playbills, and clippings constitutes a remarkably complete record of the American theatre, 1900-1950.

1009   Philippiana

The Robertson Collection of Philippiana consists of 5,000 volumes and other materials relating to the Philippine Islands.

1010   Trent, Josiah, Collection on Walt Whitman

A collection of manuscripts, poem notes, unpublished poems, and ca. 200 letters of Walt Whitman, along with various editions of **Leaves of Grass,** including the first issue (1855) and other works by and about the poet.

1011   Utopias

The Glenn R. Negley Collection of 570 volumes serves as the nucleus of a unique assemblage of materials relating to idealistic societies. Included is a Utopian work by Filippo Beroalda (1495) and a 1613 edition of Sir Thomas More's **Utopia.**

1012   Wesleyana and Methodistica

The nucleus of this denominational collection is the Frank C. Baker Collection of 14,000 items, which emphasize British Methodism of the 18th and 19th centuries. Included are holograph letters of John and Charles Wesley along with extensive materials relating to other early Methodist leaders.

Other Collections

1013   Among other outstanding special holdings are: (1) A Collection of American almanacs; (2) Joseph Bill Brown Collection in Religion, including books and music scores; (3) Thornton Shirley Graves Collection of 18th and

19th Century Drama; (4) Karl Holl Collection in Church History; (5) Gustav Lanson Collection of French Language and Literature; (6) E. C. Strisower Collection on International Law; (7) Carroll Wilson Collection of Emersonia; (8) Hispanic Collection; and (9) American Socialist Party Collection, consisting of books, pamphlets, newspapers, leaflets, and manuscripts.

Durham County Library
311 E. Main Street   27702

1014   North Carolina

ca. 15,000 volumes, including works by North Carolina authors, fiction with a North Carolina setting, non-fiction dealing with the history of or containing factual information on the state, and all books with a Durham imprint.

James E. Shepard Memorial Library
North Carolina Central University   27707

1015   Martin, Charles D., Collection

3,500 or more pre-1950 books by and about American Blacks, extensive holdings of African and Caribbean items, scattered copies of Negro newspapers and magazines dating back 100 years, and numerous works on slavery in the United States and Europe, some of which were written by slaves or ex-slaves.

1016   First Editions

Small collection of first editions, including several works of William Wells Brown, 19th century historian and social reformer.

EDEN

Rockingham County Public Library
527 Boone Road   27288

1017   North Carolina

ca. 3,725 volumes on North Carolina history with emphasis on Rockingham County.

1018   Large Print Books

ca. 1,200 volumes in large print format and covering a variety of subjects.

ELIZABETH CITY

Whitehurst Library
College of the Albemarle   27909

1019   North Carolina

Along with general North Caroliniana are local area subjects, including 15 books and many other materials on the Great Dismal Swamp, a natural wilderness extending through portions of the eastern counties, and the Dismal Swamp Canal, which connects the Chesapeake Bay with Albemarle Sound.

G. R. Little Library
Elizabeth City State University   27909

1020   Moore, P. W., Memorial Collection

Bearing the name of the University's first president, this collection of ca. 2,000 volumes is designed to support the colleges's program of Black studies in the social sciences, drama, music, art and literature.

Mary E. Griffith Memorial Library
Roanoke Bible College   27909

1021   Discipliana

ca. 200 volumes dealing with the history of the Church of Christ and the Christian Church in the United States.

ELKIN

Northwestern Regional Library
111 N. Front Street   28621

1022   Surry County

ca. 150 items, consisting of clippings, photographs, genealogies, cemetery records, and oral history tapes, which depict the history of Surry County.

1023 Yadkin County

ca. 400 items dealing with all aspects of the county's history from the 1780's to the present.

ELON COLLEGE

Elon College Library
Box 187   27244

1024 Christian Church Historical Collection

Serving as the official repository of the Southern Conference of the United Church of Christ, this collection contains source materials on and the publications of the Christian Church, which was founded by James O'Kelly in the late 18th century. The holdings include yearbooks, annual reports, the minutes of local churches and some manuscript materials.

FAYETTEVILLE

Cumberland County Public Library
Box 1720   28302

1025 Foreign Language Collection

ca. 8,000 volumes and 500 tapes and discs representing more than 40 non-English languages, with emphasis on popular titles and recorded materials for learning a language other than English or learning English as a second language. Through interlibrary loan, it serves as the state collection of library materials other than English.

1026 North Carolina

2,700 volumes, 76 maps, and ca. 6,000 vertical file items relating to North Carolina and Cumberland County history and genealogy with slides of local historical sites.

1027 Stein, Frances Brooks, Memorial Collection

More than 300 volumes in the field of education with emphasis on teaching techniques, educational trends, and the philosophy of education.

Davis Memorial Library
Methodist College   28301

1028   Lafayette, Marquis de

14 original letters and notes of Lafayette; ca. 200 books, including many first editions, 150 pamphlets and articles, and several newspapers dating back to 1797 and containing information on the Marquis de Lafayette. Also included are artifacts, such as cuff links and badges, two music scores prepared in honor of Lafayette, and maps of North Carolina and Fayetteville covering the period from 1757 to 1834.

1029   Huske, May Catherine, Collection

Varied collection of 476 books and numerous letters: 14 letters of Mary Ann Morrison (Mrs. Stonewall) Jackson, Varina Howell (Mrs. Jefferson) Davis, George Washington Custis Lee, Myra Clark Gaines, and Letitia Tyler Semple; more than 30 volumes which belonged to Judge David Davis, Supreme Court justice and administrator of the estate of Abraham Lincoln; and the library of Wharton J. Green, Congressman and son of General Thomas Jefferson Green of the Mier Expedition.

GASTONIA

Gaston County Public Library
115 W. Second Avenue   28052

1030   Genealogy

More than 325 volumes and ca. 60 genealogical manuscripts dealing with residents of Gaston, Lincoln, Cleveland, Mecklenburg, and Rutherford counties and adjoining counties in South Carolina. Includes copies of family histories, cemetery records, marriage bonds, wills, and other materials.

1031   Local History

ca. 400 volumes, manuscripts, and a file of clippings which cover more than 50 years of the history of Gastonia and Gaston County.

1032   Loray Strike

ca. 65 items, including books, manuscripts, articles and clippings, an unpublished drama, and tapes of recollections of this strike of textile workers in Gastonia in 1929.

GREENSBORO

Thomas F. Holgate Library
Bennett College   27420

1033   **Afro-American Women's Collection**

Over 350 items, including books, records, filmstrips, pamphlets and other materials by or about Afro-American women.

1034   **Cuney, Norris Wright**

More than 300 items of personal and business correspondence of Norris Wright Cuney, Black Texas Republican of the Reconstruction period.

1035   **Palmer Memorial Institute**

Included in the Bennett College Archives is a considerable amount of material on the now-defunct Palmer Memorial Institute.

Geensboro Public Library
201 N. Greene Street   27402

1036   **Porter, William Sydney**

ca. 50 books by and about O. Henry, along with newspaper and periodical articles, notes of his biographer, Dr. C. A. Smith, some manuscript material, photographs and other memorabilia of this native short story writer.

1037   **North Carolina and Local History**

6,750 books and pamphlets about North Carolina and by North Carolina authors; extensive collection of clippings and pamphlets accumulated since 1902; census, court, land, and marriage records; and a file of the **Greensborough Patriot** and other local newspapers.

Guilford College Library
5800 Friendly Avenue   27410

1038   **The Quaker Collection**

Papers of the North Carolina Yearly Meeting of the Religious Society of Friends, 1680 to date, comprised of ca. 625 volumes of minutes of monthly, quarterly and yearly meetings along with birth, marriage and death records of monthly meeting members, minutes and records of missionary committees, and special committees of the yearly meeting.

Of particular historical interest are:

1039   Papers of the Standing Committee of the Yearly Meeting, 1759-1823, a volume of minutes covering the on-going concerns of the Yearly Meeting, especially regarding the issues of slavery, war, and church discipline.

1040   Papers, 1824-1881, of the Meeting for Sufferings, which replaced the Standing Committee in 1824, including 3 volumes of minutes and ca. 250 items of correspondence and other materials relating to slavery and the transporting of freed slaves to free territory.

Quaker Leaders

Papers of many outstanding Quaker leaders, primarily in North Carolina, including:

1041   Binford, Raymond, 1900-1952, 28 ms. boxes.

1042   Coffin, Addison, 1894-1896, typescript of his unpublished **Early Settlement of Friends in North Carolina.**

1043   Collins, John B., 1869-1887, 5 items including illustrated journals of travels to North Carolina by this Quaker artist from New Jersey.

1044   Cox, Clara I., 1929-1932, ca. 25 items.

1045   Cox, Levi, 1830-1914, ca. 1,000 items including letters and estate papers of relatives and friends of this Quaker minister in Randolph County, North Carolina.

1046   Crenshaw, John B., 1861-1865, 270 items including letters from this Richmond, Virginia, Quaker and North Carolina Friends in seeking to assist Quaker conscientious objectors who had been conscripted or imprisoned by the Confederate Army.

1047   Dixon, Gurney, 1853-1903, including letters written while a student at New Garden Boarding School (1853-1859) which later became Guilford College.

1048   Elliott, Aaron, 1808-1885, ca. 100 items including estate papers and records of the African fund of the North Carolina Annual Meeting.

1049   Hackney, Priscilla Benbow, 1892-1918, 178 items including letters from Addison Coffin describing his travels and accounts of Quaker activities.

1050 Haworth Family, 1875-1967, ca. 1,300 items.

1051 Hockett Family, 1856-1883, ca. 50 items including letters to and from an imprisoned conscientious objector during the Civil War.

1052 Jay, Allen, 1875-1887, 24 items, mostly letters concerning this Indiana Quaker who came to North Carolina during the Reconstruction Period to revive the Society of Friends.

1053 Jordan, Richard, 1797-1800, typed copy of journal recounting travels in the Quaker ministry.

1054 King, Francis T., 1872-1890, mostly letters concerning the transition of New Garden Boarding School to Guilford College.

1055 Korner, Russell and Gertrude, 1920-ca. 1960, including letters from Lewis L. Hobbs, noted educator and church leader.

1056 Martin, Zenas L., ca. 1901-1929, letters concerning the director of the Friends mission in Cuba.

1057 Peck Family, 1837-1849, letters between Harriet Peck, one of the first Quaker teachers in North Carolina, and her family in Rhode Island.

1058 Pearson, James Larkin, 1947-1974, 8 items concerning Pearson as Poet Laureate of North Carolina.

1059 Penney, Norman, 1908, list of books sent to North Carolina Friends in 1746.

1060 Reynolds, Delilah, 1830-1852, including a diary written in code when she was a student in the first class (1837) of New Garden School.

1061 Taylor, Nellie Moon, 1879-1955, including letters from Mary Moon Meredith, prominent Quaker minister of the late 19th century.

1062 **Genealogy**

Extensive collection of histories of North Carolina, South Carolina, Georgia, Tennessee, and Virginia Quaker and allied families, including Bible records and privately printed and unpublished histories.

1063 **Oral History**

15 tapes of reminiscences of Quakers from Monthly Meetings of 8 Quaker groups in North Carolina and memories of student days at New Garden Boarding School, later Guilford College.

F. D. Bluford Library
North Carolina Agricultural and Technical State
University   27411

1064   Ethnic Studies

Over 1,600 volumes of selected ethnic literature with emphasis on Black Studies material, but also including resources on the culture of the Caribbean and the East Indian and Oriental countries.

Walter Clinton Jackson Library
University of North Carolina at Greensboro   27412

1065   Bell, Thelma Harrington

Manuscripts, 1960-1972, 20 items of children's books written by Thelma H. Bell and illustrated by Corydon Bell.

1066   Carroll, Ruth Robinson

ca. 135 manuscripts and drawings of books by Ruth and Latrobe Carroll, including **Tough Enough's Trip** and **Salt and Pepper**.

1067   Coit, Margaret Louise

Original manuscripts, 3 linear feet, of her **John C. Calhoun; John C. Calhoun, American Portrait;** and **Mr. Baruch.**

1068   Current, Richard Nelson

Manuscripts, 1 linear foot, of his **The Lincoln Nobody Knows** and **Lincoln the President: Last Full Measure** by James G. Randall and Richard N. Current.

1069   Dickinson, Emily

Over 100 volumes of first editions, variant bindings and early works by and about Emily Dickinson.

1070   Green, Paul Eliot

Collection, 2 linear feet, including diaries, letters and manuscripts relating to the life and literary career of this Southern playwright and novelist.

1071   Greene, Nathanael

Typed copy of Letter Book, January-February, 1781, containing 173 letters of Major General Nathanael Greene to Revolutionary War officers, governors, and others concerning military matters during the Carolina campaign.

1072   Jarrell, Randall

Collection, 6 linear feet, of manuscripts, correspondence and other items relating to Jarrell, and ca. 200 volumes, including first, foreign and other editions of his works.

1073   Lenski, Lois

Collection, 1922-1974: 12 linear feet, including manuscripts of ca. 50 books, original illustrations and other items concerning her works, along with first, foreign and other editions of all the books illustrated or written by Lois Lenski.

Of special interest is the collection of ca. 700 18th and 19th century American children's books presented to the library by Lois Lenski.

1074   Pound, Ezra Loomis

Letters, 1951-1961: 40 items written by Pound to Elizabeth Winslow, containing information on his recent publications.

1075   Silva, Luigi, Cello Collection

Over 300 books including early treatises on the cello and ca. 2,000 published scores, parts and pieces for the cello and manuscript of his un-finished history of the cello.

1076   Winston, Ellen Black

Papers, 1891-1973; 20 linear feet, relating to Dr. Winston's career as teacher, social economist, and U.S. Commissioner of Welfare.

Other Special Collections:

1077   Book Arts

ca. 1,000 volumes on or illustrating the art of the book, with emphasis on the Victorian Period to the present but including Medieval manuscript illumination and 15th century printing.

1078   Southeastern Theatre Conference

Papers, 1950-1973: 10 linear feet including records and correspondence of the Southeastern Theatre Conference, founded by Paul Green.

1079   Woman's Collection

ca. 3,000 volumes of imprints from the 17th-20th centuries by, about, and of interest to women. Emphasis is on English and American works, including first editions of major literary figures, female writers of the Antebellum South, and a large group of suffrage pamphlets.

1080   This collection also contains the nearly 900-volume Anthony M. Ludovici Private Library of Books and Pamphlets on Woman, her history, physiology, emancipation, etc.

1081   Miscellaneous Special Collections include manuscripts, letters and other materials relating to John Herbert Beeler, Mebane Holoman Burgwyn, Elizabeth Ann Bowles, Olive Tilford Dargan, Harriet Wiseman Elliott, Sue Ramsey Johnston Ferguson, Ina B. Forbus, Clora McNeill Foust, Anna Maria Gove, Margaret McConnell Holt, Edythe Latham, Virginia Terrell Lathrop, Julia Montgomery Street, Carl Heinrich Schnauffer, and Emily Herring Wilson.

GREENVILLE

J. Y. Joyner Library
East Carolina University   27834

1082   Manuscript Collection

The East Carolina Manuscript Collection, a public manuscript depository, is comprised of more than 400 collections spanning the period from 1715 to date. Although holdings are not restricted by subject, classification, or geographical area, active solicitation is concentrated on North Carolina materials, military papers, missionary papers, and tobacco records. Material prior to 1800 is limited, but holdings for the 19th and 20th centuries are extensive and cover a wide spectrum of topics.

1083   Oral History

Complementing the manuscript holdings is a collection of oral history memoirs pertaining primarily to military history; tobacco operations in China; missionary activities in China, Africa, and Latin America; and North Carolina politics, jurisprudence, and social and cultural activities.

Sheppard Memorial Library
530 Evans Street   27834

1084   Natural History

More than 3,000 volumes in the field of natural history with special emphasis on the eastern United States and North Carolina.

HAMLET

Richmond Technical Institute Library
Hamlet   28345

1085   Automobiliana

ca. 300 books on modern and antique cars, particularly racing models and the famous car races and raceways.

1086   Railroadiana

ca. 250 volumes relating to the history of railroading, famous trains, and rail systems of the world, with emphasis on railroads of the South and especially North Carolina.

1087   North Carolina

ca. 600 volumes covering North Carolina history, culture, and people from the first settlement to the present, and including some early records of Richmond County on microfilm.

HAW RIVER

Technical Institute of Alamance
Box 623   27258

1088   **Business and Engineering Technologies**

ca. 15,000 items, including books and audiovisual materials touching nearly every phase of business and industrial technology and mechanical engineering since 1950, with particular emphasis upon automotive engineering.

1089   **North Carolina History**

Microfilm collection of 300 reels covering basic records of Alamance, Chatham, Caswell, and Orange Counties, 1750-1890, and Federal Census population records for the state of North Carolina, 1800-1850.

HICKORY

Elbert Ivey Memorial Library
420 Third Avenue   28601

1090   **Hahn, Walter A.**

16 folders of assorted papers relating to the Hahn and other local families.

1091   **Hefner, Raymond**

104 folders containing early Catawba County historical and genealogical materials, including many copies of early land grants in this area.

HIGH POINT

Bienenstock Furniture Library
High Point   27261

1092   **Furniture**

Believed to be the largest furniture library in existence, the Bienenstock collection consists of more than 4,000 volumes collected by N. I. and Bernice Bienenstock in their travels around the world.

High Point Public Library
411 South Main Street   27261

1093 Furniture Collection

More than 600 books which trace the evolution and history of furniture styles from earliest times to the present, especially valuable for the illustrations of virtually all types of furniture.

1094 North Caroliniana

ca. 4,000 books and pamphlets on the history, social life, and character of North Carolina, including Banastre Tarleton's **A History of the Campaigns of 1780 and 1781,** published in 1787, and James Sprunt's own copy of his **Chronicles of the Cape Fear River** with his revision notes for the second edition.

JACKSONVILLE

Coastal Carolina Community College
222 Georgetown Road   28540

1095 Onslow County

Extensive microfilm file of Onslow County records, including land entries, 1712-1928; marriage register, 1851-1961; and Index to Wills, 1765-1961.

Marine Corps Air Station Library
New River   28545

1096 Reading Resource Collection

ca. 600 items, including high interest, easy books, U. S. Office of Education materials, and other publications relating to remedial reading.   **R**

JAMESTOWN

Learning Resource Center
Guilford Technical Institute   27282

1097 Guilford County History

Microfilm collection of ca. 240 reels of Guilford County records, 1771-1920, including **Voices of Guilford,** a pictorial and oral history of the county.

KENANSVILLE

Dorothy Wightman Library (Duplin County)
Seminary Street   28349

1098   Duplin County

Clipping file from local newspapers, 1940 to date, of items relating to Kenansville and Duplin County.

KINGS MOUNTAIN

Mauney Memorial Library
100 S. Piedmont Avenue   28086

1099   Genealogy

Volumes, occupying 15 linear feet, on the Mauney Family and other local families.

KINSTON

Learning Center
Lenoir Community College   28501

1100   Local History

Microfilm of the 18th-20th century basic records for the following North Carolina counties: Beaufort, Bertie, Camden, Carteret, Chowan, Craven, Duplin, Edgecombe, Greene, Halifax, Jones, Lenoir, Northampton, Pasquotank, Perquimans, Pitt, and Wayne. Numberous long runs of records of churches in New Bern, and in Jones, Lenoir, and Onslow Counties.

LAURINBURG

DeTamble Library
St. Andrews Presbyterian College   28352

1101   Scottish Collection

A miscellaneous assortment of ca. 750 volumes dealing with the literature and history of Scotland, including a few incunabula and manuscripts.

LEXINGTON

Davidson County Public Library
224 South Main Street   27292

1102   **Walser, Richard**

A collection of 25 books, written or edited by Walser, a native of Lexington and Professor of English at North Carolina State University, including collections of North Carolina poetry, drama, and folk tales.

1103   **Genealogy**

ca. 30 items consisting of church and cemetery records and histories of a number of Davidson County families and ca. 500 items relating to tracing genealogical records of North Carolina families.

LOUISBURG

Cecil W. Robbins Library
Louisburg College   27549

1104   **North Carolina**

A collection of ca. 600 books on North Carolina history with emphasis on the Louisburg area and a small assemblage of printed genealogical materials on families of Franklin and early Granville counties.

LUMBERTON

Robeson County Public Library
101 N. Chestnut Street   28358

1105   **Biggs, Kate Britt, Collection**

Local history of Robeson County along with   both printed and manuscript materials on the Britt and Biggs families.

1106   **Local History and Genealogy**

Microfilm copies of the basic records of Robeson County, census records from 1800 to 1850, and published materials on Robeson and other counties of Southeastern North Carolina and families native to this area.

MANTEO

Research Library
Cape Hatteras National Seashore   27954

1107   The Outer Banks

General reference material associated with coastal and marine ecosystems, ca. 750 books oriented to North Carolina, plus over 1,000 separate items in the Technical and Historical Files. Included is a collection dealing with the resource management problems and practices of the Outer Banks and ca. 100 titles of special references to man's relationship with the sea.

1108   Environmental Collection

ca. 25 reports, including drafts and final copies of Environmental Impact Statements of particular interest to the Cape Hatteras Group.

Children's collection of 100 volumes for use in environmental education. The books are transferred to the Children's Environmental Center, "The Sandcastle," during peak visitation periods and returned to the Research Library during the off-seasons.

1109   English Colonial History

ca. 500 pieces and 100 titles relating to 16th century English colonial history and traditions, including the valued set of John White's drawings (books).

1110   Wright Brothers

Collection of the papers of Orville and Wilbur Wright from 1867 to 1912, 100 volumes plus 300 items relating to the Wright Brothers and their experiments and other activities on the Outer Banks. Replicas of the Wright Brothers' plane is on display in the Visitor's Center.

1111   Lifesaving Service Records

Bound volumes of the Annual Reports of the U. S. Lifesaving Service, 1800-1915, plus ca. 500 miscellaneous reports on this subject.

Dare County Library
Manteo   27954

1112 **Dare County Map Collection**

ca. 85 maps, including flood-prone areas of the state, North Carolina Transportation System maps, the John White series of historical maps and geological, topographic and hydrographic maps of the Outer Banks area, along with David S. Clark's **Index to Maps of North Carolina in Books and Periodicals.**

1113 **North Carolina Collection**

ca. 2,350 vertical file items and ca. 1,000 books and periodicals relating to North Carolina.

MARS HILL

Memorial Library
Mars Hill College   28754

1114 **Appalachian Room**

A collection of ca. 3,000 volumes relating to the history and culture of the Southern mountains, including local history, fiction and folklore; microfilm copies of 60 dissertations on topics related to the Appalachian Region; and more than 500 prints, 1915 to date, reflecting the people and places in Appalachia. On display are over 400 items of 19th century furniture, farm tools, and household implements.

1115 **Baptist History**

600 items, comprised of minutes and records, 1830 to date, of Baptist associations in North Carolina, including the French Broad Association of Western North Carolina.

1116 **Long, James**

Papers, ca. 1890-1940: 22 notebooks and scrapbooks, sermons, religious pamphlets, and articles by Long.

1117 **Lunsford, Bascom Lamar**

Papers, 1900-1970: More than 3,000 items, including personal and family letters; correspondence and memorabilia relating to Lunsford's career as a folk song collector, performer, and festival organizer.

1118   Mountain Music

Recorded music, 1925 to date, including over 200 records of traditional music and 25 taped field recordings of both instrumental and vocal music.

1119   Ruskin, Gertrude

69 volumes relating to the Cherokee Indians along with more than 300 projectile points, game stones, and other Cherokee artifacts.

MISENHEIMER

G. A. Pfeiffer Library
Pfeiffer College   28109

1120   Mary Fisher Floyd Archives

Included in the archival records of Pfeiffer College are the records of its antecedents, Pfeiffer Junior College, 1935-1954; Mitchell Home School, 1903-1934; and Oberlin Home and School, 1885-1902.

MONROE

Union County Public Library
316 East Windsor Street   28110

1121   Local History

A collection of ca. 100 books and typed manuscripts, which is primarily concerned with local history and the genealogy of more than 30 Union County families.

MONTREAT

The Historical Foundation of the Presbyterian and Reformed Churches
Montreat   28757

1122   The Foundation Library

A collection of ca. 80,000 volumes, 28,000 pamphlets, 17,000 bound periodicals, and 37,000 photographs, all of which concern the Presbyterian and Reformed churches of the world. As the repository for the official records of the Presbyterian Church United States, the Foundation collection is comprised of hundreds of manuscript volumes representing the synods, presbyteries, and sessions of that body. In addition, there are complete files of the minutes of the General Assemblies (or Synods) of the following: Presbyterian churches of England, Ireland, Canada, Mexico, the United Presbyterian Church in the United States, along with those of the United Presbyterian Church, the Orthodox Presbyterian Church, the Reformed Church in America, the Reformed Church in the United States, and the Evangelical and Reformed Church. The minutes of the General Assembly of the Cumberland Presbyterian Church are almost complete.

L. Nelson Bell Library
Montreat-Anderson College   28757

1123   Kester, Howard

Papers, 1923-1972: 14 microfilm reels including correspondence, writings, and other materials regarding this social reformer. (Originals are in the Southern Historical Collection of the University of North Carolina, Chapel Hill)

MORGANTON

Morganton-Burke Library
204 South King Street   28655

1124   Local History and Genealogy

25 oral history tapes including accounts of local events (the establishment of the Lake James Power Plant) and interviews with citizens along with the histories of 24 local families.

MOUNT AIRY

Mount Airy Public Library
Mount Airy   27030

1125   Carter Collection

Papers of William Carter, longtime mayor of Mount Airy, include programs, clippings, photographs and mementos from the 1880's through the 1940's.

MOUNT OLIVE

Moye Library
Mount Olive College   28365

1126   **Free Will Baptist Historical Collection**

More than 5,000 items, including books, broadsides, diaries, minutes, and other materials relating to Free Will Baptist history. Although the collection represents the 19th and 20th centuries, there are a few 18th century items. Also included are associational materials relating to the English General Baptists and the Continental Anabaptists. Although not restricted by state or division of the denomination, the greatest concentration is on North Carolina and the Southeast.

MURPHY

Nantahala Regional Library
101 Blumenthal Street   28906

1127   **Cherokee Indian Collection**

Over 100 volumes on the Cherokee Indians in North Carolina, especially their early history. Includes Matthew Stirling's **Peachtree Mound and Village Sites, Cherokee County, North Carolina.**

NEW BERN

Craven-Pamlico-Carteret Regional Library
400 Johnson Street   28560

1128   **Genealogy**

Extensive holdings of genealogical records of most of the eastern North Carolina counties, covering the 17th through the 19th centuries, with emphasis on Carteret, Craven, Jones, and Pamlico counties.

NEWTON

Catawba County Historical Association
1716 South College Drive   28658

1129   **Eaton, D. M.**

Papers, 1920-1960: 2,500 items including personal correspondence and letters from associates in the fields of education, music, fashion, and horticulture.

1130   **Long Island Collection**

Papers, 1860-1865: 78 items of correspondence between a Confederate soldier and his family.

OXFORD

Richard H. Thornton Library
Oxford   27565

1131   **Hays, Francis Bacon**

Scrapbooks compiled by F. B. Hays, 1867-1959, in 142 volumes relating to persons and events in Oxford and Granville and Vance counties.

RALEIGH

Reference Library
North Carolina Museum of Art   27611

1132   **Valentiner, Wilhem R., Collection**

ca. 2.200 books and exhibition catalogs bequeathed by the first director of the Museum and noted art historian. Emphasis is on Dutch and Flemish Baroque painting and Italian Renaissance sculpture.

1133   **Cunliffe-Owen Collection**

Unusual collection of books and periodicals on costume and design, which were donated by Lady Marcia Cunliffe-Owen, a New York fashion designer.

1134   **Judaic Collection**

Books and materials relating to Jewish artists and Jewish Ceremonial Art.

1135 North Carolina Artist Collection

Ex.ansive vertical file material on ca. 900 North Carolina artists.

North Carolina State Department of Archives and History
Raleigh   27611

1136   As the official archival agency of the state, the Department of Archives and History serves as the repository for non-current official records of North Carolina as both colony and state, including: (1) Journals and other legislative records, beginning in 1689; (2) Executive records, including papers of the governors, 1694 to date; and (3) Judicial records since 1690.

1137   Of special significance is the collection of the original papers of North Carolina under the Lords Proprietors and the original Carolina Charter.

1138   Also included are the non-current records of North Carolina counties; U.S. Census records of North Carolina, 1800-1880; and copies of materials in the British Public Records Office relating to North Carolina as a royal colony.

1139   Records of a number of military leaders and papers relating to all wars in which North Carolinians have engaged are represented in the collection.

1140   Papers of many North Carolina Congressmen have been deposited in the Department of Archives and History.

North Carolina State Library
109 East Jones Street   27611

1141 Genealogy

A collection of ca. 7,000 genealogical items, consisting largely of secondary materials relating primarily to North Carolina and the states from which North Carolinians came.

D. H. Hill Library
North Carolina State University   27607

1142 Burlington Textile Library

A collection of 15,000 volumes consisting of materials in the areas of textile technology and textile chemistry, which is supplemented by sub-scriptions to 300 current textile journals and files of technical bulletins and trade literature.

1143　**Lyons, Harrye B., Design Library**

17,263 volumes along with ca. 40,000 slides and other materials relating to basic design, art, architecture, and urban planning, including an extensive collection of work by and about R. Buckminster Fuller.

1144　**Metcalf, Z. Payne, Collection**

1,100 volumes and 24 vertical files of research materials relating to the Hemiptera and Homoptera orders, and particularly on Auchenorryncha.

1145　**Tippmann, Friedrich F., Entomological Collection**

6,200 volumes of books and journals relating to entomology with 123 items designated as rare, including Carl Linnaeus' **Systema Naturae**, 1758-59.

1146　**History of Transportation**

Books and periodicals on the economic, social, and technological history of railroad, automotive, water, and air transportation, primarily in North America, with emphasis on railroad history.

1147　**Winston, Sanford Richard, Collection**

ca. 2,000 volumes, with annual additions, of works on music: bibliographies, criticism, history, librettos, and scores, selected for the sophisticated listener rather than the musicologist.

St. Mary's College Library
900 Hillsborough Street　27611

1148　**Wolfe, Thomas**

ca. 800 items by and about Wolfe, including 30 dissertations in xerographic form, 3 unpublished letters, and Aline Bernstein's own copy of an important letter from Wolfe discussing autobiographical writing.

Learning Resources Center
Shaw University　27611

1149　**Yergan Collection**

More than 1,400 volumes pertaining to African history, description, and travel, along with a number of classics in Afro-American literature.

1150   Schomburg Collection

A microfilm copy (687 reels) of the famous Schomburg Collection of materials on the life, literature, and history of the Negro.

Wake County Public Libraries
104 Fayetteville Street   27601

1151   Local History

Collection of ca. 4,000 volumes, 300 reels of microfilm (largely files of local newspapers), 500 documents and 8 vertical files of clippings which relate to the history of Raleigh, Wake County and the state of North Carolina, with little genealogical material included.

1152   Mollie H. Lee Collection (in Richard B. Harrison Branch)

Black Literature: More than 7,000 volumes and other materials, including fiction as well as non-fiction and both adult and juvenile, by and/or about Blacks.

ROCKINGHAM

Sandhill Regional Library System
1104 East Broad Avenue   28379

1153   Anson County Collection (in Anson County Public Library, Wadesboro)

Papers relating to local families and the early history of Anson County are found in the W. K. Boggan, Lilly Doyle Dunlap, and the Annie Blythe Ingram collections. Also included are the county's census records, 1800-1890 (except 1880), microfilm copies of local newspapers, the earliest being 1848, and the 1841 journal of James R. Plunket, operator of the Old Buck Tavern in Wadesboro.

1154   Hoke County Collection (in Hoke County Public Library, Raeford)

Census records of Cumberland and Robeson Counties, 1800-1880, with slave schedules for 1850 and 1860. Cumberland and Robeson are the parent counties from which Hoke was formed in 1911.

1155   Montgomery County Collection (in Montgomery County Public Library, Troy)

Microfilm copies of the "Core Collection" of Montgomery County Court House records, county census records of the 1800's, and miscellaneous files of local history along with **Facts about Montgomery County and Environs,** compiled by William Reaves, and 30 articles based on interviews with older citizens of the county.

1156   **Moore County Collection** (in Moore County Public Library, Carthage)

"Core Collection" of Moore County Court House records, microfilm copies of local newspapers, the earliest being 1887, county census records of the 1800's, files of genealogical materials and local history, and Rassie Wicker's **Miscellaneous Ancient Records of Moore County.**

1157   **Richmond County Collection**

Microfilm copies of Richmond County Court House records and local newspapers, beginning in 1884, county census records of the 1800's, files of genealogical and local history materials, and "Richmond Remembers," tapes of interviews with 12 elderly residents of the county.

ROCKY MOUNT

Thomas Hackney Braswell Memorial Library
344 Falls Road   27801

1158   **Genealogy**

More than 800 items, including census records, 1800-1880, for Nash, Edgecombe and adjacent counties along with extensive genealogical records for Granville, Bladen, Nash, and Elgecombe counties as well as neighboring counties in Virginia.

1159   **North Carolina**

Over 1,400 items relating to the state with emphasis on North Carolina biography, poetry, the novels of Thomas Wolfe, and local newspapers, beginning in 1920.

North Carolina Wesleyan College Library
US 301, North

1160   **Black Mountain College**

ca. 7,000 items, including books, prints and memorabilia, relating to Black Mountain College, 1933-1956.

SALISBURY

Corriher-Linn-Black Library
Catawba College

1161 **Poetry Council of North Carolina**

A collection of 720 volumes, plus 7 boxes of correspondence, covering the period from 1940 to date.

1162 **The Evangelical and Reformed Church**

This archival collection of the Southern Chapter of the Historical Society of the Evangelical and Reformed Church consists of ca. 5,000 items relating chiefly to the German Reformed Church and the Evangelical and Reformed Church in North Carolina, beginning in 1770 but particularly strong coverage from 1831 to 1955.

Hood Library and Heritage Hall
Hood Theological Seminary   27144

1163 **Walls Collection**

International in scope, this collection of more than 3,000 volumes is concerned with the history of minority groups with special attention to the African Methodist Episcopal Zion Church and Livingstone College.

1164 **Jordon Collection**

Records, documents, microfilms and oral history tapes designed to present more than 100 years of the C.M.E., A.M.E., and A.M. E. Zion Church.

Andrew Carnegie Library
Livingstone College   28144

1165 **The American Negro**

A collection of 3,384 volumes including the history and records of the A.M.E. Zion Church, 50 letters from Booker T. Washington to John Dancy, Sr., and manuscripts of books by W. J. Walls.

1166 **Dancy, John C.**

935 volumes, pictures and scrapbooks of Dancy, long-time executive

director of the Detroit Urban League along with the manuscript of his book, **Sands Against the Wind.**

SOUTHERN PINES

Southern Pines Public Library
Broad Street   28387

1167   North Carolina

ca. 500 volumes, including fiction and nonfiction, of works about the state or by North Carolinians.

SYLVA

Southwestern Technical Institute Library
Webster Road   28779

1168   North Carolina

A collection of ca. 1,500 volumes about North Carolina or by North Carolinians along with 78 reels of microfilm of the records of Jackson and Macon counties from 1820.

TARBORO

Learning Resources Center
Edgecombe County Technical Institute   27886

1169   Edgecombe County

Included in a collection of ca. 200 volumes relating to North Carolina are a number of official publications and microfilm records of Edgecombe County.

TRYON

Lanier Library Association
114 Chestnut Street   28782

1170   Morgan, Sidney H. Collection

210 volumes on the creative arts along with 18 portfolios of prints by the

old masters, and 75 volumes on the performing arts, selected for little theatre use. **R**

WAKE FOREST

Library
Southeastern Baptist Theological Seminary   27587

1171   **Baptist Beginnings in England**

Microfilm collection of 110 reels of early materials — books, tracts, and sermons — of Baptist work in Great Britain.

1172   **History of Southern Baptists**

Proceedings of local associations and state conventions of Southern Baptists and of the Southern Baptist Convention, including the annuals of the Southern Baptist Convention, 1855 to date, and annuals of the North Carolina Baptist Convention, 1830 to the present.

1173   **Church Curriculum Materials**

ca. 1,000 items, consisting of current and relatively current materials prepared by the Southern Baptist Convention for the various educational programs of the churches.

1174   **Johnson, Walter Nathan**

Papers, 1900-1952, comprised of several hundred items including manuscripts of published and unpublished works, some on ethical questions which did not become issues in society for two decades or more after the death of this North Carolina denominational leader.

1175   **McDowell, Edward Allison, Jr.**

Papers, 1933-1975, ca. 5 feet of materials relating to the leadership of this Southern Baptist minister and seminary professor in the field of race relations.

1176   **Turner, John Clyde**

ca. 3,000 manuscripts, ca. 1903-1972, including sermons, personal papers, and memorabilia of this prominent pastor and trustee of Southern Baptist institutions.

WASHINGTON

George H. and Laura E. Brown Library
122 Van Norden Street   27889

1177   **Warren, E. J.**

More than 700 items, including papers and letters of the North Carolina senator, beginning before the Civil War and going through the Reconstruction period.

1178   **Wiswall, Martha Matilda Fowle**

Xerox copies of 66 items, including 19th century letters and papers and the Civil War diary of Mrs. Wiswall, a sister of Governor Dan Fowle.

1179   **19th Century Business Records**

These collections include: Dunstan Papers, 192 items relating to Isaiah Respass and his business; Fowle-March Papers, 7 packets of xerox copies of business records of this early North Carolina shipping firm; B. F. and Jonathan Havens Collection, extensive collection of the business records of the wealthiest local citizens during the latter half of the 19th century; and Charles F. Warren Collection, 479 items of business transactions of eastern North Carolina lumber companies prior to 1900.

WENTWORTH

Rockingham Community College Library
Wentworth   27375

1180   **State and Local History**

ca. 700 volumes pertaining to North Carolina history and literature; two vertical files of items relating to Rickingham County, including some genealogical material; and 30 oral history tapes concerning the local area during the first half of the 20th century.

WHITEVILLE

Columbus County Public Library
Health Center Road   28472

1181 North Carolina and Whiteville

ca. 250 volumes on the history and literature of North Carolina, a pamphlet and clipping file of local history items, and runs of area newspapers, including the Whiteville **News Reporter,** 1924 to date.

Southeastern Community College
Whiteville 28472

1182 North Carolina Newspapers

A collection of 635 reels of microfilmed newspapers from the following North Carolina cities: Asheville, Charlotte, Durham, Elizabeth City, Fayetteville, Goldsboro, New Bern, Raleigh, Salisbury, Wilmington, and several others. The files range in date from 1783 to 1935.

1183 Southeastern North Carolina County Records

359 reels of microfilm of the records of the following North Carolina counties: Bladen, Brunswick, Columbus, Duplin, New Hanover, Onslow, Robeson, and Sampson. Dates range from 1807 to 1967.

WILKESBORO

Wilkes Community College Library
Wilkesboro 28697

1184 Oral History Collection

50 tapes, some video tapes, photographs, and transcripts of interviews on the history of Wilkes County.

1185 Pearson, James Larkin

Scrapbook of newspaper articles and other items relating to Larkin, Poet Laureate of North Carolina, 1950's to date.

WILMINGTON

Library/Learning Resource Center
Cape Fear Technical Institute 28401

1186   Carraway, Thomas B., Jr., Collection

A miscellaneous collection of ca. 50 volumes, including 5 18th century imprints and 11 works of the 19th century Southern novelist, John Esten Cooke — all part of the Institute's Living Museum.

New Hanover County Public Library
(formerly Wilmington Public Library)
409 Market Street   28401

1187   North Carolina Collection

ca. 5,700 volumes on North Carolina history and literature, ca. 8,000 pamphlets and clippings, over 1,200 reels of microfilm of local newspapers from 1799 to date, North Carolina census data from 1800 to 1880, and the basic county records for five southeastern North Carolina counties.

WILSON

Wilson County Public Library
Nash and Jackson Streets   27893

1188   Drama

ca. 2,000 volumes, including plays, collections of plays, and books on acting and the theatre, predominately English and American but classical and modern international drama represented.

1189   Local History

ca. 1,200 items, consisting of books and pamphlet materials on Wilson and Wilson County, primarily 20th century with some genealogical data included.

WINSTON-SALEM

Forsyth County Public Library
660 West Fifth Street   27101

1190   North Carolina Room

ca. 10,000 volumes about North Carolina or North Carolinians, extensive vertical files of local history and genealogy, North Carolina census records from 1790 through 1880, and microfilm files of local newspapers and the basic records of Forsyth, Stokes, Surry, and Rowan counties.

Moravian Archives
4 East Bank Street

1191 Moravian Collection

ca. 2,000 volumes and more than 10,000 manuscript pages, dating from 1753, and relating primarily to the Moravian settlement in North Carolina, known as Wachovia. The collection is comprised of letters, diaries, church records, and manuscript music.

The Moravian Music Foundation
20 Cascade Avenue 27108

1192 Peter Memorial Library

ca. 6,000 books and music scores dealing with music of the 18th and 19th centuries, with strong emphasis on American and Moravian music and music history.

1193 Lowens, Irving, Collection of Americana

Over 1,000 18th and 19th century tunebooks, containing sacred music used in American churches during that period along with hymnals without tunes and some secular music.

1194 Herbst, Johannes, Collection

ca. 500 manuscripts of over 1,000 compositions of Moravian choral music of the 18th and early 19th centuries, from the personal music library of Moravian Bishop Johannes Herbst, 1735-1812.

1195 Sheet Music Collection

ca. 2,500 itmes of sheet music, mostly songs and piano music for the 1820-1860 period.

1196 Other Collections:

Salem Congregation Collection, ca. 700 manuscripts of nearly 2,000 compositions formerly used for services at the Home Moravian Church in Salem, North Carolina; Salem Collegium Musicum Collection, ca. 600 pieces used by the community orchestra and ensembles in Salem; Salem Band

Collection, ca. 300 compositions used by the 26th North Carolina Regimental Band during the Civil War; Salem Lovefeast Odes, ca. 2,000 texts to anthems and other music used in the church at Salem; and Salem Copybooks, ca. 100 items of music copied in manuscript by residents of Salem during the 18th and 19th centuries.

Museum of Early Southern Decorative Arts
924 South Main Street   27108

1197   MESDA Documentary Research File

Typescript of ca. 30,000 items with excerpts from pre-1821 newspapers, court records, and other documents concerning the decorative arts in Maryland, Virginia, North Carolina, South Carolina, Georgia, Kentucky, and Tennessee, and particularly the craftsmen working in these areas.

1198   MESDA Photo Research File

Folders with ca. 3,000 items, consisting of photographs with data concerning objects of the decorative arts in North and South Carolina and five other Southern states, as found in private and public collections. Including furniture, silver and other metals, paintings, and textiles, most objects are of pre-1821 vintage.

Research Department Library
R. J. Reynolds Tobacco Company   27102

1199   Tobacco

An extensive collection of materials relating to tobacco agronomy and the various aspects of the tobacco industry, including aluminum technology and packaging.

Z. Smith Reynolds Library
Wake Forest University   27109

1200   Crittenden, Ethel T., Collection

North Carolina and Southern Baptist History collection, comprised of manuscript records of 96 North Carolina Baptist churches; microfilm records of 520 Baptist churches in the state; 9,300 volumes and 1,550 bound periodical volumes; 205 private collections of personal papers; vertical files of information on North Carolina churches and past and present pastors; and a few genealogical folders.

1201 Artoum, Camillo, Collection

Extensive news library and morgue of **The Reporter,** a magazine of world affairs, published in New York, 1949-1968. Donated to Wake Forest in 1975 by the founder and editor, Max Ascoli.

1202 Other Collections

Rare Books, with emphasis on author collections of 19th and 20th century English, American, and Irish literature in first and significant editions; The Charles H. Babcck Collection, composed of English first editions, 16th-20th centuries, American literature, 19th-20th centuries, and a collection of Southern authors; The Oscar T. Smith Collection of first editions, including the Kelmscott Chaucer; and among the collections of ephemera are the Hubert Evans Book Plate Collection and the Collection of Confederate Broadside Verse.

C. G. O'Kelly Library
Winston-Salem State University   27102

1203 Black Studies Collection

A gift from the Southern Association of Colleges and Schools, these selected books are representative of the numerous publications on Afro-Americans and African culture.

VII

SPECIAL COLLECTIONS
IN
LIBRARIES OF SOUTH CAROLINA

Compiled
By
Laura F. Pitzer

AIKEN

Aiken-Bamberg-Barnwell-Edgefield Regional Library
224 Laurens Street   29801

1204   **South Carolina**

ca. 2,000 volumes, both fiction and non-fiction, about South Carolina or by South Carolinians. Included in the collection are a number of genealogies of South Carolina families and microfilm files of Aiken and Barnwell newspapers, one of which covers 100 years.

Gregg-Graniteville Library
University of South Carolina at Aiken   29801

1205   **May Collection**

400 volumes pertaining to Southern history, including diaries and first person narratives of Civil War experiences and items of local history.

ANDERSON

Anderson County Library
202 East Greenville Street   29621

1206   **State, Local, and Family History**

More than 1,500 volumes of works by and about South Carolinians, city directories and histories of the Anderson area, and the **Book of the Dead,** which lists the persons buried in all the cemeteries in the county. Along with scattered genealogies from South Carolina and neighboring states, the collection contains microfilm copies of Anderson County census records, 1790-1880.

Research & Development Division Library
Clark-Schwebel Fiberglass Corporation
2200 South Murray Avenue   29622

1207 **Reinforced Plastics**

A collection of 500 volumes, supplemented by 50 periodical subscriptions, 700 microfiche, and 2,000 SEM, pictures and other audio-visual materials on glass fiber reinforced plastics. **R**

BEAUFORT

Beaufort County Library
700 Craven Street   29902

1208 **Busch, James, Collection**

600 books, pamphlets, and maps relating to the Civil War.

1209 **Beaufort Historical Society**

51 research papers, dealing with various facets of the history of Beaufort and the surrounding Sea Islands, which have been presented before the Society, along with short histories of a number of local families.

1210 **State and Local History**

The handwritten **Journal of the Proceedings of the Trustees of the College of Beaufort, 1795-1868** and a first edition of William Elliott's **Carolina Sports by Land and Water,** published in Charleston in 1846, are among the 728 volumes in this collection of state and local history. The Library also serves as a depository for Beaufort County documents.

United States Navy
Marine Corps Air Station   29902

1211 **Library**

Military arts and science in general and the history and maintenance of aircraft in particular are subject interests in this collection of ca. 20,000 volumes. **R**

BENNETTSVILLE

Marlboro County Library
Market Street   29512

1212   **Marlboro County**

The manuscript of Colonel C. W. Dudley's **History of Bennettsville** (1876) and copies of D. D. McColl's **Sketches of Old Marlboro** and the **Cemetery Records of Marlboro County** are included in this collection of several hundred books and manuscripts relating primarily to local history, area families, churches and societies of Marlboro County and the Pee Dee section of South Carolina.

CAMDEN

Kershaw County Library
1304 Broad Street   29020

1213   **Local History**

Included in a small South Carolina collection are ca. 200 volumes relating to the history of Camden, one of the oldest inland towns of the state and the scene of 14 battles during the American Revolution.

CENTRAL

Library-Learning Center
Central Wesleyan College   29630

1214   **Wesleyana**

A collection of ca. 900 items, including original letters, manuscripts, photographs, and artifacts relating to John Wesley, early Methodism, Wesleyan Methodist Church history, and Central Wesleyan College. A number of these items concern the work of Roy S. Nicholson, for whom the special collections room is named.

CHARLESTON

Charleston County Library
404 King Street   29403

1215   **South Carolina**

Extensive collection of current and historical material on South Carolina with emphasis on Charleston, including transcripts of wills and miscellaneous legal records of Charleston County, 1600-1800's; original records of Charleston births and deaths in the 1800's; the South Carolina census, 1790-1880, on microfilm; and an unpublished index to South Carolina items in the Charleston **News and Courier,** 1930 to date.

Charleston Library Society
164 King Street   29401

1216   Manuscript Collection

DuBose Heyward's **Porgy** and **The Log Book of the "Shenandoah,"** a Confederate destroyer, are among the 700 items in the manuscript file of letters, business and military papers, novels, and journals. Correspondence includes that of John C. Calhoun, Nathanael Greene, William G. Hinson, John Paul Jones, Francis Marion, William Moultrie, Andrew Pickens, Charles Cotesworth Pinckney, John Rutledge, and George Washington.

1217   Microfilm

The microfilm collection of 1,482 reels consists primarily of Charleston newspapers from 1732 to date. Also included are Charleston city directories, census listings, and a file of the **Virginia Gazette.**

1218   Courtenay, William Ashmead, Collection

Along with more than 200 books, many of which relate to the history of South Carolina, and ca. 800 pamphlets are portraits, maps and manuscripts, presented by the Honorable William Ashmead Courtenay in 1906.

1219   Hinson, William Godber, Collection

The nucleus of this collection of more than 5,000 items, dealing primarily with the history of the South, was bequeathed to the Society by William Godber Hinson in 1919. Appropriate additions have since been made to this collection of books, clippings, pamphlets, and manuscripts.

1220   Garden Club of Aiken

ca. 200 volumes ranging from L'Obel's **Plantarum** (1591) and Gerard's **Herbal** (1597) to 70 volumes from American presses covering every phase of the art of gardening.

1221   Staats, Henry P., Collection

Comprised of such titles as **Works in Architecture** (1773-1822) by Robert and James Adam, **The Gentleman and Cabinet-maker's Director** (1754) by Thomas Chippendale, and **The Cabinet-maker and Upholsterer's Drawing Book** (1794) by Thomas Sheraton, this collection of ca. 90 volumes on architecture and furniture was placed in the Society Library by Architect Henry P. Staats in 1958.

Charleston Museum Library
121 Rutledge Avenue   29401

1222   Museum Collection

ca. 20,000 items supporting the scientific research of the curators and the preparation of exhibits, with special emphasis on local and natural history, ornithology, and the decorative arts. Materials include maps, scrapbooks, sheet music, photographs, periodicals, letters, manuscripts, and autographs of such notables as John James Audubon, John Bachman, and members of the Drayton, Gibbes, Martin, and Ravenel families.

Among the most valuable holdings are a first edition of Mark Catesby's **Natural History of Carolina** (2 volumes, 1731-1743) and Robert Mills' **Atlas of the State of South Carolina** (1825), and an extensive file of pamphlets relating to South Carolina, 1800 to date.   **R**

1223   Heyward-Washington Collection

This collection of 242 volumes, representing many interesting works of the 18th century, is housed in the Heyward-Washington house, erected about 1770.   **R**

1224   Manigault Collection

Ranging from 1750 to 1815, this collection of ca. 42 books was owned by the Manigault family, in whose Meeting Street residence they are housed.   **R**

1225   Aiken, Governor William, Collection

Reflecting the habits and tastes of the upper class, 1820-1880, and housed in the Aiken home, this collection consists of ca. 500 volumes, numerous magazines, and more than 5,000 pieces of sheet music.   **R**

1226 **South Carolina Imprints**

Listed in a separate section of the Museum Library's shelf-list are those works in all the collections which were printed in South Carolina. **R**

The Citadel Memorial Archives-Museum
The Citadel   29409

1227 **Capers, Ellison**

Papers, comprised of ca. 200 letters and hand-drawn maps covering the Civil War period, of Ellison Capers, Confederate Brigadier General and Protestant Episcopal Bishop of South Carolina.

1228 **Clark, General Mark**

ca. 40 linear feet of manuscripts and ca. 10,000 photographs, 1941 to date, covering the career of General Mark Clark as World War II General and as president of The Citadel.

1229 **Ruge, Frederick**

20 linear feet of German operations orders during World War II, correspondence with famous commanders on both sides of the conflict, and diaries and other personal papers of Frederick Ruge, Naval Advisor to General Erwin Rommel.

1230 **Rivers, L. Mendel**

To be used by permission of Mrs. Rivers, this collection of letters and papers, occupying ca. 160 linear feet, covers the Congressional career of L. Mendel Rivers, 1945-1970.

1231 **Summerall, General Charles P.**

ca. 5 linear feet of manuscripts, papers, and speeches, 1928-1953, of General Charles P. Summerall, former Chief of Staff of the U.S. Army and president of The Citadel. However, his major collection is in the Library of Congress and his uniforms and artifacts are at the Smithsonian Institution.

1232 **Westmoreland, General William**

On deposit is a collection of memorabilia, pictures, scrapbooks, medals and other items, 1955-1972, belonging to General William Westmoreland, former head of the Joint Chiefs of Staff, U.S. Department of Defense, and president of The Citadel. This collection does not include his papers.

Robert Scott Small Library
College of Charleston   29401

1233   **Manuscript Collection**

Comprised of (1) Business papers (ca. 20 volumes) of 18th, 19th and 20th century ledgers of Charleston merchants and the Bank of Charleston; (2) Land papers (ca. 50 items) 18th and 19th century deeds, indentures, wills, and plats of prominent Low Country families; (3) Literary letters (ca. 250) of Paul Hamilton Hayne, Hugh Swinton Legare, Ludwig Lewisohn, N.W. Stephenson, and L. M. Harris; (4) Harold Meltzer Collection of Musicians' Letters (ca. 22): Massenet, Puccini, Debussy, Mendelssohn, and others; and (5) Church, fraternal, and military records in typescript: St. John's Lutheran Church, Charleston, Records, 1767-1917; South Carolina Society, Charleston, Minutes, 1827-1888; and Washington Light Infantry, Charleston, Minute Book, 1827-1936.

1234   Also available in both manuscript and microform: (1) Fraser, Charles, Commonplace Book, 1800-1819; (2) Laurens, Henry, Ledger, 1766-1773; (3) Pinckney, Charles Cotesworth, Plantation Dairy (kept in J. Hoff's **Agricultural Almanac**), 1818; and (4) Weston, Plowden, Ledger, 1765-1769, and antebellum management account of his plantation.

1235   **Drayton and Grimke Collections**

ca. 2,000 pamphlets, including speeches and articles, on education, religion, slavery, temperance, tariff, and other public issues of early and mid-19th century, presented by the Reverend John Drayton and Thomas Smith Grimke.

1236   **Caroliniana**

ca. 500 volumes, including many first editions, of books of importance in South Carolina historiography and belles-lettres, portraits of distinguished Charlestonians, and photographs of the Carolina Low Country.

1237   **Izard, Ralph, Collection**

ca. 1,000 volumes from the private library of Ralph Izard, an 18th century Carolina expatriate. Included are early editions of **The Wealth of Nations, L'Esprit des Lois,** and Johnson's **Dictionary.**

1238 **Frampton and King Collections**

ca. 6,530 volumes presented by Lingard A. Frampton in 1853 and Mitchell King in 1860, strong in 18th and early 19th century sets and treatises on classical archaeology, lexicography, ecclesiastical history, voyages, and life sciences.

1239 **Levi, Wendell, Collection**

ca. 1,200 monographs and 15 journals, 1920-1974, covering all aspects of the breeding, care, racing, and marketing of pigeons.

1240 **Miles, J. W., Collection**

Comprised of ca. 1,000 volumes related to Oriental and Semitic languages, Biblical history, and patristical studies.

1241 **World Wars I and II**

ca. 400 pamphlets, including speeches, articles, and other materials on World War I along with ca. 75 posters concerning enlistment, war bonds, and other aspects of American life during World Wars I and II.

Gibbes Art Gallery Library
135 Meeting Street   29401

1242 **Johnson, George W., Collection**

1,191 photographs of the Charleston area, 1875-1930, with emphasis on the architectural details of Charleston houses.

Huguenot Society of South Carolina
25 Chalmers Street   29401

1243 **Library**

More than 3,000 volumes relating to Huguenot history and genealogy, including the **Transactions** of the Society, 1888 to date, and publications of the Huguenot Society of London.

Marine Resources Center
217 Fort Johnson Road

1244 Library

Combined holdings of the College of Charleston's Marine Biology Program and the South Carolina Marine Resources Division, ca. 20,000 volumes, 15,000 journals, and 20,000 reprints in all areas of marine biology, ichthyology, oceanography, coastal zone management, and the economics of marine resources.

Waring Historical Library
Medical University of South Carolina   29401

Historical Collections

1245 Babcock, James Woods, Papers, 1885-1920 (200 items) including notes and correspondence related to Dr. Babcock's work on the identification of pellagra in the United States..

1246 Chamberlain, Olin Burnham, Papers, 1918-1941, (ca. 85 items) including typed manuscripts of articles and addresses on neurology.

1247 Davis, Theodore McCann, Scrapbooks, 1927-1966, (ca. 40 items) emphasizing material related to Dr. Davis' research in trans-urethral prostate resection.

1248 Johnson, Francis Bonneau, Papers, 1915-1954, (ca. 150 items) including correspondence regarding his contribution to a textbook on clinical pathology.

1249 Kredel, Frederick Evart, Papers, 1925-1955, (ca. 90 items) consisting of his writings and particularly those related to his study of the three-toed sloth of British Guiana.

1250 Michel, Middleton, Papers, 1846-1890, (ca. 150 items) with manuscripts of his works on various medical subjects and Dr. Michel's original drawings for his article, "Radical Cure of Reducible Hernia" (1886).

1251 Porcher, Francis Peyre, Papers, 1850-1892, (ca. 250 items) including lectures and notes on botany and materia medica.

1252 Rudisill, Hillyer, Papers, 1936-1942, (ca. 285 items) including material relating to his editorship of the **Review of Tumor Therapy**.

1253 Smithy, Horace Gilbert, Jr., (ca. 186 items) including original drawings and photographs used to illustrate the publications of this pioneer in heart surgery (1940's).

1254   Taft, Robert Burbridge, Papers, 1917-1945, (ca. 300 items) including the first draft of his book, **Radium Lost and Found.**

1255   Waring, Joseph loor, Papers, 1923-1973, (ca. 250 items) including correspondence and articles by the curator of the Waring Historical Library.

1256   Weston, William, 1914-1932, (ca. 80 items) on acrodynia.

1257 **Pinehaven Sanatorium**

ca. 150 items, comprising the existing records, 1925-1952, of the defunct tuberculosis sanatorium in Charleston.

1258 **Roper Hospital**

Papers, 1845-1942, ca. 450 items, including the Minutes of the Board of Trustees, 1845-1868, and the Board of Finance, 1923-1934, along with other materials relating to Roper Hospital, which is owned and operated by the Medical Society of South Carolina.

1259 **Naturopathy**

Papers, 1947-1961, ca. 55 items, relating to the controversy concerning naturopathy in South Carolina as collected by William D. Workman, editor of **The State** in Columbia.

1260 **Art in Medicine**

Prints, 1736-1950, ca. 220 items, comprised of engravings, lithographs, watercolors, and medical caricatures by Daumier, Cruikshank, and others.

South Carolina Historical Society
100 Meeting Street   29401

1261 **Library**

ca. 3,000 books and 4,000 pamphlets relating to South Carolina history, 2,000 volumes of historical journals covering 40 states, and ca. 1,200 linear feet of manuscripts. Notable among the manuscript holdings are:

1262 **Laurens Collection**

Papers of Henry Laurens, 1747-1796, 38 volumes and 673 items, relating to his career as merchant, planter, and President of the Continental Congress;

and the papers of John Laurens, Revolutionary War officer and envoy to France, including his correspondence, 1777-1781.

1263   Middleton, Arthur

Papers, 1767-1783, 99 items relating to this lawyer, planter, and member of the Continental Congress.

1264   Pinckney Family

Papers, 1745-1863, 4 volumes and 93 pieces, including the correspondence of Eliza Lucas Pinckney, who is identified with the development of indigo as a staple in colonial South Carolina; Charles Cotesworth Pinckney, 1777-1778, 1 volume relating to him as U. S. Senator and diplomat; and Thomas Pinckney, 1790-1813, 7 volumes, relating to him as Revolutionary War officer, governor, and minister to Great Britain.

1265   Allston, Robert F. W.

Papers, 1774-1926, 6 volumes and 30 boxes, relating to him as planter, civil engineer, and governor, and to members of his family.

1266   Poinsett, Joel R.

Papers, 1806-1847, 84 items, concerning this first United States minister to Mexico and Secretary of War, who developed the poinsettia in this country from a Mexican flower.

1267   Heyward, DuBose

Papers, 1880-1940, 25 boxes relating to him as novelist, poet, and playwright.

CLEMSON

Clemson University Library
Clemson   29631

1268   Agricultural Societies

Papers, 22 boxes and 3 volumes, of minutes and membership lists of the agricultural societies of South Carolina: Pendleton Farmers' Society, 1815-1965; South Carolina State Grange, Patrons of Husbandry, 1873-1905; and Farmers' State Alliance, 1875-1909.

1269   Behrend, Bernard A.

ca. 1,000 items, 1886-1932, including pamphlets, notebooks, and reprints on electrical engineering collected by Behrend, inventor and author of **The Induction Motor.**

1270   Brown, Edgar Allan

Papers, 1911-1975, 233 document boxes and 29 scrapbooks, including correspondence, speeches, pictures, clippings, and memorabilia relating to his career of five decades in state government and founder of the Council of State Governments (1925).

1271   Byrnes, James Francis

Papers, 1930-1968, 226 document boxes and 32 scrapbooks, of correspondence, photographs, and memorabilia collected in government service in the U. S. Congress, U. S. Supreme Court, the office of the U. S. Secretary of State, and as Governor of South Carolina.

1272   Calhoun, John Caldwell

Papers, 1784-1888, occupying ca. 4½ linear feet and comprised of correspondence with eminent men of the period as well as with members of the family; surveyor's book, 1784-1818; and pamphlets relating to statesmanship and states' rights.

1273   Clemson, Thomas Green

Papers, 1831-1888, 5 document boxes of personal correspondence, including letters from the family of John C. Calhoun, Clemson's father-in-law, and letters from Belgium, where Clemson was **Chargé d'Affaires,** 1844-1851, and correspondence and miscellaneous items relating to the establishment of Clemson Agricultural College as a state-supported institution.

1274   Related to the Calhoun and Clemson Collections is the correspondence of Richard Kenner Cralle, 1818-1856, 240 items, largely concerning politics in the antebellum South.

1275   Lever, A. Francis

Papers, 1908-1940, 34 document boxes, a scrapbook and other materials relating to Lever's Congressional duties, 1901-1919, during which he co-sponsored the Smith-Lever Act of 1914, which provided for cooperative agricultural extension work between land-grant colleges and the U. S. Department of Agriculture.

1276 Pickens, General Andrew

Papers, 1780-1819, 129 items, consisting largely of photostatic copies of original manuscripts in other repositories, and including 15 letters from General Nathanael Greene.

1277 Quattlebaum, Paul

Papers, 1910-ca. 1964, 26 document boxes and 8 storage boxes including the early drafts of his book, **The Land Called Chicora, the Carolinas under Spanish Rule, 1520-1670,** genealogical information on Horry County families and records of the Quattlebaum Light and Ice Company, 1910-1920.

1278 Ravenel, Henry William

Correspondence, 1841-1886, 215 items, mostly letters from leading American and European botanists and agriculturists concerning fungi, grapes and other plants, and related to **The Private Journal of Henry William Ravenal, 1859-1887,** published by the University of South Carolina Press in 1947.

1279 Robertson, Ben (Benjamin Franklin) Jr.

Papers, 1924-1969, 5 boxes, including materials about the journalist, letters concerning his three books — **Traveler's Rest, Red Hills and Cotton,** and **I Saw England** (manuscript) — and information on the launching of the **SS Ben Robertson.**

1280 Tillman, Benjamin Ryan

Papers, 1897-1918, 220 document cases, including family information, photographs, political pamphlets, and correspondence relating to Tillman as governor, senator, and champion of Southern agrarianism.

CLINTON

James H. Thomason Library
Presbyterian College   29325

1281 Caroliniana

A collection of 2,000 items relating to South Carolina history, with some Presbyteriana, mainly from the libraries of Frank Dudley Jones, Ellison Smythe, Louise Jones DuBose, and William Plumer Jacobs, founder of the college. Included is an original edition of Mark Catesby's **The Natural History** of Carolina, Florida and the Bahama Islands (1731) and a number of mid-19th century pamphlets.

Library
Whitten Village   29325

1282   Mental Retardation

ca. 150 volumes of historical records of training the mentally retarded, emphasizing habilitation, education, and medical treatment and including **Annual Reports** of the South Carolina Training School for the Feebleminded, 1918-1968.

COLUMBIA

J. Drake Edens Library
Columbia College   29203

1283   Early Children's Books

ca. 65 items of religious literature for young readers published prior to 1850.

Columbia Museums of Art and Science Library
1112 Bull Street   29201

1284   Exchange Catalogs

A collection of 230 exchange catalogs of museums and other organizations throughout the United States.   **R**

1285   Kress Collection

ca. 100 volumes relating to the Italian Renaissance paintings in the Kress Art Collection.   **R**

William S. Hall Psychiatric Institute Library
2100 Bull Street   29202

1286   Psychiatry, Neurology, and Psychology

ca. 10,000 volumes on all aspects of mental health, including a historical collection on mental institutions and asylums from 1621. Along with a basic medical collection, subject emphases are on schizophrenia, behavior therapy, psychoanalysis, child psychiatry, and sex therapy.

1287 Pastoral Care

ca. 200 books on pastoral counseling, death and dying, and medicine and religion.

Lineberger Memorial Library
Lutheran Theological Southern Seminary
4201 Main Street   29203

1288 German Pietism

2,000 volumes of devotional materials which are representative of the German pietist of the 17th, 18th, and 19th centuries.

1289 Hazelius Library

A collection of 150 volumes in various languages on a broad range of subjects, which were in the personal library of Lewis Hazelius, professor at the Moravian Theological Seminary, 1833-1852.

1290 Manuscripts

Letters and documents, ca. 5 boxes, pertaining to South Carolina and Alabama, from the collection of John Marquart (also spelled Markart), pastor in the Orangeburg, South Carolina, territory, ca. 1830-1870.

1291 German Hymnbooks and Catechisms

500 hymnbooks and catechisms of the Reformed and Lutheran churches with German and American imprints, mostly 18th century.

Lyles, Bissett, Carlisle & Wolff
Gervais and Sumter Streets   29202

1292 Architecture Library

ca. 3,000 volumes, 200 journal subscriptions, 9,000 technical reports, and 2,000 manufacturers' catalogs relating to various aspects of architecture and architectural engineering. **R**

Richland County Public Library
1400 Sumter Street   29201

1293 **South Carolina**

ca. 2,435 volumes of primarily printed materials, consisting of South Carolina history, biography, description, and travel; books by South Carolina authors; state, and Richland County documents; and city and town directories.

1294 **Genealogy**

ca. 578 volumes, including general genealogical works with emphasis on South Carolina family histories and including armorial and family crests.

1295 **D.A.R. Collection**

The South Carolina State Collection of the Daughters of the American Revolution consists of 627 volumes plus microfilm, including the DAR Lineage Series, South Carolina town histories, family genealogies, and DAR journals.

1296 **Ensor-Brown Collection**

ca. 1,110 volumes published in the 19th century on a variety of subjects, including travel in the Middle and Near East and Latin America, world history, Free Masonry, religion, science, and literature.

1297 **Columbia Philatelic Society Collection**

ca. 50 volumes and 4 periodical subscriptions relating to stamps and stamp collecting.

South Carolina Department of Archives and History
1430 Senate Street   29211

Library

The major holdings of the South Carolina Department of Archives and History consist of official public records of South Carolina as a proprietary colony, royal province, and state; these holdings total over 12,000 cubic feet. Nearly all significant state records from 1671 to 1940, and many after 1940, are included.

1298 The state records contain many notable manuscripts: constitutions; legislative journals (1671-   ); other legislative papers (1788-   ); "Indian Books" (ten, 1710-18; 1750-65); engrossed laws (1691-   ); Executive papers; Treasury records (1725-   ); Judicial records (1671-   ); and records of numerous other state agencies. Most extensive are the Secretary of State records (1671-), with the land records being the largest group.

1299   More than 2,900 cubic feet (including over 3,000 microfilms) of municipal, parish, and county records have been brought to the Archives by the Department's Local Records Section.

1300   Other important holdings include extensive microfilms and transcriptions relating to South Carolina, British, Federal, Confederate, and other sources, such as from records in the British Public Record Office (London), 1663-1782; Federal Revolutionary War Pension and Bounty Land Applications (National Archives Microfilm Publications, M804 on 2,670 microfilm reels); Freedman's Bureau Records, Federal Census of South Carolina, 1790-1880; and the films of local governmental records produced by the Genealogical Society of the Church of Jesus Christ of the Latter Day Saints.

Tree of Life Congregation
2701 Heyward Street   29250

1301   The Hennig Library

This collection of Judaica and Hebraica, comprised of 3,000 volumes in English, Hebrew, and Yiddish, contains classical, as well as secondary, reference works.

South Caroliniana Library
University of South Carolina   29208

1302   South Caroliniana

The South Caroliniana Library contains printed, manuscript, cartographic, and pictorial materials in South Carolina history. Its holdings include ca. 2,000,000 manuscripts, dating from 1675; 62,000 books, pamphlets and periodicals; extensive original and microfilmed newspaper files, dating from 1732; a picture file of more than 13,500 items; sheet music, from 1800, and recordings; more than 2,000 maps; a complete file of the University of South Carolina theses and dissertations; and over 8,100 reels of microfilm, chiefly newspapers and manuscripts.

1303   Special units within the collection are (1) the A. S. Salley Collection of the works of William Gilmore Simms, ca. 400 items; (2) the Henry P. Kendall Collection of books, pamphlets, pictures, and maps of South Carolina and adjoining states, 1580-1830; and 415 maps by the Sanborn Map Company, 1884-1935.

1304   Manuscript holdings consist primarily of personal and family papers, but include numerous business, corporate and institutional records. Some of the families represented by substantial collections are: (1) Bacot, (2) Ball, (3) Blanding, (4) Bratton, (5) Butler, (6) Calhoun, (7) Charles, (8) Childs, (9) DeSaussure, (10) Fouché, (11) Fraser, (12) Gibbes, (13) Guignard, (14) Hammond, (15) Hampton, (16) Haynesworth, (17) Izard, (18) Janney-Leaphart, (19) Jenkins, (20) Kincaid-Anderson, (21) Law, (22) Lawton, (23) Lebby, (24) Lide-Coker, (25) McMaster, (26) Manigault, (27) Manning, (28) Mean-English-Doby, (29) Middleton, (30) Montgomery, (31) Moore, (32) Norton, (33) Obear, (34) Palmer, (35) Pickens, (36) Pinckney, (37) Porcher, (38) Renwick, (39) Richardson, (40) Rutledge, (41) Sams, (42) Seabrook, (43) Seibels, (44) Shand, (45) Sheppard, (46) Singleton, (47) Tennent, (48) Thomas, (49) Thompson-Jones, (50) Townes, and (51) Wingard.

1305   A selection of individuals represented by significant holdings include (1) David Wyatt Aiken, (2) Martin F. Ansel, (3) Lewis Malone Ayer, (4) John Shaw Billings, (5) Milledge Luke Bonham, (6) Rosamonde Ramsey Boyd, (7) Iverson L. Brookes, (8) Preston S. Brooks, (9) Pierce Butler, (10) Pierce Mason Butler, (11) John C. Calhoun, (12) Louis W. Cassels, (13) Mary Boykin Chesnut, (14) David R. Coker, (15) John Ewing Colhoun, (16) Thomas Cooper, (17) William Courtenay, (18) Robert Means Davis, (19) Edwin DeLeon, (20) W. J. B. Dorn, (21) Louise Jones DuBose, (22) William Elliott, Jr., (23) John Gary Evans, (24) Martin W. Gary, (25) John Temple Graves, (26) Wil Lou Gray, (27) James H. Hammond, (28) Wade Hampton, (29) Butler B. Hare, (30) Oliver Hart, (31) Paul Hamilton Hayne, (32) John J. Hemphill, (33) Robert W. Hemphill, (34) Duncan Clinch Heyward, (35) Ralph Izard, (36) Richard M. Jefferies, (37) Olin D. Johnston, (38) August Kohn, (39) Henry Laurens, (40) Hugh Swinton Legare, (41) Francis Lieber, (42) Charles S. McCall, (43) Duncan D. McColl, (44) Samuel McGowan, (45) William J. Magrath, (46) Blondelle Malone, (47) Richard .I. Manning, (48) Wyndham M. Manning, (49) William Moultrie, (50) Benjamin F. Perry, (51) William C. Preston, (52) Henry W. Ravenel, (53) William M. Reid, (54) Robert Barnwell Rhett, (55) Archibald Rutledge, (56) Alexander S. Salley, Jr., (57) Eulalie Chafee Salley, (58) William Gilmore Simms, (59) William D. Simpson, (60) Elihu P. Smith, (61) Mendel L. Smith, (62) Mary A. Snowden, (63) Yates Snowden, (64) John E. Swearingen, (65) James H. Thornwell, (66) Strom Thurmond, (67) Henry Timrod, (68) William H. Trescott, (69) Samuel P. Verner, (70) Patterson Wardlaw, (71) Emory O. Watson, (72) George A. Wauchope, (73) James Woodrow, and (74) James T. Williams.

1306   Among the numerous business records are the mercantile papers and account books, 1790-1840, of Laurens County merchant, John Black, and account books of the Graniteville Manufacturing Company, 1823-1900. Corporate and institutional holdings include original and typed copies of church records of all major denominations in South Carolina.

Thomas Cooper Library
University of South Carolina   29208

1307   Rare Book Collection

Comprised of more than 20,000 volumes of rare non-South Carolina materials, this collection contains incunabula, early imprints, and color-plate items. It is particularly strong in natural history, early sciences, American history, and English and American literature.

1308   Civil War

Over 3,000 volumes, including an outstanding collection of regimental histories of the Northern Army.

1309   Historical Children's Literature

ca. 2,500 children's books, including many first editions and emphasizing 19th century publications.

1310   Frost, Robert

A collection of ca. 95 first and variant editions of the works of Frost, many of which were signed by him.

1311   Whitman, Walt

ca. 75 first and variant editions of Whitman's works, most of which were published during his lifetime. Included is a first issue of **Leaves of Grass.**

1312   Bridges, Robert

ca. 200 volumes, with first editions of every published title, this is the finest extant collection of Bridges' works.

1313   Ornithology

A collection of ca. 75 rare items, including the elephant folio of Audubon's **Birds of America** and the works (with color plates) by Bonaparte, Brasher, Cassin, Catesby, Gould, Selby and Wilson.

CONWAY

Horry County Memorial Library
1008 Fifth Avenue   29526

1314   **Local History**

ca. 300 volumes and 40 oral history tapes relating to the history of Conway and Horry County are supplemented by the manuscript materials for the **Independent Republic Quarterly,** which is published by the Horry County Historical Society.

DENMARK

Library
Voorhees College   29042

1315   **The American Negro**

ca. 50 reprints of early editions by the Arno Press, which depict the history and literature of the American Negro.

DUE WEST

Library
Erskine College   29639

1316   **Associate Reformed Presbyterian**

A collection, occupying ca. 100 linear feet, includes periodicals and other publications in bound and/or microfilm form of the synod, presbyteries, and local churches of this denomination.

1317   **Agnew, Dr. Samuel A.**

ca. 700 items of handwritten sermons by this ARP minister of South Carolina and later Mississippi, along with his notes, scrapbooks, family letters, and other data.

1318   **Genealogy and Local History**

This collection is comprised of books and a few manuscripts on area and ARP families, a file of the Abbeville (S. C.) **Press and Banner** from 1846 to date, and ca. 70 items from the diary of John Pratt, a Due West resident, with recollections from the 1880's.

1319   **Erskiniana**

Included in this collection of materials relating to Erskine College and Erskine Theological Seminary are publications and memorabilia of Due West

Female College and Bryson College, both of which merged with Erskine College.

DUNCAN

Cryovac Division
W. R. Grace and Company   29334

1320   Duncan Technical Library

ca. 3,500 volumes, 180 journal subscriptions, 480 microforms, and 10,000 technical reports relating to industrial chemistry and packaging.   **R**

EASLEY

W. F. Lowell Engineering Library
Platt Saco Lowell Corporation   29640

1321   U.S. Textile Machinery Patents

This collection is comprised of more than 50,000 copies of U. S. patents in the textile machinery arts from 1795 to date.

1322   Foreign Textile Machinery Patents

In addition to ca. 18,000 British textile machinery patents, dating from 1735, are more than 3,000 specialized patents from 15 non-English speaking countries. Plans are to limit the British collection to 20th century patents; many of the patents prior to 1900 will be transferred to the Textile Collection of the Greenville County Library.

1323   Textile Machinery

ca. 3,000 publications by more than 50 manufacturers of textile yarn machinery, dating from the late 1890's, along with ca. 300 publications of the Platt Saco Lowell Corporation and its predecessor companies.

FLORENCE

Florence Museum
600 Spruce Street   29501

1324   Evans Research Center Library

More than 2,000 volumes, including materials on museology, primitive art, antique furniture, pewter, colonial lighting, and silver and porcelain identification marks.

The James A. Rogers Library
Francis Marion College   29501

1325   The Arundel Room

ca. 3,000 volumes of South Caroliniana with special emphasis on the Pee Dee Section of the state. The core of this collection is the private library of A. M. Quattlebaum of Arundel Plantation, whose primary interest is the Colonial and Revolutionary period. Also included are area maps, wildlife and sporting books, and an extensive collection of works by and about George Henty.

1326   Salem (Black River) Presbyterian Church

ca. 1,700 volumes which formerly comprised the library of this historic Presbyterian church near Mayesville, South Carolina. Although the church was founded ca. 1759, the earliest book extant was acquired in 1831. On permanent loan to the James A. Rogers Library, this collection is on exhibit as an example of an early Pee Dee library.

1327   Rankin, Hugh F.

The original manuscripts and galley proofs of the biography, **Francis Marion: Swamp Fox** by Dr. Hugh F. Rankin, professor of history at Tulane University, occupies ca. 3 cubic feet and includes the first handwritten draft.

GEORGETOWN

Georgetown County Memorial Library
Highmarket and Screven Streets   29440

1328   Local History

Miscellaneous collection including files of Georgetown newspapers since 1801; area photographs collected by William Doyle Morgan, mayor of Georgetown, 1892-1906; and Waccamaw Parish records, 1819-1954.

Winyah Indigo Society
Cannon and Prince Streets   29440

1329 **Society Library**

More than 1,500 books, including rare atlases and ca. 100 bound newspapers, along with records and papers of the Winyah Indigo Society, which was organized in 1740 and chartered by George II at the Court of St. James in 1758. Membership dues, paid in indigo, were used to found one of the first free schools in America.

GREENVILLE

James B. Duke Library
Furman University   29613

1330 **Baptist Historical Collection**

ca. 1,500 volumes of bound minutes of various South Carolina Baptist Associations, State Baptist Convention annuals, and biographical materials.

Furman Family

Included in this collection:

1331   Richard Furman's correspondence, 1777-1825, 164 items to/from this Revolutionary patriot, Baptist clergyman, and denominational leader.

1332   The James Clement Furman Papers, 1827-1890, 1,300 items comprised of correspondence concerning the Baptist denomination in South Carolina and his work as teacher and first president of Furman University, and 800 sermons and addresses.

1333   Furman Family correspondence, 1782-1960, ca. 1,800 items.

State Baptist Leaders

Other collections relating to Baptist leaders in South Carolina include:

1334   Botsford, Edmund, Letters, 1785-1819, 105 items largely concerning Baptist churches in the Low Country of South Carolina.

1335   Cook, Harvey Toliver, Papers, 1882-1930, 250 items of correspondence and miscellaneous writings.

1336   Davis, Jonathan, Papers, 1821-1851, 66 items.

1337   Hammett, Horace Greeley, Papers, 1959-1969, 19 feet of correspondence relating to his service as secretary-treasurer of the South Carolina Baptist Convention.

1338   Johnson, William Bullein, Papers, 1831-1862, 233 items, chiefly correspondence concerning church discipline, the founding of the Southern Baptist Convention, and other matters of denominational interest.

1339   Judson, Charles Hallette, Papers, 1851-1902, ca. 500 items of correspondence and business, chiefly relating to his work at Furman University.

1340   Manley, Basil, Papers, 1828-1868, ca. 60 items of correspondence dealing with various aspects of denominational life.

1341   Manley, Basis, Jr., Papers, 1838-1891, ca. 350 items including diary, autobiography, sermons, lectures, original hymns, and other materials.

1342   McGlothlin, William Joseph, Papers, 1930-1932, 2,500 items of correspondence, reports, and minutes covering his term as president of the Southern Baptist Convention, and other denominational matters during the Depression years.

1343   McIver Family Papers, 1834-1844, 50 items of correspondence by members of this family of Society Hill.

1344   Mims, James Sessions, Papers, 1835-1855, 300 items, along with other papers of the Mims Family, 1834-1878, 129 items.

1345   Sims, Charles Furman, Correspondence, 1942-1961, 14 feet of materials concerning the South Carolina Baptist Convention.

1346   Whiteside, William Marion, Correspondence, 1911-1961, ca. 500 items of correspondence relating to the beginnings of the Good Samaritan Hospital (later the Spartanburg General Hospital) and the Baptist denomination in South Carolina.

1347   **South Carolina**

A collection of 3,200 volumes covering all aspects of life in South Carolina.

Greenville County Library
300 College Street   29601

1348   **South Carolina Collection**

ca. 6,000 volumes, supplemented by clippings, pamphlets and maps, on South Carolina subjects with emphasis on works relating to Greenville County. A collection of oral history regarding the county was begun in 1975.

1349   **Genealogy**

ca. 1,800 volumes, including indexes and bibliographies on genealogy not only in South Carolina but in neighboring states and Pennsylvania, and census records for these states from 1790 through 1880 (except Pennsylvania, which goes through 1860).

1350   **Bicentennial Textile Historical Collection**

Begun in 1976, this collection is comprised of ca. 500 volumes on the history of textiles and textile technology and includes a file of the **Daily News Record** from 1931.

Greenville County Planning Commission Library
Court House Annex   29602

1351   **Technical Library**

ca. 6,000 volumes, along with journal subscriptions and the Urban Land Institute technical reports, relating to urban planning.

GREENWOOD

Greenwood County Library
North Main Street   29646

1352   **Local History**

Miscellaneous collection of pamphlets, clippings, photographs, diaries, and letters on various aspects of local history. Comprised of ca. 1,500 items, this collection is the property of the Greenwood County Historical Society.

1353   **DAR Genealogical Collection**

ca. 300 items, including printed and manuscript material on South Carolina and Virginia genealogy and scrapbooks containing the "Our Old Roads" series by Harry L. Watson.

1354 Ray, Ralph

ca. 50 watercolors and pen drawings by Ralph Ray, noted illustrator of children's books.

GREER

Films Division Information Center
Celanese Corporation   29651

1355 Library

ca. 800 volumes, 127 journal subscriptions and 5,500 technical reports relating to polyester film and its safety, management, and sales. **R**

HARSTVILLE

Sonoco Products Company, Incorporated
1 North Second Street   29550

1356 Research Laboratory Library

ca. 4,000 volumes, 150 journals, 10,000 technical reports and other materials on pulp and paper technology; environmental engineering; and textile, plastics, adhesives, and coatings technology. Holdings include 2,500 volumes of the **Bibliography of Papermaking and U.S. Patents,** 1900 to date, and extensive files of federal, military, and engineering societies' specifications and standards. **R**

LANCASTER

Lancaster County Library
313 South White Street   29720

1357 Local History

ca. 1,000 items of printed and manuscript materials on the South Carolina Upcountry and its families with particular emphasis on Lancaster County.

LAURENS

Laurens County Library
321 South Harper Street   29360

1358   **South Carolina**

ca. 500 items, concentrating on Laurens County, which was part of the Old Ninety-Six District, and including genealogy, histories of local churches, Revolutionary and Civil War records, and Laurens County Court records on microfilm up to 1900.

1359   **Dunklin, James**

ca. 200 books on all types of antiques, mostly furniture, willed to the Laurens County Library by the owner of the Dunklin House, a fine example of an Up-Country town house of 1820 which is now open to the public.

1360   **Holmes, Zelotes Lee**

Copies of letters (originals were burned) written by the Reverend Zelotes Lee Holmes, 1815-1885, Presbyterian minister and educator, over a period of 30 years. In 1856, Holmes built the Octagon House, which is one of the last gravel wall octagonal structures left standing in the United States.

MARION

Marion County Library
101 E. Court Street   29571

1361   **Local History**

Parish records, including the **Register of the Episcopal Church, Prince George Winyah** and the **Register Book for the Parish** (Prince Frederick Winyaw, 1713); Oral histories depicting life in Marion in the early 1900's.

NEWBERRY

Wessels Library
Newberry College   29108

1362   **Historical Collection**

ca. 2,500 volumes and manuscripts pertaining to the history of Newberry College, Newberry County, Summerland College, and the South Carolina Midlands.

1363   **Lutheran Collection**

ca. 1,200 items, including sermons, early Bibles, church history, theological studies, minutes of the United Lutheran Church of America, and the archives of the Florida Lutheran Synod.

Newberry-Saluda Regional Library
1300 Friend Street   29108

1364   South Caroliniana

ca. 1,600 books about South Carolina and about South Carolinians, with emphasis on the history and genealogy of the Midland counties.

A collection of manuscript materials of the late George Leland Summer, now the property of the Newberry County Historical Society, is housed in the library and available for public use.

ORANGEBURG

The Alex Salley Archives
Bull and Middleton Streets   29115

1365   Salley Collection

Genealogical materials of Alexander Samuel Salley, 1871-1961, South Carolina historian and secretary of the South Carolina Historical Commission, this collection is comprised of ca. 500 items of Salley family correspondence; 50 plats and indentures, mostly of the Salley family; ca. 30 pamphlets and more than 100 newspaper articles by Dr. Salley; and other records relating to Orangeburg County families and history.

Learning Resources Center
Orangeburg-Calhoun Technical College   29117

1366   Non-traditional Power Sources

ca. 90 volumes on non-traditional power sources, tracing the historical development and current practices of the use of the sun, wind, water, methane, and wood as sources of energy.

Orangeburg County Library
510 Louis Street   29115

1367   Local Genealogy

A collection of ca. 60 books, mostly manuscripts, on families in the Orangeburg area and lower South Carolina.

1368 Salley, Alexander Samuel

ca. 50 books and manuscripts pertaining to the history of South Carolina with a descriptive bibliography of Dr. Salley's works.

Miller F. Whittaker Library
South Carolina State College 29117

1369 Black Collection

ca. 13,000 volumes, 20 periodical subscriptions and daily and weekly newspapers giving historical and current coverage of Blacks. Four special collections in microform are the Armistad Collection of Dillard University (S.C. manuscripts); Atlanta University Black Culture Collection; Doctoral research on the Negro, 1933-1966; and Slave Narrative Collection (Works Progress Administration).

ROCK HILL

Ida Jane Dacus Library
Winthrop College 29733

1370 State and Local History

This collection, occupying 49 linear feet, is comprised of individual and family histories, organizational records, and items of historical interest on York County and South Carolina. Noteworthy are the papers of Robert O'Neill Bristow, Mary E. Frayser, Thomas S. Gettys, Robert L. McFadden, and Frances Lander Spain, and the **Records** of the South Carolina Home Economics Association, 1914-1975, and the South Carolina Homemakers Extension Council, 1917-1976.

1371 Draper Manuscript Collection

135 microfilm reels copied from the original collection of Draper's manuscripts on frontier Indians, including Indians of South Carolina.

1372 Johnson, David B.

Included in the Winthrop College Archives are the papers of Dr. Johnson, founder of the college and its first president, 1886-1928. This collection contains much information on higher education for women.

1373 Spratt Cookbook Collection

Named for its donor, Roy Spratt of Fort Mill, this collection of ca. 250 volumes contains an interesting variety of early and unusual cookbooks, especially appropriate for Winthrop's role in Home Economics education and Home Demonstration work.

York County Library
325 South Oakland Avenue   29730

1374 Catawba Indians

ca. 5,000 items, comprised of books, manuscripts, correspondence, and clippings on the Catawba Indians, including the manuscript of Douglas S. Brown's **The Catawba Indians: the People of the River** (1966).

1375 Local History and Genealogy

ca. 8,000 items relating to history of York County, Rock Hill and to the families in the north-central area of the state.

SPARTANBURG

Gwathmey Library
Converse College   29301

1376 Music

Extensive collection of reference materials, ca. 5,000 phonograph records, and music scores, primarily Renaissance and Baroque and, secondarily, Romantic and Modern; performing scores for brass, brass ensemble, and opera; a 20th century collection which is comprised of folk, rock, and jazz materials along with classical items. Also included is a number of letters to Radiana Pazmore, Converse voice instructor, from contemporary composers, such as Ravel, Ives, and Milhaud.

1377 Taylor, A. B.

ca. 900 titles, collected and presented by A. B. Taylor, Spartanburg business executive, of books that were awarded as prizes to students in English schools and colleges.

Hoechst Fibers Industries
American Hoechst Corporation   29304

1378 Technical Information Center

ca. 1,000 volumes, including journals, on polymer chemistry and synthetic fibers.   **R**

Technical Library
Milliken Research Corporation   29304

1379 Textile

ca. 3,500 volumes, 275 journal subscriptions and audio-visual materials in chemistry, textile technology and the textile industry, including complete sets of Beilstein, Bornstein, and Houben-Wehl.   **R**

Spartanburg County Public Library
333 South Pine Street   29304

1380 Genealogy and Local History

Miscellaneous collection of genealogical materials, including Spartanburg County wills as early as 1787, family histories, local cemetery records, and the files of the Pinckney District Chapter of the South Carolina Genealogical Society. The library serves as a depository for the publications of the Spartanburg Planning and Development Commission and the Spartanburg Office for Budget and Planning.

1381 Garden Center

More than 300 volumes on vegetable and flower growing and flower arrangements.

Sandor Teszler Library
Wofford College   29301

1382 South Caroliniana

ca. 700 18th to 20th century items, consisting of books, maps, pamphlets and ephemeral materials relating to South Carolina. Included is a typed rough draft of Julia Peterkin's **Scarlet Sister Mary,** with holograph emendations by the author; a 1792 London edition of **Bartram's Travels;** and a 4-volume set of D.D. Wallace's **History of South Carolina** with glossolia in the author's hand.

1383   **Church History**

ca. 450 volumes on sectarian religions and the history of religion, with emphasis on Methodism and 19th century works.

Closely allied are the **Bible Collection,** comprised of ca. 130 editions of the Bible from the 17th to the 20th century, including a Christopher Sauer **Bible** in German, published at Germantown, Pennsylvania, in 1763; and **Hymnody Collection** of ca. 200 church hymnals of various denominations from mid-19th to first quarter of the 20th century.

1384   **Wofford Library Press**

A collection of 55 titles of books produced by students at the Wofford Library Press during interim semesters from 1969 to 1977. The students designed, set the type, printed and bound their books in 50-copy editions.

1385   **The Secondi Collection**

ca. 50 items relating to the Sacco-Vanzetti case, including a 6-volume transcript of the Sacco-Vanzetti trial, books, articles, and a collection of 8x10 photographs of the trial area by Joseph Secondi.

1386   **Rare Books Collection**

20 volumes printed in Europe, 1516 to 1599, including folios and both leather and vellum bindings; 43 European publications of the 17th century; 103 titles of works published by Matthew Carey and successor Philadelphia firms (now Lea and Feibiger) from 1794; 90 volumes of the London "Folio Society" publications, and ca. 90 works published by Heritage Press, Nonesuch Press, and the Limited Editions Club along with ca. 75 American private press books; 25 miniature volumes under three inches in height and a complete file of **The Miniature Book Collector;** and examples of both hand-bound and machine-bound volumes from the 15th century to date.

Also ca. 2,200 rare volumes from the 17th through the 19th century in various disciplines, including the Norton facsimile of Shakespeare's First Folio, Samuel Johnson's **Dictionary of the English Language** (1775) and numerous descriptive works on early exploration in North America.

STATE PARK

Professional Library
State Park Health Center   29147

1387   Respiratory Diseases

ca. 10,000 volumes and 30 professional journals, the majority of which deal with tuberculosis, emphysema, and other respiratory diseases.

SULLIVAN'S ISLAND

Black Heritage Research Center
The Old Slave Mart Museum   29482

1388   Museum Artifacts

Provenance files, accession books, and catalog cards on ca. 800 items, mainly slave-made handcrafts and African art and crafts related to them.   **R**

1389   Wilson, Miriam B., Collection

Manuscripts, papers, books, photographs, correspondence, and other materials on Miriam B. Wilson, founder of the Old Slave Mart Museum, Black history, and South Carolina history.   **R**

1390   Chase, Judith Wragg, Collection

Manuscripts, papers, books, photographs, correspondence, and other materials on Black cultural history, both African and Afro-American, along with correspondence with contemporary Black artists and items of oral history, including Gullah dialect, rural church music, and interviews with Black artists.   **R**

SUMTER

Sumter County Library
111 N. Harvin Street   29150

1391   South Carolina Reference Collection

ca. 1,500 titles with concentrations on the history of Sumter County, the city of Sumter, and local family histories.

UNION

Union Carnegie Library
300 East South Street   29379

1392 **South Caroliniana**

This collection of 890 volumes is comprised largely of historical works, including Union County histories and genealogies; Union County wills, 1777-1900; and files of local newspapers since 1900.

Union Regional Campus Library (USC)
401 East Main Street   29379

1393 **Genealogy**

Materials on the early settlers of Union County, including a file of 18th and 19th century epitaphs in the cemeteries of the county.

WALTERBORO

Colleton County Memorial Library
600 Hampton Street   29488

1394 **Local History**

Published and unpublished local history and genealogical materials, including records of the Stoney Creek Independent Presbyterian Church, 1743-1910; records of the South Carolina Baptist Association, 1879-1974; a file of the **Press and Standard,** beginning in 1873 and complete from 1906 to date; and local history tapes.

WINNSBORO

Fairfield County Library
Garden and Washington Streets   29180

1395 **Lauderdale Collection**

568 beautifully leather-bound volumes in the Lauderdale collection of English literature, which is housed in the Governor's Mansion in Columbia.

VIII

SPECIAL COLLECTIONS
IN
LIBRARIES OF TENNESSEE

Compiled
By
John David Marshall

ARNOLD AIR FORCE STATION

ARO, Incorporated
Arnold Engineering Development Center   37389

1396   Technical Library

    ca. 16,000 volumes, 83,000 technical reports, and 575 journals on aerospace science, including aerodynamics, aeronautical propulsion and related subjects. **R**

ATHENS

Merner-Pfeiffer Library
Tennessee Wesleyan College   37303

1397   Methodist Historical Collection

    1,431 volumes by denominational leaders and about Methodism, 1780 to date, including handwritten ledgers and other manuscript materials.

Blountville

Sullivan County Library
205 Main Street   37617

1398   Local History and Genealogy

    A collection of ca. 100 items of printed and manuscript materials, including church histories, genealogies of ca. 15 local families, and historical records of early Blountville and Sullivan County.

Chattanooga

Chattanooga-Hamilton County Bicentennial Library
1001 Broad Street   37402

1399   Genealogy

A collection of compiled genealogies, including the Southeastern states with emphasis on the eastern counties of Tennessee; county records and county histories; Federal census records, 1790-1880; and a surname index to family sketches in various genealogical journals and other publications.

1400   Hamilton County History

ca. 500 items, including printed histories and county records; Chattanooga Board of Aldermen Minutes, 1859-1911; city directories, beginning in 1871; papers of local organizations and family histories.

Combustion Engineering, Inc.
911 West Main Street   37402

1401   Research Library

ca. 8,000 volumes relating to metallurgical research, including metallography, metallurgy, and nuclear engineering.   **R**

Hunter Museum of Art
10 Bluff View   37403

1402   Library

ca. 1,000 items, comprised of volumes on American art, a file of dealer and exhibition catalogs, and art auction serials.

Library
University of Tennessee at Chattanooga   37401

1403   The Civil War

ca. 3,000 volumes, comprising three collections: the Edwin Young Chapin Collection; the Charles R. and Anne Bachman Hyde Collection, reflecting the Southern point of view; and the Wilder Collection, established by the Lilly Foundation as a memorial to General John T. Wilder, and presenting the Federal viewpoint.

1404 Preston, Frank W., Collection

ca. 10,000 pieces on state and local government, ca. 1930-1960, including material on state constitutional revision, executive veto, state finances, state Legislative journals and Blue Books, municipal government and Civil Service.

1405 Rauston, Agnes and Leonard, Collection

ca. 400 volumes, largely Southern history with emphasis on Tennessee.

CLARKSVILLE

Felix G. Woodward Library
Austin Peay State University   37040

1406 Dix, Dorothy

A collection of 9 volumes, letters, clippings, and travel diaries, 1908 to 1952, of Elizabeth Meriwether Gilmer, who pseudonomously syndicated her advice to the lovelorn under the name of Dorothy Dix.

1407 Local History

A collection comprised of printed, manuscript, and photographic materials relating to the Clarksville area and Fort Campbell.

CLEVELAND

Library
Cleveland State Community College   37311

1408 East Tennessee

Area history as depicted in the J. D. Clemmer collection of scrapbooks, 35 volumes covering the history of Polk County, 1840-1940; the John Morgan Wooten scrapbooks, including information on pioneer families of Bradley County and local church records; and one of six existing copies of J. S. Hurlburt's **History of the Rebellion in Bradley County, Tennessee** (1866).

Lee College Library
N. Ocoee Street   37311

1409 Pentecostal Research Center

A collection of 1,341 volumes along with journals and audio-visual materials on the Church of God and other Pentecostal groups.

COLLEGEDALE

McKee Library
Southern Missionary College   37315

1410 SDA Heritage Collection

As the repository for all Seventh-Day Adventists publications, this collection of ca. 8,000 volumes and all periodicals published by the church includes both materials about the church and by authors affiliated with the church.

1411 Thomas, Vernon L., Memorial

Unique combination of (1) the Lincoln Collection of John W. Fling, Jr., of Wyoming, Illinois, including 1,200 books, journals, pamphlets, pictures, oil paintings and artifacts relating to Abraham Lincoln and (2) the Civil War Collection of Dr. Russell C. Slater of LaSalle, Illinois, consisting of 1,900 volumes along with letters, manuscripts, newspapers, and other primary source materials on the War Between the States.

COOKEVILLE

Jere Whitson Memorial Library
Tennessee Technological University   38501

1412 McClain, Victor, Collection

A collection of local history materials on Cookeville, Central High School, Buck College, and Dixie College. Included are the corrective notes which Walter S. McClain made for additions to his **History of Putnam County, Tennessee.**

1413 Bryan, Charles Faulkner

All of the original music, composed and arranged by Tennessee educator-musician, Charles Faulkner Bryan, 1911-1955.

1414   **Barnes, Thomas Jefferson**

Papers, including genealogical data; church, cemetery, and public records of Warren County; a list of American Revolution pensioners; and Shellsford Baptist Church minutes, 1855-1886.

1415   **Tennessee**

Original documents and copies of books, pamphlets and other materials relating to Tennessee history and Tennessee families, with special emphasis on the Middle Tennessee counties, are being collected and housed in the Tennessee Room. Special indexes include an alphabetical name index covering genealogy, an alphabetical subject index to Tennessee sources, a military units index, and others.

ELIZABETHTON

Elizabethton Public Library
Sycamore Street   37643

1416   **Tennessee**
ca. 100 items relating to the history of Tennessee, including the genealogy of 12 local families.

GAINESBORO

Charles Ralph Holland Memorial Library
Hull Avenue   38562

1417   **Jackson County**

Local history collection, comprised of ca. 60 microfilm reels of Jackson County Court House records from 1859 to date; genealogies of ca. 20 area families; Federal census records of Jackson County, 1820-1880; and the R. G. Draper Scrapbook, containing historical clippings from the county newspaper, beginning in 1853.

GATLINBURG

Great Smoky Mountains National Park Library
Sugarlands Visitor Center   37738

1418 Oral History

ca. 100 items, tapes and transcriptions of interviews with older residents on the early rural life in the Great Smoky Mountains, communities and churches, hunting, lumbering, and farming.

1419 Naturalist

A collection of nature journals, 1935 to date, field notes and other publications, including studies and reports of staff scientists since the establishment of the Great Smoky Mountain National Park in 1926.

GREENEVILLE

Tusculum College Library
Greeneville   37743

1420 Archives

In the Tusculum College Archives are the original charter and other materials relating to Greeneville College, which was founded in 1794 and merged with Tusculum College in 1868.

1421 Rare Books

ca. 200 volumes, consisting largely of 16th and 17th century theological works, including signatures of Samuel Adams, Samuel Bradstreet, Charles Chauncey, and Jonathan Edwards.

HARROGATE

Carnegie Library
Lincoln Memorial University   37752

1422 Lincolniana/Civil War

ca. 15,000 items relating directly or indirectly to Abraham Lincoln and the Civil War, including manuscripts, pamphlets, legal briefs written by Lincoln, regimental histories of both the Union and Confederate armies, and a first edition of **Uncle Tom's Cabin.** Also included are ca. 6,000 items of sheet music of the Civil War period, including a number of Stephen C. Foster songs.

HENDERSON

Loden-Daniel Library
Freed-Hardeman College   38340

1423   Restoration Collection

>   543 books relating to the restoration of Christianity as practiced in New Testament times, A.D. 33 - A.D. 90; emphasizing the early leaders of the Restoration Movement in the United States, Alexander Campbell, Isaac Errett, Moses E. Lard, David Lipscomb, John W. McGarvey, Robert Milligan, and Barton W. Stone.

JACKSON

Jackson-Madison County Library
433 East Lafayette   38301

1424   Local History and Genealogy

>   More than 500 volumes relating to Tennessee history with emphasis on West Tennessee, Madison County, and Jackson, including an incomplete file of local newspapers from 1823; a general genealogical collection along with the history of ca. 75 West Tennessee families.

1425   Tigrett, I. B., Memorial

>   175 volumes pertaining to railroads of the United States, with emphasis on the Gulf, Mobile and Ohio and the Illinois Central lines.

J. K. Daniels Library
Lane College   38301

1426   Negro Collection

>   ca. 2,000 volumes and 35 audio-visual items by and about the Negro in Africa and America.

1427   Tree, L. C., Collection

>   More than 100 taped interviews with persons acquainted with Bishop Isaac Lane, one of the founders of the African Methodist Church and Lane College, along with other tapes relating to the early history of the college.

Shiloh Regional Library
Hamilton Hills Shopping Center   38301

1428 Tennessee

A collection of ca. 300 volumes relating to Tennessee with special emphasis on the counties of West Tennessee.

JEFFERSON CITY

Carson-Newman College Library
Jefferson City   37760

1429 Burnett, Frances Hodgson

A small collection of letters, 1892-1908, by the Anglo-American author of **Little Lord Fauntleroy,** who lived in East Tennessee from 1865 to 1877.

1430 Genealogy

Printed materials on ten East Tennessee families.

JOHNSON CITY

Sherrod Library
East Tennessee State University   37601

1431 Rare Books and Manuscripts

Along with ca. 200 rare books are ca. 100,000 manuscript items of early records of East Tennessee counties, including the State of Franklin, which was organized in 1784.

1432 Reece, Brazilla Carroll

Papers, ca. 200,000 items, of B. Carroll Reece, longtime representative from Tennessee's First District in the U.S. Congress.

Mayne Williams Public Library
205 South Roan Street   37601

1433 **State and Local History**

ca. 500 items relating to Tennessee history, including family histories, with emphasis on Washington, Sullivan, and Carter counties.

KINGSPORT

Kingsport Public Library
Broad and New Streets   37660

1434 **Palmer Regional History Collection**

ca. 3,000 items, including books, periodicals, maps and clippings, relating to the local history and genealogy of Upper East Tennessee and Southwest Virginia counties.

Tennessee Eastman Company
Eastman Road   37762

1435 **Research Library**

ca. 32,500 volumes, 650 periodical subscriptions, 1,000 items in microform, and 150 filing drawers of patents in scientific and technical fields, especially fibers, polymers, and cellulosics.   **R**

KNOXVILLE

Dulin Gallery of Art
3100 Kingston Pike   37919

1436 **Library**

ca. 800 volumes, 30 periodicals and extensive vertical file of art reference materials on art, artists, and galleries.

Environmental Systems Corporation
1212 Pierce Parkway   37901

1437 **Library**

A collection of ca. 3,500 volumes along with 200 technical reports and periodicals relating to environmental systems, particularly cooling towers and water wastes.   **R**

Glass Memorial Library
Johnson Bible College   37920

1438   **Restoration Movement**

ca. 600 volumes and pamphlets representing the writings of early leaders in the Christian Church/Churches of Christ.

Knoxville-Knox County Public Library
500 West Church Avenue   37902

1439   **Blount, William**

Papers, ca. 1791-1835, ca. 500 items, largely personal and official correspondence of Blount, who was Governor of the Territory of the United States south of the Ohio River, U. S. Senator from Tennessee, and a signer of the United States Constitution.

1440   **Brown, William R., Family**

Papers, ca. 1825-1900, 3,500 items reflecting the commercial life and social conditions of Greeneville during the 19th century, including references to the Andrew Johnson family. Brown was the employer of the president's son, William.

1441   **Houk, L. C., and Houk, J. C.**

Papers, 1863-1923, 124 boxes, including correspondence, speeches, and legal papers of Leonidas Campbell Houk, lawyer, judge, and Congressman; and his son, John Chiles, lawyer and state legislator. Included is material on the Republican and Progressive Parties and the coal miners' insurrection in Anderson County in 1891.

1442   **Nelson, Thomas Amis Rogers**

Papers, 1782-1873, 19 volumes and 21 boxes of correspondence, speeches, professional papers and scrapbooks relating to Nelson as lawyer, judge and Congressman, including his Unionist sympathies during the Civil War and his role as defense counsel during the impeachment trial of Andrew Johnson.

1443   **Rothrock, Mary Utopia**

Papers, ca. 1905-1976, ca. 36 boxes of correspondence, diaries and other writings of Miss Rothrock as public librarian in Knoxville, librarian of the

Tennessee Valley Authority, president of the Southeastern Library Association, 1922-1924, and president of the American Library Association, 1946-1947.

1444   Rule, William

Papers, 1860-1927, 6 boxes of correspondence, diaries (1863-1865), speeches and other materials documenting Rule's career as Union soldier, journalist and mayor of Knoxville. Included is material on dueling and on Tennessee's historical figures.

1445   Tyson, Lawrence Davis

Papers, ca. 1917-1929, ca. 84 boxes, mainly correspondence of Tyson as soldier, businessman, and U. S. Senator, including source material on textile manufacturing, mining, and publishing.

Other Collections include:

1446   Ault, Frederick Armstead, Papers, 1797-1912, 1 box, relating to Knoxville civic leader and the McClung family.

1447   Boren Family, Papers, 1839-1909, 1 box containing correspondence, receipts, distillery records, and other materials of a Carter County family.

1448   Broome, Harvey, Papers, ca. 1924-1968, ca. 2,000 items of correspondence and other materials relating to Broome as lawyer, conservationist, and naturalist.

1449   Brownlow, Walter Preston, Papers, 1882-1894, 1 box of personal and political correspondence of this Jonesboro journalist.

1450   Buffat Family, Papers, 1831-1925, 3 boxes of correspondence, memoirs, scrapbooks, and other materials on a Swiss family which settled in Knox County and engaged in the milling business.

1451   Cabaniss, Septimus D., Papers, 1805-1887, 2 boxes of correspondence of this lawyer and state legislator of Madison County, Alabama, and the family of James White McClung, 1798-1848.

1452   Cannon Family, Papers, 1806-1888, 2 boxes of correspondence, account books, pamphlets and survey maps of Hamilton, Monroe, and Roane counties.

1453   Caswell, William Richard, Papers, 1805-1900, 2 boxes of correspondence muster rolls, documents and other materials relating to Caswell as lawyer, Confederate Army officer, and railroad executive of Knox County.

1454 Coffin, Charles, Papers, 1800-1853, ca. 2,000 pieces, including correspondence and diaries of this Presbyterian minister who served as president of East Tennessee College (now the University of Tennessee).

1455 Crozier-French, Lizzie, Papers, 1880-1926, ca. 1,000 pieces relating to this educator and advocate of women's rights.

1456 Graham, Hugh, Papers, 1805-1886, 2 boxes of business records of this Irish-born merchant of Tazewell.

1457 Hall-Stakely Family, Papers, 1825-1952, 15 boxes of correspondence, diaries, and genealogical records, covering the Civil War, slavery, and 19th century life.

1458 Heiskell, Frederick Steidinger, Papers, ca. 1816-1882, ca. 500 pieces, including personal, political and business correspondence of this pioneer printer, publisher, and politician along with the records of the Knoxville Library Company, 1817-1826.

1459 Jaques, Joseph, Papers, 1851-1884, 1 box of correspondence, reports, and legal and family papers of this railroad executive, banker, and mayor of Knoxville.

1460 Lenoir, William Ballard, Papers, 1798-1882, 3 boxes of personal and business correspondence, bills and deeds relating to the Lenoir family in North Carolina and Tennessee, the removal of the Cherokee Indians to Oklahoma, and cotton manufacturing.

1461 Luttrell, James Churchwell, Papers, ca. 1855-1858, ca. 300 pieces, relating to this Knoxville merchant and politician.

1462 Lynn, May, Papers, 1780-1949, 1 box of membership lists, anti-abolitionist statements and other records of the Kingsport (Tennessee) Presbyterian Church, including material on the history of Kingsport and trade between Virginia and the West Indies during the American Revolution.

1463 McClung Family, Papers, 1861-1943, 9 boxes, correspondence, memorabilia and pamphlets concerning Calvin Morgan McClung, Knoxville businessman, and his family.

1464 McGhee, Charles McClung, Papers, 1857-1907, 31 boxes and 14 volumes, relating to McGhee as financier, railroad executive, state legislator and philanthropist of Knoxville, including correspondence, treasurer's account books of the American Cattle Trust, and materials on coal mining, iron manufacturing, and politics.

1465 McTeer, Will A., Papers, 1828-1925, 42 boxes and 45 volumes covering correspondence and other records of this Blount County lawyer, banker, and state legislator.

1466 Nelson, Seldon, Papers, 1875-1921, correspondence and papers of this local historian and genealogist.

1467 Nenny, Charles Grandison, Papers, 1822-1963, 5 boxes of materials on this farmer and agent for East Tennessee and Virginia Railroad.

1468 Netherland, John, Papers, ca. 1813-1900, ca. 1,000 pieces concerning this lawyer and Whig politician of Rogersville and including historical materials on the Netherland Inn, a house museum in Kingsport.

1469 Park, James, Papers, ca. 1800-1912, ca. 500 pieces relating to this Presbyterian minister, including letters of political significance written to Park's father by U. S. Senator Hugh Lawson White.

1470 Ross, William Cary, Jr., Papers, ca. 1925-1951, 41 pieces, including letters from artistic and literary figures of the time.

1471 Sanford, Hugh Wheeler, Papers, 1886-1963, 2 boxes of materials relating to Sanford as industrialist, inventor, financier, and author.

1472 Seymour, Charles Milne, Papers, ca. 1905-1958, ca. 2,500 pieces, regarding this Knoxville attorney and corporation lawyer.

1473 Watterson Family Papers, 1780-1908, 2 boxes of correspondence and other records of this Irish family which settled in Hawkins County.

1474 Welcker, Charles Freeling, Papers, 1801-1859, 5 boxes of correspondence and business records of this merchant and farmer of Roane County, including materials on farming, navigation, and river improvement.

1475 Welcker, George Lewis, Papers, 1836-1963, 1 box of family and business correspondence, particularly of J. H. Welcker of Welcker's Mines in Kingston.

1476 Williams-Coffin Family, Papers, 1822-1958, ca. 500 pieces of family correspondence collected by Ella Williams, an aunt of Playwright Tennessee Williams, and including letters from Tennessee and his brother, Dakin.

1477 Young, David King, Papers, ca. 1801-1939, ca. 2,500 pieces, relating to this lawyer and Tennessee circuit court judge.

Tennessee Valley Authority Technical Library
400 Commerce Avenue   37902

1478   **TVA History**

Hundreds of thousands of items on the history of the Tennessee Valley Authority as an agency of the Federal Government and on the areas of TVA projects, including the printed archives of TVA, administrative files, internal reports, photographic collection, published histories and critical and analytical articles, and a file of newspaper clippings, 1933 to date.

1479   **History of Fertilizer**

This collection is in the Muscle Shoals Technical Library, a branch of the TVA Technical Library. See Muscle Shoals, Alabama.

James D. Hoskins Library
University of Tennessee   37916

Comprised of more than 800 separate collections, the special collections consist of both volumes and manuscript items, 1783 to date, and relating chiefly to Tennessee.

1480   **Literary Manuscripts**

ca. 300 pieces, 1895 to date, including manuscripts of (1) Gray Blanton; (2) Smiley Blanton; (3) North Callahan; (4) Alfred Leland Crabb; (5) Robert Drake; (6) Will Allen Dromgoole; (7) May Justus; (8) Harry Harrison Kroll; (9) Joseph Wood Krutch; (10) David Madden; (11) Richard Marius; (12) Jane Merchant; (13) Harvey Swados; (14) Lately Thomas, pseudonym of Robert V. Steele; and (15) all University of Tennessee Press manuscripts.

1481   **Baker, Howard H.**

Papers, 1951-1965, ca. 60,000 pieces, including legislative files, correspondence, speeches, and other materials associated with the political careers of Baker and his wife, Irene Bailey Baker, who were representatives from the Second Congressional District of Tennessee.

1482   **Brown, Clarence L.**

Papers, 1920-1952, ca. 20,000 pieces, including shooting scripts, still photographs, scrapbooks, and other items relating to the career of this renowned motion picture director.

1483   **Claxton, Philander Priestley**

Papers, 1890-1955, ca. 30,000 pieces, including correspondence, speeches, articles and other materials related to Claxton's career as U. S. Commissioner of Education, Provost of the University of Alabama, and as outstanding educational leader.

1484   **Frazier, James B.**

Papers, 1898-1914, ca. 25,000 pieces, including correspondence, speeches, scrapbooks and other materials concerning Frazier as Governor of Tennessee and as United States Senator.

1485   **Hartman, Robert S.**

Papers, 1946-1973, 100 linear feet of correspondence, original manuscripts of publications, research notes, reprints, and other materials concerning this renowned philosopher.

1486   **Kefauver, Estes**

Papers, 1935-1963, 1,204 linear feet, including personal and political correspondence, manuscripts for **Crime in America** and **A Twentieth Century Congress,** political files, speeches, and other materials concerning the colorful political career of this Senator from Tennessee.

1487   **Ramsey, James Gettys McGready**

Papers, 1790-1912, ca. 650 items, including correspondence, scrapbooks, family and financial records, and other materials relating to Knoxville and Tennessee history, the Confederate treasury, the Tennessee Historical Society, and Anderson's East Tennessee Mining Company.

1488   **Steele, Robert V.**

Papers, 1957-1973, ca. 18,000 pieces, including literary manuscripts, galley proofs, research notes, and other materials pertaining to the published works of Lately Thomas, pseudonym of Robert V. Steele.

1489   **Steinhaus, Arthur H.**

Papers, 1914-1966, ca. 60,000 pieces, including correspondence, personal records, manuscripts, journals, pictures, and other materials relating to this distinguished physiologist.

1490   Temple, Oliver Perry

Papers, 1832-1900, ca. 9,400 items, including correspondence, speeches, memoranda for books, pictures and other materials relating to this outstanding Tennessee writer, historian, and political figure.

1491   Walters, Herbert S.

Papers, 1939-1972, ca. 200,000 pieces, including personal, business, and political files as well as scrapbooks, photographs, and other materials concerning Walters as prominent business man, political leader, and United States Senator from Tennessee.

1492   Civil War Diaries

ca. 250 diaries and personal narratives, 1860-1866, including accounts by both Confederate and Union soldiers as well as others involved in the war.

1493   Radiation Biology Archives

Papers, 1908-1970, ca. 100,000 pieces, including research and laboratory notes, correspondence, lectures, reprinted articles, and other materials assembled by such noted international radiation biologists as Charles C. Congdon, Louis Harold Gray, George de Hevesy, Alexander Hollaender, Antoine Lacassagne, Douglas E. Lea, Egon Lorenz, and Karl G. Zimmer.

1494   Ruskin Co-operative Association

Records, 1894-1899, ca. 500 items, including minutes of meetings, membership certificates, a manuscript history of the colony, catalog of the Ruskin library, and clippings from **The Coming Nation,** published by the colony, which was founded in Dickson County in 1894.

LOOKOUT MOUNTAIN

Anna Emma Kresge Memorial Library
Covenant College   37350

1495   Kresge Rare Books

A collection of ca. 600 volumes, 1540 to 1800, consisting largely of Bibles, works on English Puritan theology, along with notable literary editions, including Samuel Rutherford's **Lex Rex.**

MADISON

Outdoor Universal Training
Academy Drive   37115

1496   **Outdoor Living Library**

Unique collection of ca. 1,400 volumes, supplemented by 27 periodical subscriptions and audio-visual materials, on wilderness survival, backpacking, camping, mountaineering, edible wild plants and medicinal plants, food preservation, soap-making and nature crafts.

MARTIN

Paul Meek Library
The University of Tennessee at Martin   38238

1497   **Tennessee Collection**

ca. 1,400 volumes by or about Tennesseans or about the State of Tennessee, with particular emphasis on works concerning West Tennessee. The collection includes 21 books by Harry Harrison Kroll, who was on the faculty of the University of Tennessee at Martin.

MARYVILLE

Blount County Library
300 East Harper Street   37801

1498   **Genealogy**

262 volumes, with emphasis on early Blount County history and genealogy, including county court records, wills, and deeds, dating back to 1795.

Lamar Memorial Library
Maryville College   37801

1499   **Hunter Research Library**

1,973 physical units of microfiche covering world events, 1758-1889, with essays on history, religion, science, literature and economics as well as texts of important historical documents.

McKENZIE

Burroughs Library
Bethel College   38201

1500   Cumberland Presbyterian Church

ca. 100 volumes dealing with the history of the Cumberland Presbyterian Church, with emphasis on the years prior to 1906, including biographies and memoirs of ministers, doctrinal works, creedal statements, and related materials.

McKenzie Memorial Library
135 North Broadway   38201

1501   Browning, Governor Gordon

A collection of papers, correspondence, 300 personal books, pictures, and other memorabilia collected during Governor Browning's 86 years, including World Wars I and II and the governorship of Tennessee, 1937-39 and 1949-1953.

1502   Genealogy

ca. 1,050 books, 104 of which comprise the Reverend William Thorne Collection and 250 volumes and 120 feels of microfilm for Tennessee genealogical research, including Carroll County records, 1822-1900, census records beginning in 1830, and extensive files of local family histories.

1503   Oral History

22 tapes of programs and personal interviews prepared by the Carroll County Historical Society.

MEMPHIS

Brooks Memorial Art Gallery
Overton Park   38112

1504   Library

ca. 10,000 volumes of reference works in the fine arts, graphic arts, photography and design.

Agricultural Chemicals Group
W. R. Grace and Company   38127

1505   Technical Services Library

ca. 7,000 volumes and 2,000 items in microform relating to agriculture, agricultural statistics, feeding of animals, trade literature and patents in agricultural chemistry.   **R**

Memphis District Corps of Engineers
668 Federal Building   38103

1506   Library

ca. 4,500 volumes, 250 journals and extensive microform holdings in civil and military engineering, flood control, and ecology.   **R**

Memphis/Shelby County Public Library & Information Center
1850 Peabody Avenue   38104

1507   America-at-War Collection

Papers, 1861 to date, 6 linear feet, including newspapers, correspondence, maps, posters, and ration books relating to U. S. military conflicts from the beginning of the Civil War.

1508   Foundation for World Literacy

66 linear feet of papers, 1955-1960, comprised of the records of the first international literacy program.

1509   McKeller, Kenneth D.

Papers, 1911-1952, comprised of over a million items relating to McKeller, who served six terms in the U. S. Senate, 1916-1953.

1510   Malone, Walter

Papers, 1883-1919, 12 linear feet of correspondence, newspaper clippings, and manuscripts of Judge Walter Malone, Memphis author and poet.

1511   Yellow Fever

6 linear feet of manuscripts and scrapbooks relating to yellow fever epidemics in Memphis, especially the scourge of 1878. Included are ca. 100

items, comprising the papers, 1900-1956, of Joseph A. LePrince, pioneer in the control of this dreaded disease.

1512   **Genealogy**

ca. 10,000 volumes of genealogical reference including Randolph Papers and other family manuscripts and surname indexes to various genealogical collections.

1513   **City-County Archives**

More than 2,000 volumes and other materials measuring 2,000 linear feet, devoted to the official records of the City of Memphis and Shelby County.

1514   **Memphis Room Collections**

3,000 books and pamphlets and 500 historical maps relating to Memphis and surrounding area in addition to:

1515   "Memphis Belle" Papers, 1942-1971, including inspection book of the Flying Fortress and correspondence relating to the "Memphis Belle" monument.

1516   Newspaper clipping file of Memphis and surrounding area, occupying 300 linear feet.

1517   File of 13,000 photographs of Memphis and vicinity and ca. 200 glass plate negatives.

1518   Oral History Collection, comprised of 300 hours of tapes and transcripts relating to Memphis and Tennessee.

1519   Goodwyn Institute records, 1911-1970.

1520   Carley, John Ogden, 1848-1878, 10 linear feet of manuscripts relating to this newspaperman and authority on flood control.

1521   Downs, Captain Rees, Papers, 1880-1950, including significant materials on Mississippi River steamboats.

1522   Greene, Colton, Papers and pictorial sources, 1874-1880, 6 linear feet of materials relating to this Memphis businessman, who founded the Memphis Mardi Gras, the forerunner of the Cotton Carnival.

286

1523   Halle, A. Arthur, Papers, 1900-1960, 20 linear feet of this Memphis retailer, a promoter of the Cotton Carnival.

1524   Hughn, Hugh Higbee, Papers, 1890-1909, 12 linear feet of materials relating to this Memphis theatre critic.

1525   Loeb, Henry, 200 feet of papers on this mayor of Memphis, 1967-1971.

1526   McIntyre, Florence, Papers, 1890-1962, 30 linear feet, regarding Memphian arts.

1527   Martin, John, Papers, ca. 1890-1965, of this U. S. District Judge, occupying 150 linear feet.

1528   Montgomery, H. A., Papers, 1853-1865, 35 items on the establishment of the telegraph in the Memphis area.

1529   Scruggs, Susanne Coulan, Papers, 1864-1945, of this pioneer in children's services.

1530   Snowden School PTA Papers, 1910-1970, 15 scrapbooks and manuscripts of the first Parent Teacher Association in Memphis.

University Libraries
Memphis State University   38152

1531 Coffee, Andrew Jackson

Papers, 1804-1882, 78 letters, including correspondence of the Coffee family and 11 letters and notes of Andrew Jackson along with six miscellaneous family papers.

1532 Ford, Jesse Hill

Papers, 1967-1974, 19,000 items, including correspondence with friends in the literary world; manuscripts of 5 published novels, screenplays, and plays; 60 published stories and articles; and unpublished novels, plays, poems, and essays.

1533 Kroll, Harry Harrison

Papers, 1922-1965, 15,000 items, including correspondence, notes, scrapbooks, manuscripts, lectures, articles, contracts, certificates, and reviews.

1534 Malone, Walter

Papers, 1879-1937, 6,000 items, including correspondence, manuscripts of poems, articles, and plays by the author of **Songs of the North and South** and **Hernando de Soto.**

1535 Winslow, Anne Goodwin

Papers, 1921-1958, 16,000 items, including manuscripts of published and unpublished novels, poems, essays, and **The Dwelling Place** (memoirs), along with reviews and correspondence with friends and publishers in the literary world.

1536 American Jewish Archives

Papers, 7,000 items, including articles, correspondence, history, constitutions of congregations, speeches, sermons, portions of **The Occident,** diaries, and other materials relating to Southern Jews.

1537 Circus Collection

ca. 12,000 items, 1800's to date, including posters, handbills, films, costumes, banners, photographs, business records of individual circuses, and models.

1538 Theatre Collection

65,000 items, 1700's to date, including broadsides, posters, photographs, manuscripts, personal papers of actors and actresses, screenplays, moviescripts, and other materials.

1539 Confederate Veterans Historical Association

Papers, 1874-1925, 8,000 items, including minutes, applications, cash books, newsclippings, ledgers, rosters, financial records, and an index.

1540 Southern Tenant Farmers Union

Papers, 1934-1968, 2,000 items, including contracts, newsletters, manuscripts of books, articles, correspondence, and scrapbooks.

1541 Freedman's Bureau

Records, 1862-1866, 200 items, including correspondence, army rosters, payrolls, financial records, and maps issued by the Freedman's Bureau of the U. S. War Department.

1542 **Lantern Slides**

ca. 6,000 slides, 1890-1920, covering various historical sites and travel scenes, educational series, and miscellaneous subjects. The projector is also of historical interest.

Other Holdings include:

1543 Forshey, Caleb Goldsmith, Diaries, 1838-1873, 200 items of diaries, correspondence, reports and articles.

1544 Gowen, Emmett, Papers, 1921-1976, 50,000 items, including correspondence, diaries, photographs, business records, and manuscripts of published and unpublished novels, short stories and articles.

1545 Grider, George, Papers, 1964-1966, 26,000 items, including correspondence, campaign files, constituent cases, speeches, and legislation regarding this West Tennessee Congressman.

1546 Hale, Wiley Pope, Letters, 1848, 9 items, written while serving in the Mexican War.

1547 Harris, John Brice, Papers, 1940-1972, 1,000 items, including poetry, television skits, historical manuscripts, correspondence, photographs, and other records.

1548 Hinds, Milburn A., Papers, 1942-1965, 32,000 items, including correspondence, scrapbooks, and business files of this Shelby County sheriff.

1549 Hunter, William Washington, Papers, 1820-1860, 5,000 items, including letter concerning the Gold Rush and Texas, deeds, certificates, and daybooks.

1550 James, Edward J., Letters, 1862-1865, 42 handwritten letters from a member of the 96th Regiment, Illinois Infantry.

1551 McDowell, John H., Papers, 1863-1888, 250 items including a Civil War diary and family records of a state politician from Buntyn.

1552 Meeman, Edward J., Papers, 1938-1967, 24,000 items, including correspondence, speeches, articles, and manuscripts of newspaper materials of a former Memphis editor.

1553   Orgill, Edmund, Papers, 1940-1971, 38,000 items, including correspondence, speeches, notebooks, and office files of a former Memphis mayor.

1554   Overton, Watkins, Papers, 1915-1955, 30,000 items, including correspondence, speeches, scrapbooks, articles and political materials of this former Memphis mayor.

1555   Parks, L. H., Diaries, 1843-1887, 13 diaries of a minister.

1556   Simon, Charlie May (Mrs. John Gould Fletcher), Papers, 3,000 items, including correspondence with literary friends and others, including Albert Schweitzer.

1557   Smit, Johannes, Papers, 1946-1970, 100 items, including vocal and orchestra scores, parts, tapes, and sheet music.

1558   Stahl, Ezra M., Diaries, 1863-1865, 3 diaries written by this Union officer while in Franklin, Tennessee.

1559   Steele, William O., Papers, 1950's to date, 2 cubic feet of manuscripts of novels, scrapbooks, and correspondence of this noted author of juvenile fiction and biography.

1560   Sugarmon, Russell, Papers, 1959-1976, 500 items, including correspondence, speeches, reports, and press releases.

1561   Vermillion and Kittredge, Letters, 1861-1865, 3,000 items, including letters and forms of the 36th Iowa Regiment.

1562   Woollard, L. Guy, Papers, 1863-1874, 30 items including diaries, journals, correspondence, and petitions of Captain Woollard of the "Senatobia Invincibles."

1563   Wurzburg, Jocelyn, Papers, 1964-1975, 750 items, including correspondence, notes, and organizational newsletters.

1564   Delta Co-operative Farms, Papers, 500 items, including articles, leaflets, correspondence, and other materials.

1565   Memphis Typographical Union, Papers, 1874-1970, 10,000 items, including minutes, correspondence, contracts, and convention materials.

1566   Sanitation Workers Strike, 1968, Papers, 1968-1976, 200,000 items, including books, journal and newspaper clippings, photographs, and documents.

1567   Oral History, including the Tennessee Valley Authority, jazz and blues in Memphis, the Jewish Community in Memphis, and interviews with Southern writers.

Memphis Theological Seminary Library
168 East Parkway, South   38104

1568   Cumberland Presbyterian Archives

As the historical library and archives of the General Assembly of the Cumberland Presbyterian Church, this collection of ca. 4,000 volumes and 36 vertical file drawers consists of materials published by the church and its members. It includes official minutes of all judicatory levels.

National Cotton Council of America
1918 North Parkway   38112

1569   Library

ca. 1,000 volumes on cotton production and marketing, used primarily by the delegates of 19 cotton producing states to increase the consumption of United States cotton and cotton seed products.   **R**

Buckeye Cellulose Corporation
Proctor & Gamble Company
949 Tilman Street   38108

1570   Library

Technical collection of ca. 5,500 volumes, along with journal and microform holdings, support the company's research programs in cellulose, pulp, and paper technology and polymer chemistry.   **R**

MacCracken Memorial Library
Southern College of Optometry
1245 Madison Avenue   38104

1571   MacCracken, William P., Jr.

44 archival boxes of law office records and memorabilia of Mac-Cracken, who served as legal counsel of the American Optometric

Association, 1942-1968, along with the oral history tapes used in the compilaton of **Mr. Mac,** published by the Southern School of Optometry in 1970.

Burrow Library
Southwestern at Memphis   38112

1572   Armstrong, Walter P., Collection

21 sets and 362 individual volumes of first editions, signed editions, numbered editions, and special editions of late 19th and 20th century authors.

1573   Phelps, Ziba, Collection

Embossed revenue stamps, 1751-1817, 225 pieces, including American, English, Swedish, and Dutch stamped paper — promissary notes, bills of lading, stock certificates, farm inventories, and other documents.

University of Tennessee Center for Health Sciences Library
800 Madison Avenue   38163

1574   Wallace Memorial Collection

ca. 200 books by members of the staff and faculty of the Center for Health Sciences, which have been assembled in memory of an alumnus — William L. Wallace, known as "Bill Wallace of China," who was killed while serving as a medical missionary to Communist China in 1951.

MILLIGAN COLLEGE

P. H. Welshimer Memorial Library
Milligan College   37682

1575   Hopwood, Joseph

Papers, 1860-1935, 4 vertical files of correspondence relating to Lynchburg College in Virginia and to Milligan College, which he founded in 1881.

1576   Murch, James DeForest

Papers, 1920-1970, 5 vertical file cabinets of correspondence, manuscripts, and other publications relating to the writings of this minister of the Disciples of Christ and the religious journals, which he edited.

MURFREESBORO

Highland Rim Regional Library Center
2102 Mercury Boulevard   37130

1577   Genealogy

    ca. 500 volumes on family histories of the Southern states, with particular emphasis on Tennessee and the counties of Middle Tennessee.

Linebaugh Public Library
110 West College Street   37130

1578   Tennesseana

    ca. 300 volumes, including works by Tennesseans and books about Tennessee and the people of Tennessee.

Andrew L. Todd Library
Middle Tennessee State University   37132

1579   Tennessee

    A collection of ca. 5,000 books about the state and by Tennesseans, which is enhanced by the fact that Murfreesboro was the capital of Tennessee from 1819 to 1825.

NASHVILLE

Country Music Foundation
4 Music Square, East   37203

1580   Library and Media Center

    Consisting of 70,000 recordings, 2,500 tapes including 150 oral history tapes, 2,500 volumes, 2,000 song books, 750 films, 6,000 photographs and extensive files of biographical sketches and newspaper clippings, this collection is the largest ever assembled in the field of country music. Included are manuscripts of the American Federation of Musicians and the American Federation of Radio and Television artists, as well as the Roy Acuff Collection.

1581   Acuff, Roy

Print and non-print materials covering Roy Acuff's career from 1938 to date, including 850 recordings, 160 tape recordings, 10 feature films, 350 television films, 260 periodicals, 250 pieces of sheet music, songbooks, photographs, books, pamphlets, and personal correspondence.

Crisman Memorial Library
David Lipscomb College   37203

1582   Goodpasture Collection

ca. 1,700 volumes of primarily religious publications from the personal library of B. C. Goodpasture, long-time minister of the Church of Christ and editor of **The Gospel Advocate.**

Disciples of Christ Historical Society
1101 Nineteenth Avenue, South   37212

1583   Library

The entire collection, consisting of ca. 17,000 volumes, 10 manuscript groups, and numerous non-book materials, is concerned with the Restoration Movement and the Christian Church (Disciples of Christ), the Church of Christ, and related religious groups.

Fisk University Library
17th Avenue, North   37203

1584   Special Negro Collection

ca. 35,000 volumes, 3,050 microfilm reels, 110 journals and other serial titles, 76 newspapers, 2,000 phonograph records and tapes, theses, biography files, and other materials relating to blacks in America and Africa. Special features include the **Lincoln Bible;** first editions of Phyllis Wheatley's poems, **Les Cenelles** (1845), and William Wells Brown's **Clotel; or the President's Daughter** (1853); and **Parts of the Holy Bible, Selected for the Use of Negro Slaves in the British West-India Island.**

1585   Black Oral History

More than 500 interviews with persons who have been eyewitnesses, participants, or contributors to the black experience in America, including some African narrators.

1586 Bontemps, Arna

Papers, 1943-1965, ca. 31 boxes and filing cabinet, of this librarian, lecturer, and author of **100 Years of Negro Freedom** and **The Fast Sooner Hound,** a Caldecott Award winner.

1587 DuBois, William Edward Burghardt

Papers, 1900-1960, 128 boxes of manuscripts and other materials, relating to this renowned historian and author of **The Negro, The Souls of Black Folk,** and other studies pertaining to the Negro in America.

1588 Hughes, Langston

Papers, 1921-1965, ca. 13 boxes, including manuscripts and other materials relating to Hughes as poet, short story writer, and playwright, who compiled and edited anthologies of Negro poetry, short stories, and folklore.

1589 Johnson, Charles Spurgeon

Papers, 1866-1965, ca. 478 boxes and 4 filing cabinets, of this outstanding educator, sociologist, and president of Fisk University.

1590 Johnson, James Weldon

Papers, 1899-1952, 2 boxes of this noted composer, educator, and author of **God's Trombones, Seven Negro Sermons in Verse,** and other works on the American Negro.

1591 Rosenwald, Julius, Fund

The Fisk University Library serves as the archives, 1917-1948, of the Julius Rosenwald Fund, and this extensive collection fills 563 manuscript boxes.

Other Archival and Manuscript Collections include:

1592 Burt, Robert T., Papers, 5 boxes concerning this pioneer black doctor and civic leader in Clarksville.

1593 Chesnutt, Charles Waddell, Correspondence and journals, 1874-1885, of this lawyer and author.

1594 Dawson, William L., Papers, 1943-1970, ca. 3,000 items, of Dawson as Congressman.

1595 Douglas, Aaron, Collection, 1921-1974, 14 boxes, of this artist.

1596   Fabio, Sarah Webster, Collection, 1974 to date, 1 box of autographed books by this poet.

1597   Garvey, Marcus, Papers, 6 boxes, of this black leader.

1598   Haynes, George Edmund, Papers, 1909-1922, 5 boxes, relating to Haynes as sociologist, educator, and author.

1599   Hebb, Bobby, Papers, 1963, 1 box, materials by this composer, arranger, and songwriter.

1600   Holtby, Winifred, Collection, 1903-1971, 9 boxes pertaining to this English novelist and social reformer.

1601   Hopkins, Pauline, Papers, 1897-1899, 1 box, materials relating to this author, singer, and playwright.

1602   Johnson, Robert Burgette, Papers, 1947-1967, ca. 10 boxes, of this sociologist.

1603   Langston, John Mercer, Papers, 1853-1898, 6 boxes, representing Langston as educator, lawyer, and diplomat.

1604   Madgett, Naomi Long, Papers, 1941-1968, 1 box, of this poet.

1605   Manley, Effa, 21 items in a continuing collection of black baseball players.

1606   Myrtle Brady Collection on Booker T. Washington, 1901-1922, 1 box.

1607   Napier, James Carroll, Papers, 1880-1917, 5 boxes.

1608   Toomer, Jean, 1897-1963, 74 boxes, concerning this author, poet, and lecturer.

1609   Work, John Wesley, III, Papers, 1915-1971, 18 boxes, of this professor, author, and composer.

Memorial Library
John A. Gupton College
2507 West End Avenue   37203

1610   Mortuary Science

ca. 100 books and pamphlets, 10 cassette tapes, and 48 slides dealing with all aspects of death, grief, and bereavement; funeral customs of different countries; and the technical aspects of preparing the body for burial.

Joint University Libraries (George Peabody College for Teachers,
   Scarritt College, and Vanderbilt University)
419 Twenty-first Avenue   37203

1611   Horn, Stanley, Collection

Papers, 1780-1905, ca. 650 items, including Andrew Jackson papers, documents concerning the Aaron Burr conspiracy, Tennessee land grants, 40 letters written during the Civil War period, and William Blount's letters concerning Indian affairs.

1612   Cheney, Brainard

Papers, 1932-1970, 13 linear feet, including manuscripts of **Lightwood, River Rogue,** and 4 other novels, newspaper and periodical articles, speeches, play manuscripts and 5 tapes of the production, **I Chose to Die,** and literary correspondence.

1613   Davidson, Donald

Papers, 1917-1968, 16 linear feet, including correspondence, articles by and about Davidson, speeches, poetry manuscripts and typescripts, and research notes for **The Tennessee** and **American Composition and Rhetoric.**

1614   Lytle, Andrew Nelson

Papers, 1868-1961, ca. 3,000 items, comprised of correspondence, biographical and genealogical data, dairies and other writings, including manuscripts of his **At The Moon's Inn, The Lost Sheep, The Gold Dust Family,** and **New Ground.**

1615   Owsley, Frank Lawrence

A collection of more than 2,000 items, consisting of articles, addresses, correspondence, manuscripts of **King Cotton Diplomacy, Plain Folk of the Old South,** and **State Rights in the Confederacy,** and miscellaneous writings.

1616   Ransom, John Crowe

This collection, occupying less than a linear foot, contains manuscript letters of Ransom to Robert Graves, with comments on the poetry of each as well as the work of Laura Riding; signed poems; and extensive correspondence between Ransom and Arthur Mizener, the majority pertaining to the **Kenyon Review,** of which Ransom was editor.

1617 Rice, Grantland

ca. 500 items articles, short stories, manuscript verse, columns of "The Sportlight" and other sports writings, radio scripts and correspondence, much of which is concerned with Football All-Americans.

1618 Riding, Laura

A small collection comprised of letters discussing her own work and that of the **Fugitive** and manuscripts of her poetry.

1619 Tate, Allen

Papers, 1931-1971, 1 linear foot, including family correspondence, letters from publishers, and articles by and about Tate. Related is the correspondence with Arthur Mizener, 1939-1972, concerning literature, criticism and research.

1620 Wills, Jesse Ely

Papers, 2 linear feet, including literary correspondence, 1952-1974, manuscripts of his poems since 1920, Old Oak and Coffee House Papers, and drafts and proofs of his **Early and Late, Nashville and Other Poems, Conversation Pieces,** and other publications of this member of the Fugitive group.

1621 Grand Ole Opry

Papers, 1928-1967, 3 linear feet of Opry souvenir programs, books, sheet music and songbooks by Opry performers, photographs and advertisements, and the company's 1963 biography, **Presenting the Grand Ole Opry** by Anne Walker.

1622 Southern Politics

A collection, 14 linear feet, consisting primarily of drafts and research materials for **A Two-Party South?** and **Southern Politics in State and Nation** by V. O. Key, Jr. and Alexander Heard. Transcripts of interview used in the preparation of both works are included.

1623 I'll Take My Stand

The original manuscript of **I'll Take My Stand,** the agrarian manifesto of Donald Davidson, John Gould Fletcher, Lyle H. Lanier, Henry Blue Kline,

Andrew Lytle, Frank Lawrence Owsley, John Crowe Ransom, Allen Tate, John Donald Wade, and Stark Young.

1624   Tennessee Academy of Science

Papers, 1912-1968, 9 linear feet, including financial records, membership lists, programs, minutes and records of meetings, 1912-1947, along with clippings and articles concerning the Academy.

Other Special Collections include:

1625   Barnard, Edward Emerson, Papers, 1882-1923, 20 linear feet, including correspondence, 3 books, articles, and astronomical photographs along with the typescript of the autobiography of this renowned astronomer.

1626   Binkley, William Campbell, Papers, 18 linear feet, including correspondence, 1920-1970, manuscript of his writings, typescript of **The Texas Revolution,** and significant records of the Mississippi Valley Historical Association, 1936-1962, and the Southern Historical Association, 1930-1960.

1627   Burman, Ben Lucien, represented by a carbon typescript of **Blow a Wild Bugle for Catfish Bend,** worksheets and galley proofs of **Look Down that Winding River,** and photocopies of **The Sign of the Praying Tiger.**

1628   Caldwell, John Cope, Papers, 1943-1966, 19 linear feet, including correspondence, articles, and manuscripts of books in the "Let's Visit" and "Our Neighbors" series.

1629   Griswold, Rufus Wilmont, Papers, 1834-1856, of Edgar Allan Poe's first editor and critical biographer.

1630   Haun, Mildred, Papers, 8 linear feet, including correspondence, diaries, 350 folksongs, short stories, and the edited manuscript of **The Hawk's Done Gone.**

1631   Jackson, George Pullen, Papers, 1930-1951, comprised of correspondence, hymnbook collection, materials on Sacred Harp music, and songs in manuscript.

1632   McKendree, William, Collection of a Methodist minister of the 1700's, including a diary, sermons, a chart of circuit riders, and a letter from John Wesley.

1633   McTyeire, Holland N., 163 sermons by Bishop McTyeire, prepared from 1844 to 1850.

1634   Mann, Delbert, Papers, 1947-1977, 20 linear feet of scripts, screenplays, and other materials relating to 60 productions directed by Mann for the theatre, television, and motion pictures.

1635   Mims, Edwin, Papers, 1902-1959, including the manuscripts for his **Lee's Life after the Civil War, History of Vanderbilt, Adventurous America,** and other writings.

1636   Moore, Frederick W., Papers, 1903-1906, correspondence and notes and lecture notes on the social and political aspects of the Civil War South.

1637   Sanborn, Herbert Charles, 15 linear feet, including 101 published works in philosophy, psychology and other fields.

1638   Sims, Cecil, 10 linear feet of materials relating to this Tennessee State Senator.

1639   Taylor, John Lark, Papers, 1879-1944, comprised of music, plays, and stories along with other materials relating to Taylor as a member of the Sothern and Marlowe Shakespearean Company.

1640   Taylor, Warren, Papers, 1925-1946, including music and theatre programs in the Nashville area and letters and memorabilia of the famous Fugitives.

1641   Tigert, John J., IV, Papers, 1840-1957, 3 linear feet, comprised of sermons, correspondence, documents, and papers relating to the founding of Vanderbilt University.

1642   Tillett, W. F., Papers, 1889-1934, ca. 100 items, including the manuscript of his **Hymns and Hymn Writers of the Church.**

1643   Turner, F. Hill, represented by letters, poems, and manuscripts of his publications in field of higher education.

1644   Weakley, Samuel Anderson, Research notes and maps of the historic roads in the Nashville area, including the Natchez Trace and the Franklin Pike.

1645   Weaver, Richard Malcolm, ca. 3 linear feet of papers of this educator and manuscripts of his **Ideas Have Consequences** and **Visions of Order.**

1646   Wilkes, John Summerfield, represented by a number of items relating to him as Tennessee Supreme Court Judge, who was known as "the humorist of the American bench."

Public Library of Nashville and Davidson County
222 Eighth Avenue, North   37203

1647   Local History and Genealogy

ca. 6,000 volumes pertaining to Nashville and its history along with maps, memorabilia, and portraits by Washington Cooper, early Nashville portrait-painter; and ca. 4,000 genealogical items relating to the counties of Middle Tennessee.

1648   Nashville Authors

In an effort to collect the works of all Nashville authors, the library has assembled 1,500 books, including the writings of the Fugitives, Alfred Leland Crabb, and historian Stanley Horn.

1649   Weil, Carrie Mae, Collection

This collection is comprised of the library which Harry C. Monk assembled during a lifetime study of ornithology and lepidoptera. Along with ca. 300 volumes are Monk's diaries, covering almost 60 years of keen observation of the birds and butterflies in the Nashville area.

1650   Naff Collection

500 items, including posters, handbills, programs, and pictures relating to theatrical performances in Nashville's Ryman Auditorium.

Dargan-Carver Library
Southern Baptist Historical Commission
127 Ninth Avenue, North   37234

1651   Baptist History

This collection of more than 50,000 books and 65,000 volumes of periodicals is devoted to Southern Baptist history. The Baptist Union Catalog, maintained by the Dargan-Carver Library, provides a guide to denominational resources in the libraries of the six Southern Baptist seminaries as well as Furman University, Wake Forest University, Mercer University, Stetson University, and the University of Richmond.

Manuscripts

Among the major manuscript holdings are the collections of:

1652   Alldredge, E. P., 1919-1948, ca. 15,000 items.

1653   Bouldin, George, 1904-1967, ca. 10,000 pages

1654   Carver, W. O., 1874-1950, ca. 2,000 pages

1655   Compere, E. L., 1853-1945, ca. 4,100 items

1656   Crouch, Austin, 1893-1956, ca. 2,500 items

1657   Dargan, E. C., 1892-1913, ca. 1,350 items

1658   Day, Samuel Stearnes, 1825-1912, ca. 10,000 pages

1659   Dixon, A. C., 1870-1925, ca. 6,100 items

1660   Flake, Arthur, 1930-1946, 200 items

1661   Frost-Bell Collection, primarily consists of the official correspo
James Marion Frost and Theodore Percy Bell, the first two cor
secretaries of the Sunday School Board, 1891-1916, ca. 17,000 item

1662   Hastings, Robert J., 1948-1970, ca. 3,000 pages

1663   Hays, Brooks, 1957-1959, ca. 5,000 items

1664   Hobbs, Herschel H., 1949-1972, 37,400 items

1665   Holcomb, T. L., 1935-1945, 18 linear feet

1666   Keagan, Kearnie, 1904-1967, ca. 11,000 pages

1667   Leavell, Frank H., 1913-1950, ca. 3,300 items

1668   Leavell, L. P., 1902-1929, ca. 300 items

1669   McKinney, B. B., 1921-1967, 2,100 items

1670   Moore, Hight C., 1884-1956, ca. 10,000 items

1671   Newman, A.H., 1879-1933, ca. 1,000 pages

1672	Newton, Louie D., 1946-1948, ca. 150 items
1673	Norris, Frank, 1928-1952, ca. 29,000 items
1674	Rice, Luther, 1802-1825, 24 items
1675	Spilman, B. W., 1871-1941, ca. 3,160 pages
1676	Weaver, Rufus, 1918-1946, 1,750 items

1677 Archives

The Archives in the Dargan-Carver Library consist chiefly of materials of two Southern Baptist agencies: the Historical Commission and the Sunday School Board. Included in this collection are annuals of associations, state conventions, the Southern Baptist convention and the Woman's Missionary Union; Baptist state papers; biographical data files, bound volumes of periodicals of the Sunday School Board, Mission Boards, the WMU and the Brotherhood; Church Architecture Department drawings; materials related to the commissions of the Convention; official records of the Convention; pamphlets, pictures, and many other materials.

Minnie Ritchie & Joel Owsley Cheek Library
Tennessee Botanical Gardens   37205

1678 Botany

ca. 4,000 volumes dealing with various aspects of horticulture and botany, including landscape architecture and Tennessee wildflowers.

Tennessee State Library and Archives
403 Seventh Avenue, North   37219

1679 Henley, David

Papers, 1794-1808, 50 items relating to this Revolutionary Army officer, including correspondence concerning Indian affairs in the territory south of the Ohio River and a list of the people killed by the Indians in the Mero District.

1680 Jackson, Andrew

Papers, 1800-1845, ca. 1,500 items, including correspondence, military records, documents, marriage bond, will, and papers relating to the duel between Jackson and Charles Dickinson in 1806, and articles and other materials about Jackson and members of his family.

1681 **Johnson, Andrew**

Papers, 1846-1875, ca. 100 items, including correspondence, documents signed by Johnson, a scrapbook, broadside, and other materials regarding the 17th president of the United States.

1682 **McAlister, Hill**

Papers, 1806-1956, ca. 1,000 items, including correspondence, speeches, reports, biographical and genealogical information and memorabilia of McAlister, who served as governor of Tennessee from 1832 to 1836.

1683 **Polk, James Knox**

Papers, 1832-1848, ca. 100 items, including correspondence, sketches and information concerning homes of the Polk family in Tennessee.

1684 **Robertson, James**

Papers, 1784-1814, 376 items, comprised of correspondence, documents and other materials relating to this pioneer, army officer, Indian agent, and Tennessee legislator. Correspondence includes letters from pioneers in the Cumberland settlements, Indian chiefs, and a letter signed by George Washington.

1685 **Sevier, John**

Papers, 1752-1839, ca. 100 items, including correspondence, orders issued by Sevier, biographical sketches of this pioneer, militia officer, governor, and U.S. Representative from Tennessee.

1686 **Stokes, William B.**

Papers, 1811-1888, ca. 300 items concerning Stokes as Union officer, lawyer, and U. S. Representative from Tennessee.

Other notable manuscript collections include papers of the following:

1687 Adams, Adam Gillespie, 1857-1958, 1,200 items

1688 Barclay, Robert Edward, 1854-1961, ca. 11 linear feet

1689   Buell, George P. and Brien, John S., 1805-1943, ca. 10,000 items

1690   Cheatham, Benjamin Franklin, 1834-1893, ca. 800 items

1691   Cox-McCormack, Nancy, 1911-1960, ca. 300 items

1692   Dickinson, Jacob McGavock, 1812-1946, ca. 40,000 items

1693   Drane Family, 1719-1928, ca. 900 items and 7 volumes

1694   Faw, Walter Wagoner, 1819-1956, ca. 62,500 items

1695   Fergusson, Family, 1824-1927, ca. 7,000 items

1696   Gaines, John Wesley and Gaines, Edmund Pendleton, 1793-1926, ca. 100
items

1697   Goodloe, Hallum Wood, 1863-1956, ca. 7,500 items

1698   Hollowell, Miss Frank, 1834-1961, ca. 1,600 items

1699   Lauderdale Family, 1812-1909, ca. 150 items

1700   McGavock, Randal W., 1848-1898, ca. 200 items

1701   Rankin, Anne Porterfield, 1887-1941, ca. 2,000 items

1702   Simpson, Samuel Robert, 1862-1906, ca. 300 items

1703   Wall, Bernhardt, b. 1872, 52 items and 12 volumes

1704   Whyte, Robert, 1755-1882, ca. 1,200 items

1705   Montgomery Bell Academy minute books, 1852-1950, 4 volumes

1706   Nashville Public Schools Collection, 1710-1958, ca. 20,000 items

1707   Rugby Papers, 1872-1904, ca. 200 items relating to the colony for
younger sons of Englishmen founded by Thomas Hughes at Rugby, Tennessee

1708   Ruskin Co-operative Association Records, 1896-1963, ca. 50 items
relating to a cooperative colony, which was established by Charles Augustus
Wayland in Dickson County, Tennessee, in 1894

1709   Sam Davis Memorial Association Records, 1930-1961, ca. 1 linear foot

1710 Tennessee Turnpike Records, 1830-1910, ca. 4 linear feet

Tennessee State Planning Office
660 Capitol Hill Building   37219

1711 Library

      ca. 20,000 volumes and 180 journal subscriptions relating to comprehensive planning and Tennessee public affairs. Along with state documents, the library maintains a Tennessee Information Center collection.

Mackey Library
Trevecca Nazarene College   37210

1712 Church of the Nazarene

      Currently consisting of ca. 1,500 items, this continuing collection is comprised of manuals, histories, and other materials relating to the Church of the Nazarene and to Trevecca Nazarene College.

United Methodist Publishing House
201 Eighth Avenue, South   37202

1713 Library

      This Methodist Historical Collection consists of ca. 40,000 items, including published histories, disciplines, hymnals, journals, photographs, and church publications and curriculum materials. Also on file are family histories of Methodist ministers, 1773 to date, including those of the United Methodist Church, the Methodist Episcopal Church, South, and other related Methodist groups.

The Upper Room
1908 Grand Avenue   37203

1714 Library

      Along with thousands of volumes of devotional literature, this collection contains 70 original letters of John Wesley, 25 first editions of Wesley's publications, and photocopies of most of the correspondence of Francis Asbury, the first Methodist bishop.

SAVANNAH

Hardin County Library
1013 Main Street   38372

1715   State and Local History

>   In this collection of ca. 350 volumes and other materials relating to Tennessee are two histories of Hardin County and a set of taped interviews with local senior citizens which have been transcribed and edited.

SEWANEE

Jessie Ball duPont Library
The University of the South   37375

1716   Sewanee Review

>   Papers, 1892 to date, 2,150 items, including most of the manuscripts accepted for publication in the **Sewanee Review** since 1943 and correspondence and reports of former editors and business managers of this scholarly journal.

1717   Autograph Letters of Bishops

>   1,200 letters of Protestant Episcopal Bishops, 1729-1796 and 1861-1914, along with those of 160 later bishops. These letters relate to the prelates' business, clerical, and personal concerns and to the University of the South.

1718   Beard, William Ewing

>   Manuscripts of this journalist, historian, and chairman of the Tennessee Historical Commission, including **Gettysburg, Eighty Years After** (1943) and **Tennessee and the War.**

1719   DuBose, William Porcher

>   Papers, 1844-1918, 3 linear feet of material relating to this Episcopal clergyman, chaplain of Kershaw's Brigade of the South Carolina infantry, and professor of theology at the University of the South.

1720   Green, Elisha

>   2 linear feet of materials, including the manuscript of his autobiography,

which was used by Elizabeth and Arthur Ben Chitty for **Ely, Too Black, Too White,** and research materials, commentaries, and pictures.

1721   **Kirby-Smith, Edmund**

Papers, 1782-1969, 300 items relating to Confederate General Kirby-Smith and his family, including biographical data, correspondence, and photographs.

1722   **Otey, James Hervey**

Family papers, 1834-1884, ca. 150 letters, clippings and other materials concerning Otey, the first Episcopal Bishop of Tennessee and first chancellor of the University of the South.

1723   **Polk, Leonidas**

Papers, 1830-1864, 6 linear feet of correspondence, diaries and other materials relating to Bishop Polk.

1724   **Radford, P. M.**

Papers, 1825-1902, consisting of histories of 97 Episcopal churches, sermons, and miscellaneous items collected by this historiographer of the Diocese of Tennessee.

SHELBYVILLE

Argie Cooper Public Library
100 South Main Street   37160

1725   **Genealogy**

A collection of ten histories of local families and a list of all the cemeteries in Bedford County with map and index.

TULLAHOMA

Space Institute
University of Tennessee   37388

1726   **Library**

ca. 10,000 technical volumes, selected to support a graduate-level instruction/research program in the "space-related" sciences.

IX

SPECIAL COLLECTIONS
IN
LIBRARIES OF VIRGINIA

Compiled
By
Ardie L. Kelly

ACCOMAC

Eastern Shore Public Library
Accomac   23301

1727   **Eastern Shore of Virginia**

> ca. 500 items including manuscripts, typescripts, microtexts, maps and 230 volumes on description, local history, and genealogy of the Eastern Shore of Virginia, 84 volumes on fishing, 62 volumes on sailing, and 49 volumes on shipwrecks.

ALEXANDRIA

Alexandria Library (Lloyd House)
220 North Washington Street   22314

1728   **Virginiana**

> 5,112 volumes of Virginia history and biography, including a comprehensive local history collection with emphasis on materials relating to Alexandria from 1749 to the present.
> A microfilm collection of 7,825 items includes various city and county land records as well as the microfilm edition of the Alexandria **Gazette,** 1784 to date.

1729   **McKnight Papers**

> Miscellaneous papers of Captain John McKnight (b. 1769) and other members of the McKnight Family of Alexandria, including correspondence, personal data, and records collected in the long course of the family's shipping business.

1730   **Early Library**

> A museum collection of 3,393 volumes which comprised part of the holdings of the Alexandria Library Company, a private subscription library established in 1794 and predecessor of the present Alexandria Library.

JHK & Associates Technical Libraries
4660 Kenmore Avenue   22304

1731   **Transportation Planning**

Over 1,000 documents relating to traffic and transportation in Maryland, Pennsylvania, Virginia and the District of Columbia.   **R**

1732   Also available from JHK's West Coast Library in San Francisco are 1,000 to 1,500 documents on each of the following subjects: Bicycle Riding, Pedestrians, Motor Communications and Public Transit. The Bicycle and Motorist Aid Communications files comprise the largest known collections on these subjects.

AMHERST

Amherst County Public Library
Box 370   24521

1733   **Virginia**

ca. 350 items including history, legends, genealogy with special emphasis on Amherst County materials, supplemented by a vertical file collection of local newspaper clippings and photostats.

APPOMATTOX

Appomattox Court House National Historical Park
Box 218   24522

1734   **Historical Collection**

More than 750 volumes on the Civil War, the Confederacy, and the cultural history of the South, 1800-1870.

ARLINGTON

American Gas Association
1515 Wilson Boulevard   22209

1735 Natural Gas

ca. 10,000 volumes covering all aspects of the natural gas industry — distribution, transmission, gas appliances and equipment. **R**

American Patent Law Association
2001 Jefferson Davis Highway   22202

1736 Patent

A collection devoted to patents, trademarks, copyrights and related subjects, occupying ca. 800 linear feet. **R**

Arlington County Department of Libraries
1015 N. Quincy Street   22201

1737 Virginiana

ca. 3,100 books and documents on regional, state, and local history, ranging from the era of Indian habitation to the current century. The Library-Zonta Oral History Collection is comprised of 60 hours of interviews with local citizens on various aspects of Arlington life in an earlier day.

1738 Francis and Elizabeth Booth Silver Memorial

An illustrator's collection of 267 titles plus catalogs of various exhibitions of individual artists. Selected as examples of outstanding illustrations in children's books, it contains works by both American and foreign artists, including original illustrations by Crane, Caldecott, Cruikshank, Rackham and others.

1739 Old Timers' Collection

500 books from the late 19th and early 20 centuries, many with unusual bindings and illustrations, of special interest to students of American literature and oldsters who enjoy a nostalgic visit with the originals.

Hardwood Plywood Manufacturers Association
Box 6246   22206

1740 Wood

ca. 500 volumes, 400 of which are devoted to hardwood, plywood, and veneer along with 50 books on building codes.

ASHLAND

Walter Hines Page Library
Randolph-Macon College   23005

1741   **Methodist Collection**

ca. 2,400 volumes and 500 non-print items including Methodist church histories, biographies, hymnals and doctrinal works, supplemented by manuscript diaries of itinerant ministers, with emphasis on the Methodist Church in Virginia, 1773-date.

1742   **Childs/Casanova Collection**

3,000 books and printed items, largely with 18th century imprints, on French history and foreign relations, and including many editions and translations of Casanova's **Memoirs,** and 97 volumes attributed to Ange Goudar.

1743   **Childs/Miller Collection**

200 books and other printed items by and about Henry Miller along with an original watercolor by Miller and four recordings made by Miller; and 50 items of correspondence between the author and J. Rives Childs.

BLACKSBURG

Carol M. Newman library
Virginia Polytechnic Institute and State University   24061

1744   **Tyler, James Hoge**

50 linear feet of personal, political and business papers of the Tyler Family from 1832 to the 1930's, including 38 volumes of official correspondence while Tyler was governor of Virginia, 1898-1902.

1745   **20th Century American and British Authors**

First editions of 27 20th century authors in 2,200 volumes with letters and other materials relating to Sherwood Anderson, W. H. Auden, Max Beerbohm, Erskine Caldwell, Robert Graves, Joseph Hergesheimer, Henry James, and Dylan Thomas.

1746   Account Books

200 volumes of account books of general stores, lime kiln, produce company, furnace and mining companies in five counties of Southwest Virginia.

1747   Landis, John

ca. 53 linear feet of papers of Landis' work with the Babcock and Wilcox Company of Lynchburg, Virginia, 1954-1967, relating to nuclear engineering projects, nuclear ships, etc.

BRISTOL

Bristol Public Library
701 Goode Street   24201

1748   Genealogy and Local History

570 volumes of local histories, court records and other primary sources of the history of Southwestern Virginia and Northeastern Tennessee. Included are 60 printed genealogical volumes covering Washington County, Virginia, and Sullivan County, Tennessee, from the Colonial period through the Civil War.

BRIDGEWATER

Alexander Mack Memorial Library
Bridgewater   22812

1749   The Brethren Collection

1,500 volumes and 500 pamphlets on the Church of the Brethren and by members of the Church, several of which are dated in the 1700's.

CHARLOTTESVILLE

Mineral Resources
McCormick Road
Box 3667   22903

1750 Minerals

20,953 volumes and 4,500 maps pertaining to Geology and Mineral Resources.

Institute of Textile Technology
Box 391   22902

1751 Roger Milliken Textile Library

Extensive holdings in all areas of textile technology with emphasis on textile processing from raw material to textile marketing, concentrating on publications since 1945 but including many earlier editions.

Alderman Library
University of Virgnina   22901

Manuscript Collections

1752   ca. 9,100,000 items, chiefly manuscripts but also including ca. 100,000 small prints and photographs, 7,300 microfilm reels of manuscripts, 834 audio recordings, and other materials. The main strengths of the collection lie in the history of Virginia and the Southeastern United States and in Virginia and American literature.
Notable are:

1753   19th century Virginia family papers with some 18th century as well.

1754   Papers of Virginia political figures from the late 18th to the 20th centuries with emphasis on recent political history.

1755   Business records for the 19th and early 20th century.

1756   National figures of the entire period of American history, including (1) Thomas Jefferson (ca. 3,000 original manuscripts and copies of all known obtainable manuscripts, which along with books by, about, and belonging to Jefferson make this the most comprehensive collection of Jefferson materials in existence), (2) Arthur Lee, (3) Richard Henry Lee, (4) James Madison (along with 300 pamphlets bequeathed to the University by Madison), (5) James Monroe, (6) John Hartwell Cocke, (7) R. M. T. Hunter, (8) Carter Glass, (9) Harry F. Byrd, (10) Edwin M. "Pa" Watson, and (11) Edward R. Stettinius, Jr.

Virginia Literature

1757   16,900 manuscripts, including manuscript material of the following authors with approximate dates covered and number of items:

1758   Cabell, James Branch, 1886-1956, 2,500 items

1759   Glasgow, Ellen, 1880-1954, 2,000 items

1760   Johnston, Mary, 1898-1936, 4,000 items

1761   Keyes, Frances Parkinson, 1950-1965, 3,000 items

1762   Neal, Harry Edward, 1930-1970, 4,500 items

1763   Rives, Amelie (Princess Troubetzkoy), 1887-1938, 300 items

1764   Thompson, John Reuben, 1842-1926, 500 items

1765   Tucker, George, 1775-1861, 60 items

1766   **Dos Passos, John**

ca. 50,000 items including the author's personal collection of manuscripts, research materials and drafts of novels, and extensive correspondence.

1767   **Faulkner, William**

Manuscript holdings, 12,000 in number, along with 2,500 volumes (consisting of every first edition and all available printings and translations of Faulkner's works) make this the most complete collection of this Nobel prize-winner.

1768   **Poe, Edgar Allan**

Significant collection of ca. 15,000 items and extensive printed materials, some original letters, copies of all known Poe letters, and materials collected by Henry Ingram, the first biographer of Poe.

Rare Book Collections

1769   The largest portion of the material housed in the Rare Book Room — 200,000 volumes, pamphlets, broadsides, maps and other printed items — pertains to American history and American literature with emphasis on the Southeastern states, particularly Virginia.

1770 Barrett, Clifton Waller, Library

American literature, 1775-1950, in a collection of 250,000 pieces, including books and manuscripts and containing, insofar as it has been possible to assemble them, all fiction, poetry, drama, .and essays published by an American in book form up to 1875 and a very nearly complete collection of the works of every American writer up to 1950. Along with the exhaustive author collections are the Wegelin Collection of American Poetry, the Wright Collection of American Fiction, and the Hill Collection of American Drama.

1771 McGregor, Tracy W., Library

The main portion of this collection of 18,000 volumes and other printed items consists of important works relating to American history, beginning with the early explorations of the 15th century with emphasis on the explorations of what is now the southeastern United States. Within the McGregor Library is the Mather Collection concerning the early New England colonies and particularly the Mathers of the 17th century.

1772 Another area of concentration is English literature, with particular emphasis on the 19th century authors. Among these are:

1773 **Kipling Collection,** 450 volumes

1774 **Tennyson Collection,** 62 items, including rare and limited editions and the manuscript of "The Charge of the Light Brigade"

1775 **Blackmore Collection** of 1,030 manuscript items by, about, and relating to Richard Duddridge Blackmore

1776 **Sadleir-Black Collection of Gothic Novels,** comprised of 2,000 works of Gothic fiction of the late 18th and the 19th centuries.

Special Collections

Extensive holdings in special subject areas, including

1777 **South Asia Collection** of ca. 100,000 volumes, which along with access to the CRL serials file forms the most complete collection of this kind of material in the world

1778 **East Asia Collection** of 35,000 volumes, including the Ma Kiam library of 11,000 volumes on traditional China

1779 **Ceylon Collection** of 3,000 volumes on all aspects of Ceylon

1780   **Tibetan Collection,** consisting of 10,000 titles of works relating to Tibet

1781   **Middle East Collection** of 18,000 volumes covering from 1962 to date

1782   **Slavic Collection** of 75,000 volumes, emphasizing Russia, Yugoslavia, Poland, and Bulgaria.

Other outstanding miscellaneous collections include

1783   **Yellow Fever Collection,** ca. 66 linear feet of material on yellow fever and specifically on the work of Walter Reed

1784   **Adolph Lomb Optical Library** of 3,000 volumes on the history and development of modern optical science

1785   **Thomas W. Streeter Collection** of 800 pieces on railroads in the Southern states

1786   **American Sheet Music Collection** of 15,000 titles of some 18th but mostly early 19th century sheet music with American imprints

1787   Several unique files, comprised of ca. 23,000 manuscripts relating to ballads, folksongs and other folk materials in the **Virginia Folklore Collection.**

CHESAPEAKE

Chesapeake Public Library
300 Cedar Road   23320

1788   **Wallace Memorial Room**

ca. 800 items relating to the history and genealogy of Virginia and North Carolina and particularly strong in the Colonial and Revolutionary War periods. Printed and genealogical records are supplemented by a complete microfilm collection of local newspapers published prior to the Civil War and a number of historical maps of the Chesapeake area.

DANVILLE

Dan River, Incorporated
Research Library   24541

1789 Research Collection

2,000 volumes dealing with the various aspects of Textile Chemistry. **R**

Danville Public Library
Patton Street   24541

1790 Genealogy and Local History

1,500 volumes and 150 non-print items including city directories, court records, county histories, parish registers, family genealogies, and Virginia census records on microfilm, 1810-1880.

EMORY

Frederick T. Kelly Library
Emory and Henry College   24327

1791 Holston Conference Archives

1,100 volumes and 850 non-print items relating to the history of the Holston Conference of the United Methodist Church, including Methodistica gathered by Richard Nye Price for his **Holston Methodism** and the manuscript of this work. Although some manuscripts, church minutes, and correspondence of parishioners are as early as 1803, the collection's primary coverage is from 1830 to the present.

FAIRFAX

Charles R. Fenwick Library
George Mason University   22030

1792 Barnes Papers

ca. 200 items, mostly letters exchanged between Lt. Col. Milton Barnes, Commander of the 97th Ohio Volunteers, and his wife from late 1861 to mid-1865. His letters graphically depict both combat and ordinary army life; hers often refer to the problems posed by the presence of numerous pro-Southerners in Ohio.

1793 Chess Collection

ca. 200 volumes including 175 volumes of monographic works on all aspects of chess and a complete file of **Chess Informant.**

1794 Federal Theater Project

Scripts, documents, photographs, and costume designs from the Works Projects Administration program in the performing arts, including 7,000 scripts; previously unknown plays by Theodore Ward, Theodore Browne, Hughes Allison and other Black writers; and unpublished early works of Arthur Miller, Betty Smith, and other distinguished American playwrights.

FALLS CHURCH

American Automobile Association
8111 Gatehouse Road   22042

1795 AAA Collection

13,000 volumes emphasizing highway safety and transportation and including 5,000 volumes on driver education and 4,000 travel guidebooks.   **R**

Falls Church Public Library
120 N. Virginia Avenue   22046

1796 Virginia Collection

1,500 volumes and 5 oral history tapes, concentrating on the City of Falls Church and surrounding areas.

FORT BELVOIR

Learning Resources Center
U.S. Army Engineer School
Building 270   22060

1797 General Bruce C. Clarke Collection

ca. 1,000 volumes and 500 non-print items comprised of papers, correspondence, photographs, policy statements and recordings, many relating to the Korean Conflict.   **R**

FORT MONROE

Fort Monroe Casemate Museum
Box 341

1798   Casemate Collection

   700 volumes with emphasis on Military History, the Civil War, and Fort Monroe Records (microfilm).

FREDERICKSBURG

Central Rappahannock Regional Library
1201 Caroline Street   22401

1799   Virginiana

   Beginning collection of 2,000 books and pamphets and 320 reels of microfilm intended for students of general, county, and local history, with emphasis on works indexed by Swem, early Fredericksburg newspaper, and local court records.

E. Lee Trinkle Library
Mary Washington College   22401

1800   Joyce, James

   233 items, consisting mainly of first and special editions of Joyce's works as well as material about him and criticisms of his work.

Fredericksburg National Military Park
1013 Lafayette Boulevard   22401

1801   Civil War Library

   ca. 5,000 volumes and 1,000 manuscript items dealing with the Civil War campaigns in the Virginia Theater (1861-65), particularly the battles of Fredericksburg, Chancellorsville, Wilderness, and Spotsylvania. Emphasis is on Federal regimental histories and reference tools for the identification of individual soldiers on both sides.

GLOUCESTER POINT

VIMS Library
Institute of Marine Science   23062

1802   Marine Science

   18,000 volumes, including 4,000 volumes on Oceanography, 5,000 volumes on Fisheries (with a special sport fishing collection) and 4,500 volumes on Marine Biology.

HAMPTON

Charles Taylor Memorial Library
4205 Victoria Boulevard   23669

1803   **Virginiana**

1,450 volumes and 440 non-print items relating to Virginia history from the 1600's with particular emphasis on Hampton and its environs. Genealogical records include the Virginia census on microfilm, histories of families in the area, and books of general interest to Virginia genealogists.

Collis P. Huntington Memorial Library
Hampton Institute   23668

1804   **Negro Literature and History**

Originally loaned and later presented to Hampton Institute by George Foster Peabody, this collection of research materials on Black history currently consists of 20,000 volumes and ca. 5,000 pamphlets, clippings and articles.

HARRISONBURG

Eastern Mennonite College
Library   22801

1805   **Menno Simons Historical Library/Archives**

This collection of Mennonitica, comprised of 11,256 volumes along with supporting periodicals and microforms, features Anabaptist and Mennonite history from the early 16th century to the present. Materials on Amish and Hutterite groups are also included.

Rockingham Public Library
45 Newman Avenue   22801

1806   **Virginiana and Genealogy**

1,735 volumes, consisting of family histories and general genealogical information and books on Virginia history (with emphasis on the Shenandoah

Valley and local counties), books by local authors and books with local imprints.

HOLLINS COLLEGE

Fishburn Library
Hollins College   24020

1807   **Lucy Winton McVitty Memorial**

Manuscripts, incunabula, and books on the history of printing and the study of incunabula. Included are five 15th century manuscripts, ca. 60 volumes of incunabula, early 16th century printed works, incunabula leaves (including Haebler's Incunabula, 280 genuine leaves), 70 handbooks and other volumes on incunabula, and the history of printing, including 8 volumes on papermaking by Dard Hunter.

1808   **Franklin, Benjamin**

ca. 250 books and miscellaneous items, including a letter written by Franklin in 1784 and paper currency issued by the various states between 1690 and 1777, along with books by and about Franklin and books printed by him.

KING GEORGE

Lewis Egerton Smoot Memorial Library
King George   22485

1809   **Virginiana**

The Northern Neck area is emphasized in this collection of ca. 100 volumes on the history of Virginia.

LANCASTER

Mary Ball Washington Museum & Library
Box 97   22503

1810   **Camp Meetings**

ca. 1,000 items, collected by Dr. James Marvin Wharton, covering denominational camp meetings during the last quarter of the 19th century and the first quarter of the 20th. Contains oral histories, recollections, letters, description of customs of revival camp services, this collection serves as the nucleus of a library of camp meeting materials in the area, in Virginia, and in the nation.

1811 Genealogy

Manuscript and printed material on a number of Lancaster families from 1600 to the present.

LAWRENCEVILLE

Brunswick-Greensville Regional Library
234 Main Street   23868

1812 Brunswick/Greensville Historical Records

Two special collections: one containing historical materials and family records of Brunswick County, 1715-1975; the other consists of historical and genealogical records of Greensville County, 1715-1970.

1813 Owen, Gorony

Papers concerning the pre-Revolutionary poet-rector of St. Andrew's Parish in Brunswick County, whose poetry is considered by Welshmen to be among the finest in their language.

LEXINGTON

George C. Marshall Research Foundation Library
Drawer 920   24450

1814 Military-Diplomatic History

18,000 volumes, 40 manuscript collections and extensive non-book material relating primarily to the life and public service of General George C. Marshall, the military and diplomatic history of the United States for the first half of the 20th century, and the Marshall Plan. Also included is the William F. Friedman collection of Cryptography with many interesting examples, photographs, and artifacts. **R**

Rockbridge Historical Society
101 E. Washington Street   24450

1815   **Local History**

1,000 volumes: A complete file of Rockbridge County newspapers along with manuscripts and ledgers of Rockbridge families and businesses.

Cyrus Hall McCormick Library
Washington and Lee University   24450

1816   **Lee Collection**

Papers, mainly correspondence and letter books, of Robert E. Lee during the period he served as president of Washington College, 1865-1870, but also includes material on Lee from as early as 1830, a few items of his father, Henry Lee, dating from the 1790's, and letters by Mrs. R. E. Lee and the Lee children. Collection consists of 5 linear feet of manuscripts, 4 linear feet of pamphlets and memorabilia, and 300 books on Lee.

1817   **Literary Society Records**

Manuscript record books and the library of the Washington Society (300 volumes; 50 manuscript record books) which was established in 1812; the Graham Society (400 volumes; 30 ms. record books) established in 1809; the Franklin Society and Library Company of Lexington, a Lexington literary-debating society, 1800-1891 (3,000 books; 30 ms. record books).

LINDEN

The Aaron Burr Association Library
Tremon, Inca Road   22642

1818   **Burr, Aaron**

110 volumes: The life, career and times of Colonel Aaron Burr, 85 volumes; other members of the Burr Family in America, including Mrs. Theodosia Burr Alston, Col. Burr's daughter, 25 volumes.   **R**

LOCUST GROVE

Germanna Community College Library
Box 339   22508

1819   **Germanna Library Collection**

Genealogy and archival material deposited by the Germanna Foundation, including genealogies of early German settlers in the area. 200 volumes, many of which are in German, and ca. 100 non-print items.

LYNCHBURG

Jones Memorial Library
434 Rivermont Avenue   24504

1820   Genealogy

Significant collection of ca. 6,200 items, including biographies; family, county, and census records; Quaker records, and other genealogical publications covering Kentucky, North and South Carolina, West Virginia, Ohio, Pennsylvania and Tennessee as well as Virginia.

1821   Virginiana

ca. 6,300 items including a variety of historical publications, records of the Virginia Company, Journals of the Council of Colonial Virginia, 1680-1775, and early state and county maps.

1822   Lynchburg

Published histories, research manuscripts and city records comprise this collection of 1,200 items, which include copies of and original local newspapers, dating back to 1794.

Lynchburg College
Lynchburg   24501

1823   The Capron Collection

Categories in this varied collection of 847 volumes and 207 maps include the history of the early iron industry in Europe and America; 15th and 16th century illuminated religious works; 18th century books on "general science;" and books, pamphlets and promotional materials on travel in 19th century America, particularly during the era of the spas.

Nuclear Power Generation Division
Babcock & Wilcox Company
Box 1260   24505

1824   Nuclear Power

Special library of 16,000 volumes, 12,000 of which are concerned with Nuclear Technology.   **R**

Lipscomb Library
Randolph-Macon Woman's College   24503

1825   Writings of Virginia Women

1,681 volumes of published writings by Virginia women.

1826   Lucy S. Howorth Collection of Women's Studies

221 items related to the general subject of women's studies.

1827   The Herbert C. Lipscomb Collection

A carefully selected collection of 132 volumes of classical literature and works indicating the classical influence on other literatures.

McLEAN

Planning Research Corporation Library
7600 Old Springhouse Road   22101

1828   Information Sciences

3,000 volumes on computers, information processing and management.   **R**

TRW Systems Technical Library
7600 Colshire Drive   22101

1829   Energy Collection

Beginning collection, organized in 1975, of publications dealing with all aspects of energy resources, technology and planning: ca. 200 books and thousands of technical reports.   **R**

MANASSAS

Manassas National Battlefield Park
Box 350   22110

1830 **Civil War Collection**

ca. 2,000 volumes on the Civil War in general and books, manuscripts, and diaries on the two battles fought at Manassas.

Prince William County Public Library
8601 Mathis Avenue   22110

1831 **Virginiana**

Virginia history, social life and customs from the late 1800's are depicted in this collection of 1,350 books and numerous pictures. Emphasis is on Prince William County materials.

MARTINSVILLE

Blue Ridge Regional Library
310 E. Church Street   24112

1832 **Virginia Collection**

615 volumes on Virginia history, government, biography, and including histories of Martinsville and Henry County, along with genealogical records of local families.

Library
Patrick Henry Community College   24112

1833 **William F. Stone Collection of Southern History**

ca. 200 volumes on the South from 1860 to the present with emphasis on the Reconstruction and post-Civil War era.

MIDDLEBURG

National Sporting Library
Box 1335   22117

1834 **Arundel-Lonsdale-Huth Collection**

Early equine literature dating back to the 17th century is found in this collection of more than 350 volumes, many of which are first editions from the libraries of Henry Huth and Lord Lonsdale in England.

1835   Foxhunting and Field Sports

ca. 200 volumes on Colonial American sports, hunting with horse and hounds, and many other varieties of the hunt in Great Britain and America.

1836   Smith, Harry Wooster, Papers

Collection consists of 20 boxes of papers and other materials on thoroughbred racing, steeplechasing, jockey clubs and trophies.

1837   White, Thomas Holden, Collection

Over 500 volumes along with photographs and pamphlets on the game of polo, with particular emphasis on polo in America.

MOUNT VERNON

Mount Vernon Ladies' Association of the Union
Mount Vernon   22121

1838   Mount Vernon

ca. 10,000 volumes dealing largely with the domestic life of George and Martha Washington, the restoration and preservation of Mount Vernon, and other topics as they relate to this historic plantation home.   **R**

NEWPORT NEWS

Captain John Smith Library
Christopher Newport College   23606

1839   Alexander C. Brown Nautical Collection

1,100 volumes on oceans, ships, navigation, naval history and memoirs.

Newport News Public Library
West Avenue at 30th Street   23607

1840   Virginiana

ca. 4,500 volumes of Virginia history with emphasis on the Colonial period and a genealogy collection which includes not only Virginia but the Carolinas, Pennsylvania and Maryland as well.

The Mariners Museum
Library 23606

1841   Research Collection

Over 55,000 volumes on regional, national and international maritime and naval history along with maps, charts, logs and ships papers, and more than 150,000 photographs.

NORFOLK

Chrysler Museum
Olney Road and Mowbray Arch   23510

1842   Art Reference Library

ca. 35,000 volumes with special emphasis upon architecture, glass, and Pre-Columbian art.   **R**

MacArthur Memorial
198 Bank Street   23510

1843   MacArthur Library

ca. 4,000 volumes collected by General Douglas MacArthur or acquired by the MacArthur Memorial since 1942. Emphasis is on military subjects, Japan, and Asia for the period 1945-1951.

1844   MacArthur Archives

In 20 record groups, the materials include Records of Headquarters of the U. S. Army Forces under General MacArthur's command in various areas of the world; messages, documents, photographs, and private correspondence of MacArthur; and the Papers of Brigadier General H. E. Eastwood and General Courtney Whitney — occupying 455 linear feet.

Norfolk Botanical Gardens
Airport Road   23518

1845   Botanical Library

1,650 volumes on plant culture, plant identification, garden design, pest control, and Bonsai.

Norfolk Public Library System
301 E. City Hall Avenue   23510

1846   **Sargeant Memorial Room**

In serving the purpose for which this room was established, 12,164 volumes and 5,745 non-print items have been collected in the areas of Norfolkiana, Virginiana, and Virginia genealogy. Microfilm collection of local newspapers begins with the year 1736.

Robert Morton Hughes Library
Old Dominion University   23508

1847   **Dr. George Gay, III, Collection**

Personal collection of 12,300 phonodiscs of largely classical but some folk music acquired between 1920 and 1972. Included are two Edison Phonograph machines and a series of Special Edison records.

PETERSBURG

Petersburg National Battlefield
Box 549   23803

1848   **Civil War**

Large number of regimental histories are included in this collection of 2,500 volumes, which emphasize the events and personages surrounding the siege of Petersburg.

Petersburg Public Library
137 S. Sycamore Street   23803

1849   **Virginia Genealogy/History**

Along with 300 volumes of Virginia genealogical materials are works of Virginia writers and ca. 500 volumes of Virginia history with emphasis on the Petersburg-Dinwiddie-Lower Chesterfield-Prince George area. Included is the definitive 3-volume **History of Virginia** (1607-1805) by John Burk of Petersburg.

Richard Bland College Library
Petersburg   23803

1850   **The Gary Thornell Chess Collection**

45 volumes on chess and its strategy, with sample games by Alekhine, Horowitz and other experts.

PORTSMOUTH

Portsmouth Naval Shipyard Museum
Box 248   23705

1851   **Marshall W. Butt Library**

4,000 volumes of naval and local history.   **R**

Portsmouth Public Library
601 Court Street   23704

1852   **Lighthouse-Lightship Collection**

65 titles collected in conjunction with the Portsmouth Lightship Museum and covering the worldwide history of lighthouses and lightships. The collection is housed on a lightship.

1853   **Portsmouth History**

ca. 200 volumes including unpublished manuscripts, published histories and other printed materials covering the city's history from 1752 to the present.

1854   **Portsmouth and Norfolk County Documents**

Copies of more than 2,500 documents from 1635 to 1925, including rare primary source material on the duel of the **Merrimac** and the **Monitor,** the Civil War on the Outer Banks of North Carolina, and the Battle of Craney Island (now a part of Portsmouth).

1855   **Genealogy**

The genealogical notes of Marshal Butt include a name index from a variety of public documents for families in Norfolk County, Virginia, in the 1600's.

QUANTICO

U. S. Marine Corps
Quantico   22134

1856   **Main Library**

Military history in general and Marine Corps history in particular are featured in this general collection of 30,000 volumes.   **R**

RADFORD

John Preston McConnell Library
Radford College   24142

1857   **Appalachian Studies**

Recent collection of 150 oral history tapes, supplemented with pictorial essays and gravestone rubbings.

1858   **Blacks in Southwest Virginia**

A unique collection of ca. 500 items on Christiansburg Institute, an institution for Blacks in Montgomery County (1866-1966), founded by a Freedmen's Bureau agent and supervised by Booker T. Washington from 1895 to 1915. Includes manuscripts, unpublished poems, sermons, records, and photographs.

RESTON

American Newspaper Publishers Association
11600 Sunrise Valley Drive   22070

1859   **ANPA Foundation Library**

Of the 3,000 volumes in this specialized collection, 2,500 are in the field of journalism.

Council for Exceptional Children
1920 Association Drive   22091

1860   Information Center Library

This Special Education collection of 20,000 volumes emphasizes education for the gifted and the handicapped, including all handicapping conditions

National Center Library
U. S. Geological Survey   22902

1861   Geology-U. S.

More than 600,000 volumes and 250,000 maps dealing with geology, mineralogy, geothermal energy, conservation of land resources and related fields.

1862   Kunz Collection on Gems and Minerals

The George F. Kunz Collection is composed of more than 2,000 items, mostly books, dealing with American and European gemmology and minerals from the 17th century to the present.

RICHMOND

Braille Circulating Library
2700 Stuart Avenue   23220

1863   Braille

The 25,000 volumes of this collection are made available (one item at a time for a period of six weeks) to any visually handicapped person in a free world-wide service.

Confederate Memorial Literary Society
1201 E. Clay Street   23219

1864   Museum of the Confederacy Library

Covering the Confederate States of America, 1861-1865, consists of 2,300 books, 1,950 Confederate imprints, 230 maps and prints, 346 bound volumes of service records, 750 photographs of soldiers and civilians of the Confederacy, and 42 linear feet of manuscripts — file folders, official reports, and soldiers' letters and diaries.   **R**

Foreign Mission Board
Southern Baptist Convention
3806 Monument Avenue   23230

1865   Jenkins Memorial Library and Archives

ca. 30,000 volumes relating primarily to missions and the customs and characteristics of countries which serve as mission fields, along with a core collection in theology. In addition to a subscription list of 239 titles, many of which are overseas periodicals, the library maintains a vertical file of information on missionaries under current appointment.

1866

The archives collection consists of Foreign Mission Board minutes; missionary and national conferences in foreign countries; missionary correspondence back to 1845; a permanent display of Lottie Moon items; and ca. 1,100 representative items from most of the countries in which Southern Baptist missionaries serve.

County of Henrico Public Library
Box 27032   27032

1867   French Literature

600 volumes of French literature in French and English and featuring the novels of Honore de Balzac with criticisms, interpretations, and bibliographies of his works.

Philip Morris, U.S.A.
Box 26583   23261

1868   Research Center Library

Textile chemistry and the cigarette and tobacco industry are featured in this special collection of 6,000 volumes.   **R**

Richmond Public Library
101 E. Franklin Street   23219

1869   Richmond Authors

Expanding collection, ca. 300 at present, of books by authors born, educated, living or having lived in Richmond.

1870 **Tucker Collection of Early British Books for Children**

Earliest volume in this collection of 275 early British children's books is dated 1715, but most of these works were published in the middle and late 1800's.

Union Theological Seminary
3401 Brook Road   23227

1871 **Presbyterian Church Archives**

750 volumes, mostly manuscripts, of the archives of the Presbyterian Church in the United States, 1750 to date. Although chiefly from the Synod of Virginia, the Synod of North Carolina is also included. In addition to the minutes of the synods and their presbyteries and scattered records of local churches, the collection contains the papers of two outstanding Virginia clergymen, William Henry Foote, 1819-1869, and Robert Lewis Dabney, 1863-1890.

Caroline Meriwether Goodlett Library, UDC
328 N. Boulevard   23220

1872 **Research Collection**

ca. 4,000 volumes devoted exclusively to the Confederate Period of American history and includes letters, diaries, and documents.   **R**

Boatwright Memorial Library
University of Richmond   23173

1873 **Virginia Baptist History Collection**

This is the archival collection of the Virginia Baptist Historical Society, and it includes ca. 1,500 volumes of manuscript minute books of Baptist churches in Virginia; ca. 1,000 minute books of district associations; ca. 10,000 books, periodicals and microfilms relating to Baptist history in the state; a complete file of **The Religious Herald,** the state Baptist paper, 1828 to date; and other materials comprised of correspondence, diaries, clippings and photographs. Although some late 18th century material is included, most of the records cover the 19th and 20th centuries.

1874 **Lutz, Caroline Stukey, Collection**

An unusual assemblage of ca. 175 books, pamphlets, periodicals, and miscellaneous items relating to puppets and puppetry.

James Branch Cabell Library
Virginia Commonwealth University
901 Park Avenue   23284

1875   **Cabell, James Branch**

The personal library of 4,000 volumes of this Richmond author, including copies of nearly every edition and printing of all of his works, along with ca. 800 items of Papers, 1890-1958, comprised of correspondence, drafts of chapters, and book reviews.

1876   **Virginia Writers**   (Especially Richmond Authors)

Books and manuscripts, including:

1877   Robert Adams, Papers, 1971-1977, of this science fiction writer, ca. 130 items.

1878   Helena Lefroy Caperton, Papers, 1918-1961, ca. 3,600 items.

1879   James D. Pendleton, Papers, 1960-1069, including drafts of 14 plays and 15 manuscript notebooks of this Richmond playwright.

1880   Herbert Silvette, Papers, 1945-1967, 25 items relating to this physician-author whose pen name was Barnaby Dogbolt.

1881   Frances Leigh Williams, Papers, 1935-1976, ca. 100 items.

1882   **Poetry Society of Virginia**

Papers, 1922 to date, consisting of correspondence, reports, minutes of meetings, ca. 300 items.

1883   **Giacomini Collection**

ca. 100 volumes of first editions of the works of Samuel Johnson, James Boswell, and Oliver Goldsmith, and ca. 100 volumes about these 18th century authors.

1884   **Cartoon and Caricature Collection**

Original drawings and newspaper clippings of several noted Richmond cartoonists along with books relating to cartoons in America, ca. 4,250 items.

1885   Meacham, Harry, Collection

ca. 160 volumes and 1,200 items of books and manuscripts regarding Ezra Pound and correspondence concerning modern American poetry, 1953-1973.

Virginia Historical Society
428 N. Boulevard   23221

1886   Manuscript Collection

ca. 3,000,000 items, 1607 to date, relating to all periods of Virginia history, and including both incoming and outgoing correspondence of those listed in the following categories. (Only a very few of the most famous Virginians represented in this extensive collection can be named here.) Papers of:

1887   Colonial leaders in Virginia William Byrd I, II, and III, Robert Carter, Robert Dinwiddie, and Alexander Spotswood.

1888   Political leaders who served chiefly during the American Revolution or the early years of the federal government: Thomas Jefferson, Richard Henry Lee, James Madison, John Marshall, James Monroe, John Randolph of Roanoke, and George Washington.

1889   19th century Virginia authors: George Washington Parke Custis, John Pendleton Kennedy, Thomas Nelson Page, and John Reuben Thompson.

1890   20th century Virginians, including Senator Harry Flood Byrd, Sr., Governor John Garland Pollard, and Rebecca Yancey Williams, author.

Virginia State Library
12th and Capitol Streets   23219

1891   Archives

Collection consists of the non-current records of the Commonwealth of Virginia and includes 15,794,110 manuscripts in the following categories: Colonial records (1607-1776); Executive records (from the Continental Congress of 1774 through World War II); Legislative records (1776-1955); Judicial (county) records; and non-archival papers of many eminent Virginians of the 18th and 19th centuries; church records (1648-1898); and business records (1752-1957).

1892 Virginiana

23,00 volumes dealing with virtually every aspect of the history, life and culture of the people of Virginia and the state in which they live.

1893 Picture Collection

2,275 broadsides and more than 60,000 prints, photographs, and drawings, chiefly of Virginia and Virginians from 1607 to date.

1894 Other Collections

Confederate States of America, 36,000 volumes, including 2,200 Confederate imprints; History of the Southern States, 34,000 volumes; Virginia newspapers, dating from the 18th century, 91 titles in 500 bound volumes and 19,300 reels of microfilm; Maps, 74,000, consisting of early and contemporary maps of Virginia and U. S. Geological Survey Topographical Quadrants; and Genealogy, 3,600 volumes, pertaining chiefly to Virginia and Southern families.

William J. Clark Library
Virginia Union University
1500 N. Lombardy Street   23220

1895 Lewis, Howard O., Collection

7,858 volumes by and about Blacks from 1837 to date, including 160 rare books, mostly slave narratives and books on slavery, and 343 microfilms from the noted Schomberg Collection on Afro-American culture and history at the New York Public Library.

ROANOKE

Roanoke Public Library
706 S. Jefferson Street   24011

1896 Browning Collection

137 volumes, including single editions and collected works of Robert Browning as well as critical and biographical material published between 1835 and 1950 with emphasis on the second half of the 19th century.

1897 Virginiana

10,026 items and 954 microforms covering the history of Virginia with

340

emphasis on local genealogy and including the complete set of 41 lithographs in Edward Beyer's **Album of Virginia.**

1898   **Black History** (Gainsboro Branch)

Comprehensive collection of 3,400 volumes along with manuscripts, art, and clippings with special emphasis on local Black source materials dating from 1921, when the collection was begun.

SPRINGFIELD

Fairfax County Public Library
5502 Port Royal Road   22151

1899   **Virginiana**

Materials dealing with all aspects of Virginia and especially Fairfax County, including genealogy, 15,250 volumes, 700 reels of microfilm and 1,200 photographs/slides.

1900   **Foreign Language Collections**

200 books written in or translated into Hungarian and 100 titles in Russian, at the Thomas Jefferson Library; 700 items in the Spanish language at the Woodrow Wilson Library.

1901   **Black Studies**

3,400 items and more than 120 reels of microfilm dealing with the Black experience in America and Africa with extensive writings on slavery and colonialism in Africa.

1902   **Theatre and the Performing Arts**

Single plays and collections, costuming and stage design, acting, theatre management and funding are included in this collection of 4,125 books, 300 pamphlets and 100 records at the Dolley Madison Library.

STAUNTON

The Woodrow Wilson Birthplace Foundation Research Library
Box 24   24401

1903 **Woodrow Wilson Papers**

100 items, including correspondence with family and friends as well as private papers of the President, 1888-1924.

1904 **Historic Photographs**

1,200 pieces, including photographs which record the life of Woodrow Wilson, the Wilson Family, the Wilson presidencies (1913-1921), and the Paris Peace Conference (1918-1919).

1905 **McClure, Wallace K., Collection**

ca. 2,000 books, 500 pamphlets and assorted papers and correspondence relating to the State Department and the League of Nations, covering the period from 1885 to the present.

1906 **Brand, Katherine, Collection**

Books and pamphlets, 1920-1970, 500 items concerning the life and times of Woodrow Wilson.

SWEET BRIAR

Mary Helen Cochran Library
Sweet Briar College   24595

1907 **Auden, Wystan Hugh**

154 first editions of W. H. Auden's works in England and America along with clippings and other materials.

1908 **Woolf, Virginia**

84 first editions of the works of Virginia Woolf in England and America, including **The Voyage Out,** 1915.

VIENNA

Wolf Trap Farm Park for the Performing Arts
Box 66   22180

1909 **American Symphony Orchestra League**

Extensive files of orchestra data and programs and periodicals.   **R**

VIRGINIA BEACH

Association for Research and Enlightenment Library
Box 595   23451

1910   **The Edgar Cayce Readings and Tape Library**

> The Psychic Readings of Edgar Cayce, typescripts of 14,250 discourses and answers given by him in response to questions while in a state of trance, covering the period from 1903 to September, 1944. 384 loose-leaf binders of Readings, 155 cassettes along with 1,400 tapes related to the readings and psychic phenomenon.

Virginia Beach Public Library
936 Independence Boulevard   23455

1911   **Princess Anne Collection**

> ca. 100 volumes and 15 reels of microfilm on the history of Princess Anne County and the city of Virginia Beach from 1600 to the present.

WARRENTON

Fauquier County Public Library
2 Court House Square   22186

1912   **Virginiana and Genealogy**

> 500 volumes including the history of Virginia, all available materials on Fauquier County; 300 items in the WPA file of local history; 150 items relating to the genealogy in Northern and Middle Virginia.

WARSAW

North Campus Library
Rappahannock Community College   22572

1913   **Genealogy**

> Basic genealogical works along with a complete file of the **Northern Neck Historical Journal** and the publications of historical societies in Westmoreland, Northumberland, and Essex Counties.

WAYNESBORO

Waynesboro Public Library
600 S. Wayne Avenue   22980

1914   **Local History and Genealogy**

ca. 250 volumes and 2,400 items on Waynesboro and Augusta County history and histories of families in the area, 1800 to date.

WILLIAMSBURG

Earl Gregg Swem Library
College of William and Mary   23185

1915   **Manuscripts Collection**

900,000 manuscripts relating chiefly to the history of Virginia from 1650 to the present, with special strength in (1) 18th and 19th century family papers, especially those of the Blows, Carters, Tuckers, Taliaferros, Barrons, Jerdones, Southalls, and Stubbs; (2) in manuscripts of such notable Virginians as George Washington, Patrick Henry, Robert E. Lee, James Madison and John Tyler; (3) in manuscripts of such illustrious alumni of William and Mary as Thomas Jefferson, James Monroe, and John Marshall; and (4) in several 20th century political collections of state and national import, including U.S. Senator A. Willis Robertson and Governors William M. Tuck and John Garland Pollard; and (5) in papers of Virginia literary figures Thomas Nelson Page and James Barron Hope.

1916   **Rare Books Collection**

The major subject emphasis in this collection of ca. 22,000 volumes is American history and culture, largely to 1865. Although there is a natural emphasis on Virginia, other aspects of special strength include anti-and pro-slavery, canal-building, temperance, and journals of exploration and travel.

Other Collections:

1917   **Peter Chapin Collection**

Comprised of 3,000 volumes, this is one of the most extensive collections in North America relating to dogs. It includes books by Ernest Thompson Seton, Albert P. Terhune, Jack London, Rudyard Kipling and other writers of note.

1918   Wright, John Womack, Collection

ca. 100 17th and 18th century books on fortifications and the campaigns of the Napoleonic Wars along with 346 maps of European military engagements.

Research Center
Colonial Williamsburg Foundation
Drawer C   23185

1919   General Research Collection

ca. 15,000 volumes focused chiefly upon the British Empire in North America during the 17th and 18th centuries, and especially Colonial Williamsburg. Concentration is on social, economic, and political history and published primary sources, but the collection is not designed for genealogical research. **R**

1920   Research Center Archives

ca. 17,500 manuscripts, 300 newspapers, and 290 manuscript volumes, including private and business correspondence, account and letter books, and maps and broadsides relating to Colonial Virginia, along with 2,200 microfilm reels of related manuscript and printed material and over 2,000 photostats. Among the manuscripts are the papers of Robert Anderson, Sir William Blathwayt, Carter and Nathaniel Burwell, Sir Guy Carleton, Richard Corbin and John Norton. **R**

1921   17th and 18th Century Books

ca. 3,000 volumes in the Research Library and in exhibition buildings of Colonial Williamsburg, relating particularly to agriculture, law, travel, medicine and craftsmanship and including a small group of Williamsburg imprints. **R**

1922   Other Collections:

The **A. L. Kocher Collection** of more than 500 books on architecture and related fine arts titles from the 16th to the 20th centuries; **18th Century Music Collection** of ca. 400 pieces or books of music, mostly English, for violin, fife and drum, including religious music and dancing tunes; **Children's Books Collection** of ca. 400 children's, miniature, and drawing books from the 17th through the 19th centuries. **R**

1923   In the Architecture Department Library:

The **Architectural Research Collection** of over 1,500 titles on 18th century American and English architecture and the architectural aspects of Williamsburg's restoration, and the **Alden Hopkins Landscape Architecture Collection** of ca. 350 volumes on gardening and landscaping from the 17th to the 19th centuries.   **R**

1924   In the Abby Aldrich Rockefeller Folk Art Collection Library:

Folk Art Collection of more than 2,500 books and exhibition catalogs pertaining to folk art, furniture, quilts, dolls and toys.   **R**

1925   In the Department of Collections:

Collections Library of over 10,000 titles on 18th century decorative arts and the techniques of museum curation.   **R**

1926   In the Audiovisual Department Library:

Audiovisuals Collections including over 400,000 photographic prints, negatives, slides, transparencies, films and sound tracks covering the entire range of scenes and activities of Colonail Williamsburg.   **R**

WINCHESTER

The Handley Library
Braddock and Piccadilly Streets   22601

1927   Virginia Room

ca. 1,800 items including books by local authors, books published locally, and books relating to the area and the families of Winchester and vicinity with the strongest coverage of the Civil War period.

Howe Library
Shenandoah College and Conservatory of Music   22601

1928   Evangelical United Brethren Church Historical Collection

550 books, journals, and yearbooks on the history and doctrines of the church along with General and Annual Conference Minutes, especially of the Virginia United Brethren Church, 1879-1946, and the Evangelical United Brethren Church, 1947-1968.

WISE

John Cook Wyllie Library
Clinch Valley College   24293

1929   **Historical Society of Southwest Virginia**

      Books, pamphlets, letters and other materials (8 drawers) relating to the history of Southwest Virginia and surrounding areas from 1780 to date. Also available as a supplement to this collection are original, microfilm and photocopies of 79 titles of Southwest Virginia newspapers, 1810 to date.

1930   **Other collections:**

      Local History items (ca. 15 drawers) in collections of Wise County merchants and newspaper publishers along with the papers of Governor John B. Floyd and lawyer-author Elihu Jasper Sutherland.

WYTHEVILLE

Wytheville Community College Library
1000 E. Main Street   24382

1931   **F. B. Kegley Library**

      ca. 1,000 items including books, pamphlets, census records and more than 300 maps on Southwest Virginia history from 18th century frontier days to the present along with genealogy of the Southwest Virginia counties.

X

SPECIAL COLLECTIONS
IN
LIBRARIES OF WEST VIRGINIA

Compiled
By
L. Josephine Fidler

ATHENS

Concord College Library
Athens   24712

1932   Goodykoontz, F. Wells, Collection

222 photographs and prints, including autographed photographs of notable individuals, 1920-1940; photographs or engravings of the U.S. presidents and first ladies from Washington to date with letters and memos relating to many; and photographs of West Virginia political figures.

BECKLEY

Raleigh County Public Library
221 North Kanawha Street   25801

1933   West Virginia Collection

700 items, including books, maps, pamphlets, reports, and periodicals with strengths in materials pertaining to the city of Beckley and to Raleigh County, as well as coal mining.

BETHANY

T. W. Phillips Library
Bethany College
Bethany   26032

1934   Campbell, Alexander

Letters, 1805-1935, 6 linear feet of correspondence, speeches, and college documents of the founder of Christian Church (Disciples of Christ) religious movement and Bethany College. Included are letters to him from leading members of the Christian Church and letters to and from members of his family and descendants.

5   Pendleton, Alexandria Campbellina

Letters, 1852-1898, 3 linear feet of correspondence to and from Alexandria Campbellina Pendleton, granddaughter of Alexander Campbell, founder of the Christian Church (Disciples of Christ) and Bethany College, and daughter of William Kimbrough, second president of Bethany College.

1936   Clark, Champ

Letters, 1905-1915, 1 linear foot of letters to and from Champ Clark, Speaker of the U.S. House of Representatives (1911-1919), member of the House (1893-1921); several letters relate to his unsuccessful attempt to receive the Democratic Party nomination for president in 1912.

1937   Cramblet, Wilbur Haverfield

Papers, 1934-1952, 1 linear foot of letters and office documents from Bethany College president's office; correspondence with nation's leading business, political, and religious leaders.

1938   Gresham, Perry Epler

Papers, 1953-1972, 20 linear feet of letters, office documents from Bethany College president's office; correspondence with noted political figures, leaders of business and labor, West Virginia notables, and religious leaders of the Christian Church (Disciples of Christ).

1939   Mahaffey, Pearl

Diaries and letters, 1908-1969, 10 linear feet of diaries of a Bethany college professor of Modern Language covering daily life at Bethany College, West Virginia's oldest degree granting college.

1940   Marshall, John

Letters, 1940-1965, 1 linear foot including letters to Marshall as U.S. Assistant Attorney General (1925-1929) and President of the Institute of Fiscal and Political Education, Washington, D.C., from prominent political figures.

BRADLEY

Appalachian Bible Institute
Bradley   25818

1941   Judaica (Okey Patteson Collection)

450 volumes on history of Judaism and doctrines, both ancient and current.

BUCKHANNON

A. M. Pfeiffer Library
W. Va. Wesleyan College
Buckhannon   26201

1942   Buck, Pearl

Manuscripts, 1920-1973, 300 items, comprised of original manuscripts along with typescripts of novels and biographies (including **The Exile** and **Fighting Angel,** two of the three works on which the Nobel Prize was based), short stories, and plays on loan from Pearl Buck Birthplace Foundation, Hillsboro, West Virginia.

1943   United Methodist Church of West Virginia

Books, journals (conference), and diaries, 1790 to date, 3,000 items related to the Methodist Church and related organizations, which are historically significant in West Virginia.

1944   Upshur County

Manuscripts and papers, 1820 to date, 750 items related to local and county history, including manuscripts, and census records pertaining to Upshur County.

CHARLESTON

Kanawha County Public Library
123 Capitol Street
Charleston   25301

1945   West Virginia Collection

8,500 items including county histories, genealogical records of western Virginia counties and West Virginia, and materials relating to coal, oil, and gas geology.

Andrew S. Thomas Memorial Library
Morris Harvey College
Charleston   25304

1946   **Kinnaman, John Allen, Memorial Collection**

ca. 200 volumes, including some primary documents and fascimile reprints, relating to American Colonial history.

1947   **Gorman, Rocco J., Memorial Collection**

405 volumes relating to the American Civil War, including biographies, first editions, and scarce items.

West Virginia Department of Archives and History
Science and Culture Center, Capitol Complex   25305

Although the Department of Archives and History is the official archival agency of the state, all of the noncurrent public records of the state are not in this repository. According to Ernst Posner's **American State Archives,** many public records of county, local and some state offices have been acquired by West Virginia University and some are in the custody of the State Records Administrator. With the establishment of the Records Management Program in 1961, the Commissioner of Finance was designated as the State Records Administrator, who has the authority to determine the disposition of public records.

1948   The Department of Archives and History has an extensive collection of Governor's papers, minutes of the Legislative Assembly of 1863, Civil War records of various kinds, court records, and the records of organizations and churches. The major collections are described below.

1949   **Atkinson, George Wesley**

Papers, 1897-1901, 736 items, including correspondence, reports, recommendations, protests, and other papers of Governor of West Virginia.

1950   **Boreman, Arthur Inghram**

Papers, 1863-69, 527 items, including correspondence, relating chiefly to Union Military affairs, educational, election and legislative material, court cases, and other papers of a political leader, jurist, and Governor of West Virginia.

1951   Conley, William Gustavus

Papers, 1929-33, 875 items including correspondence, petitions, reports, and other papers of Governor of West Virginia.

1952   Cornwell, John Jacob

Papers, 1917-21, 334 items including correspondence, reports, petitions, and other papers, relating to military matters and official duties of Governor of West Virginia.

1953   Fleming, Aretas Brooks

Papers, 1890-93, 1,041 items including correspondence, reports, and official business of a lawyer and Governor of West Virginia.

1954   Holt, Homer Adams

Papers, 1936-41, 350 items, including correspondence, reports, memoranda to heads of state government departments of a lawyer, Attorney General, and Governor of West Virginia. Much of the correspondence relates to improvements of the State Capitol building.

1955   Jackson, Jacob Beeson

Papers, 1881-85, 828 items, including correspondence, reports, petitions, and other papers, relating to education, elections, court cases, and legislative material of Governor of West Virginia.

1956   Jacobs, John Jeremiah

Papers, 1871-77, 249 items, including correspondence, petitions, reports, and other papers of a Governor of West Virginia.

1957   Mathews, Henry Mason

Papers, 1877-81, 581 items, including correspondence, petitions, reports and other papers of a Governor of West Virginia.

1958   Pierpont, Francis Harrison

Civil War papers, 1861-62, 1,264 items, including correspondence between Pierpont and his Adjutant General, H. L. Samuels, relating mainly to military matters and Union troops in their charge, petitions, protests, recommendations, and other papers of a Union Governor of Virginia.

1959 **Stevenson, William Erskine**

Papers, 1869-71, 305 items including correspondence, petitions, reports, and other papers, relating to legislative, election, and treasury material of a Governor of West Virginia.

1960 **Wilson, Emanuel Willis**

Papers, 1885-90, 63 items including correspondence, reports, and other materials relating to the contested election of 1888, and including official and private papers of a Governor of West Virginia.

1961 **Barns Family**

Papers, 1859-1931, 237 items including correspondence of Uz Barns, Jr. (1807-1879) and other members of the Barns family. Includes descriptions of Civil War campaigns in Virginia and West Virginia, and farm life in Ritchie County, West Virginia.

1962 **Coleman, Nelson B.**

Papers, 1809-90, 420 items, including correspondence, legal papers, receipts, daybooks, and financial statements, relating to Coleman's steamboat and insurance businesses (steamboat operator and insurance agent, of Malden, Kanawha Co., West Virginia).

1963 **Edwards, William Henry**

Papers, 1858-1905, 30 volumes and 3 boxes including correspondence, entomological journals, notebooks, scrapbooks, plates, and other materials of an entomologist.

1964 **Johnson Papers**

1,360 items, 1778-1848, including correspondence, land grants, court orders, receipts, and bills of sale for slaves. Persons represented include Abraham Johnson, Samuel Kercheval, John Reasoner, and other early settlers of Hampshire County, Virginia (later Mineral County, West Virginia).

1965 **Lewis, Virgil Anson**

Papers, 1790-1910, 3 boxes including papers relating to railroads, rivers roads, and turnpikes.

1966   MacCorkle, William Alexander

Papers, 1893-97, 832 items, including correspondence of a Governor of West Virginia; petitions, proclamations, invitations, and other papers relating to military and legislative matters, the building of the new State capitol; genealogy of the MacCorkle family; and maps of coal fields in Logan and Boone Counties, West Virginia.

1967   Maxwell-Bonnifield

Papers, 1840-1932, 3 feet, family correspondence, diaries, deeds, wills, speeches, and receipts, chiefly of Rufus Maxwell (1828-1907), lawyer and state legislator of Tucker County, and other members of the Maxwell family, including Hu Maxwell, author of several West Virginia county histories.

1968   Morgan, Charles Stephen

Papers, 1822-59, 1,330 items, including correspondence, addresses, invoices, court cases, and other legal papers, penitentiary record (1804-33), pension claims, and other materials pertaining to the Revolutionary War and War of 1812 of a prison warden of Richmond and state legislator of Monongalia Co, Virginia (later West Virginia).

1969   Kanawha River Steamboat

Papers, 1826-96, 226 items including correspondence, legal agreements, and other records relating to steamboat lines on the Kanawha River, primarily 1850-75. Includes papers of the following steamboats: **Active, Elk, Modoc, Resort,** and **William Phillips.**

1970   Ruffner, Donnally and Company

Records, 1832-84, 254 items including correspondence, receipts, and legal papers, chiefly 1840-60, relating to stores and salt interests of a company formed by Lewis Ruffner and Andrew Donnally in Malden, West Virginia.

1971   South Branch Valley Collection

ca. 275 items, including correspondence, accounts, affidavits, bills of sale, land grants, surveys, and other papers, of early settlers of the South Branch Valley of western Virginia (now West Virginia).

1972   Virginia Court of Appeals Records

ca. 1,250 items, including briefs, court orders, transcripts, wills, estates, and indentures, relating to cases tried in the court held at Sweet Springs and Lewisburg, Virginia (now West Virginia).

1973 **West Virginia Centennial Collection**

260 linear feet of correspondence, brochures advertising the numerous centennial activities, color slides, and other material relating to the celebration of West Virginia's centennial in 1963.

1974 **West Virginia County Courts**

Records, 1756-1971: ca. 10,650 reels of microfilm including records from county courthouses by the Genealogical Society of the Church of Jesus Christ of Latter-Day Saints, including birth and death records (chiefly after 1853), marriage records, wills, deeds, estate settlements, and other records.

ELKINS

Davis and Elkins College Library
Elkins   26241

1975 **Martin, Cecilia (Jackie)**

200 items, including technical and pictorial collection of photographer, Jackie Martin, during the early photographic growth period, 1930-1945; emphasis on continental photography.

1976 **Appalachian Collection**

856 items, including books, pamphlets, periodicals, and phonorecords relating to Appalachia with an emphasis on West Virginia.

GLENVILLE

Robert F. Kidd Library
Glenville State College
Glenville   26351

1977 **Bender Art Collection**

700 items, including museum and gallery catalogues for art exhibits and auctions held since 1950, especially Parke-Bernet descriptive auction catalogues.

HARPERS FERRY

Harpers Ferry Center
Harpers Ferry   25425

1978   Library

ca. 12,000 volumes, comprising the library of the Interpretative Design Center of the National Park Service, with emphasis on the decorative arts, museology, and the American Revolution and Civil War history. Also included are ca. 1,500 National Park Service History and Architecture reports and 700 trade catalogs.   **R**

National Historical Park
Harpers Ferry   25425

1979   Library

ca. 2,000 volumes, relating primarily to Harpers Ferry, John Brown, and local Civil War activities, especially that of the Federal arsenal there.

HUNTINGTON

Cabell County Public Library
900 Fifth Avenue
Huntington   25701

1980   West Virginia Collection

3,100 items, including West Virginia, Ohio, and Kentucky histories, marriage, birth and cemetery records; fiction of West Virginia authors (local authors well-represented); genealogical materials; and census tapes, 1810-1880.

James E. Morrow Library
Marshall University
Huntington   25701

1981   Aleshire Family

Papers, 1862-1889, ca. 300 items, primarily correspondence among family members in Gallipolis, Ohio, during and after the Civil War.

1982   Cabell-Wayne Historical Society

Papers, 1880-1973, ca. 50 linear feet of records and papers including a vertical file, many photographs, and a survey of buildings of potential historical value in the city of Huntington. (On loan from the Society)

1983   Danford, Harry Edmund

Papers, 1912-1969, 4 linear feet of correspondence and manuscripts of his books, **Soakum, The West Virginian, Trail of the Gray Dragoons, Ohio Valley Pioneers,** and **Paths of Glory.**

1984   Dugan, Irvin

Papers, 1933-1963, 10 linear feet of correspondence and papers concerning his career as staff artist for the Huntington Publishing Company, including over 500 original drawings of cartoons for publication.

1985   Enslow, Catherine Bliss

Papers, 1899-1973, 22 linear feet of papers concerning her career as a journalist and Democratic party worker in Huntington, West Virginia. Family papers and many photographs are included.

1986   Enslow, Mary Constance

Papers, 1892-1962, 4 linear feet of primarily genealogical research material including Enslow, Kelly, and Madison families. Also included are items related to her career as a commercial artist in Chicago.

1987   Gilchrist Family

Papers, 1783-1957, ca. 4 linear feet of family records including correspondence, diaries, and journals of the Anderson, Wilson, and Gilchrist families of Warren County, Ohio.

1988   Hechler, George

Letters, 1861-1865, 102 items written during the Civil War, describing troop life and campaigns through West Virginia, Tennessee, and Georgia, notably the Battle of Chickamauga, 1863.

1989   Henking, C. C.

Papers, 1795-1861, 35 items, including land patents, deeds, titles, abstracts, and indentures of properties in the present state of West Virginia, many of which are in French. (On loan from Huntington Galleries)

1990   **Hoffman, Charles Anthony**

Papers, 1945-1975, ca. 6 cubic feet of scrapbooks containing speeches made while president of the American Medical Association, awards, and other memorabilia.

1991   **Jenkins, Samuel Roy**

Diaries, 1887-1941, 41 books containing entries dating from Jenkins' high school days in Grafton, West Virginia, including discussion of college and career as florist and civil engineer.

1992   **Marshall University Oral History Collection**

Tape recordings, 1963, 1972 to date, ca. 150 taped and transcribed interviews with residents of the southern West Virginia region relating to coal mining, Appalachian customs, and folklore.

1993   **Morgan Family**

Papers, 1831-1935, 2 linear feet of correspondence and legal papers, including letters written during the Civil War and genealogical information concerning the Beale and Steenbergen families of Shenandoah County, Virginia, and Mason County, (West) Virginia, as well as the Morgan family of Putnam County, (West) Virginia.

1994   **Olafson, Sigfus Collection**

10 books of census records, 1809-1880, of Cabell, Wayne, Logan, Boone, and Wyoming counties, alphabetized and arranged for use.

1995   **Scott, Addison M.**

Papers, 1873-1924, 6 linear feet of maps, reports, contracts, construction proposals, and specifications for the Great Kanawha River Improvement, and other items relating to Scott's career as a civil engineer for the United States Corps of Engineers.

1996   **Steele, Paul Curry**

Papers, 1914 to date, 4 cubic feet of personal and family papers, including information about the Curry and Browning families of Logan County,

West Virginia, as well as manuscripts and drafts of Steele's poetry and other writings.

1997 **Stuart, Jesse**

Papers, 1929 to date, 12 linear feet of articles, poems, and stories in print, presented by the author, along with a purchased collection of first editions of his works.

1998 **Thackston-Miller Families**

Papers, 1849-1967, 1 box of correspondence and school compositions of a Cabell County, (West) Virginia, family before the Civil War.

1999 **West Virginia Association of Colleges and Universities**

Papers, 1961-1974, 23 cubic feet of records, including office files, scrapbooks, minutes, and financial records.

2000 **West Virginia Association of Health, Physical Education and Recreation**

Papers, 1933 to date, 2 cubic feet of records, correspondence, reports, programs, and financial papers.

2001 **WSAZ-TV (Television Station)**

ca. 735 reels of film containing reports of newsworthy events in Huntington, southern West Virginia, southeastern Ohio, and northeastern Kentucky, 1953-1970.

KEARNEYSVILLE

Eastern Fish Disease Laboratory Library
US Fish & Wildlife Service
Kearneysville   25430

2002 **Fish Disease**

2,100 books, 80 periodicals and 7,000 reprints pertaining to fish disease including biology, parasitology, bacteriology, and immunology of fish.   **R**

KEYSER

Mary F. Shipper Library
Potomac State College
Keyser   26726

2003   **West Virginia Collection**

31 folders of typescripts dealing with the history of Mineral County, 1700-1910, including typescript copies of land grants, deeds, property titles and wills; 9 folders including chapters of an early history of Mineral County. 1700-1850 (WPA project) with handwritten copies of the supporting data.

2004   **Genealogy**

11 folders of typescripts pertaining to early settlers of Mineral County including genealogical material on 15 original families in the area; typewritten and handwritten copies of a diary (1825-26) of a local minister, John Jacobs; and a biographical description of John Haason Thompson.

MORGANTOWN

Morgantown Public Library
373 Spruce Street   26505

2005   **State and Local History**

ca. 2,000 volumes and 3,000 archival items of West Virginia and local history, including the Moreland (James, Joseph and William) Collection of letters, papers, and other materials relating to the history of the state.

University Library
West Virginia University   26506

2006   **West Virginia Collection**

ca. 3 million manuscript items and 25,000 volumes dealing with all aspects of West Virginia from the earliest time to the present. Included is the West Virginia Historic Records Survey, 1750-1939, which is comprised of copies of records from each county in the state, listing registers of births, marriages, deaths, wills, estate settlements, and land records.

2007 Coal Mining

At least 9 separate collections covering many aspects of West Virginia's vast coal mining industry, 1900-1967, including blueprints, maps, and drawings of mining operations, wages and benefits of mine workers, and records of mine inspections and accidents.

2008 Appalachian Collection

As West Virginia lies almost entirely within Appalachia, the West Virginia Collection includes ca. 7,000 items, comprised of books and media relating to this region. Access to this collection is through the "Appalachian Bibliography," which is published biennially and "Appalachian Outlook," which appears quarterly.

2009 Jackson, Thomas Jonathan

Papers, 1845-1862, 123 items, including several original letters and photostats of many other letters written by General "Stonewall" Jackson.

2010 Montague, Margaret Prescott

Papers, 1893-1955, 6 linear feet of correspondence, manuscripts, notebooks, diaries and other materials relating to this West Virginia writer, who won the first O. Henry Memorial Prize in 1919 for her short story, "England to America."

2011 Moore, George Ellis

Manuscript, 200 pages, of Moore's **Banner in the Hills,** which presents the story of secession and the Civil War in western Virginia and traces the steps by which West Virginia was created.

2012 Tyler, John

Papers, 1739-1930, ca. 200 items, comprised of research notes and copies of the correspondence of John Tyler as collected by Oliver Perry Chitwood for his biography, **John Tyler, Champion of the Old South.**

2013 East Africa

ca. 6,500 volumes dealing with all aspects of East African history.

PARKERSBURG

Ohio Valley College
College Parkway   26101

2014   Goodpasture, B. C., Collection

A collection of 255 volumes, consisting primarily of religious books with emphasis on the Church of Christ, presented by B. C. Goodpasture.

2015   Restoration Collection

ca. 200 volumes relating to Alexander Campbell and the Restoration Movement in this country.

PHILIPPI

Pickett Library Media Center
Alderson Broaddus College   26416

2016   Baptist History

4,500 items, including books, 1811 to date; Baptist periodicals, 1868 to date; pamphlets, annuals of Northern Baptist Convention, 1919 to date, West Virginia annuals, 1866-1965; and local church history.

SOUTH CHARLESTON

South Charleston Public Library
312 Fourth Avenue   25303

2017   Ecology

As the Ecology Information Center of the Kanawha Valley, the library houses extensive files of environmental materials from deep mining and strip mining to air pollution.

WEST LIBERTY

Paul N. Elbin Library
West Liberty State College   26074

2018 Krise, Nelle M.

270 items, rare books and fine editions, comprised of cuneiform, hieroglyphic and manuscript examples, as well as printed materials, including a 1523 Aldine Press book.

2019 Local History

Included in the collection of 1,200 items relating to West Liberty State College is historical material on the town of West Liberty, 1769 to date.

WHEELING

Oglebay Institute Mansion Museum Library
Oglebay Park   26003

2020 Brown Collection

ca. 100 volumes and other materials on the history of Wheeling, including the only known copy of Wheeling's first newspaper.   **R**

2021 Stifel, Arthur, Collection

A collection of more than 2,000 glass plates of photographs of Wheeling and vicinity in the late 19th century.   **R**

Ohio County Public Library
52 Sixteenth Street   26003

2022 Wheeling Collection

ca. 1,000 volumes and other materials on the history and genealogy of Wheeling and Ohio County.

XI

GEOGRAPHICAL INDEX
CORPORATE INDEX
GENERAL INDEX

Compiled
By
G. Sheppeard Hicks

XI

I

GEOGRAPHICAL INDEX

Asterisks indicate those cities which reported Genealogy and/or Local and County History collections. State collections are listed in the General Index.

Washington 554*
Watkinsville 555*
Waycross 556*
Young Harris 557

KENTUCKY 558-757

Ashland 558-559*
Augusta 560*
Bardstown 561-562
Benton 563-564
Berea 565-567
Bowling Green 568-582
Campbellsville 583
Columbia 584
Covington 585-586
Cynthiana 587-588
Danville 589
Eddyville 590
Edmonton 591
Fort Campbell 592
Fort Knox 593
Fort Mitchell 594-595
Frankfort 596-609 (598)*
Georgetown 610
Grayson 611
Greenup 612
Hardinsburg (613, 614)*
Harlan 615-616
Harrodsburg 617-618*
Hawesville 619
Hazard 620-622 (621)*
Hopkinsville 623
Lexington 624-663 (628, 629)*
Louisville 664-722
Mayfield 723
Maysville 724*
Midway 725-726
Morehead 727-728
Murray 729-738
Owensboro 739-742*
Paducah 743
Paintsville 744
Paris 745-746
Pippa Passes 747
Prestonsburg 748
Princeton 749-750
Richmond 751
Trappist 752
Vancleve 753-754
Wilmore 755-756
Winchester 757*

MISSISSIPPI 758-931

Aberdeen 758-762 (758, 762)*

Bay St. Louis 763-764
Biloxi 765-769 (765)*
Blue Mountain 770*
Booneville 771*
Brookhaven 772*
Clarksdale 773-774
Cleveland 775-779 (775)*
Clinton 780
Columbus 781-782
Corinth 783
Ellisville 784
Greenville 785-786
Greenwood 787-788*
Grenada 789*
Gulfport 790-794 (790)*
Hattiesburg 795-802 (795)*
Holly Springs 803
Jackson 804-856 (810, 841)*
Kosciusko 857*
Laurel 858
Macon 859*
Meridian 860*
Mississippi State 861-876
Natchez 877
New Albany 878*
Ocean Springs 879
Philadelphia 880
Picayune 881
Pontotoc 882
Port Gibson 883
Stoneville 884
Tougaloo 885-898
Tupelo 899-900
University 901-928
Vicksburg 929-930
Yazoo City 931*

NORTH CAROLINA 932-1203

Albemarle 932
Asheboro 933-934*
Asheville 935-937
Banner Elk 938
Beaufort 939
Belmont 940-943
Boiling Springs 944-946
Boone 947
Buies Creek 948
Burgaw 949
Carthage 1156
Chapel Hill 950-978
Charlotte 979-989 (980)*
Clinton 990*
Davidson 991-994
Dobson 995*
Durham 996-1016
Eden 1017-1018

Elizabeth City 1019-1021
Elkin 1022-1023
Elon College 1024
Fayetteville 1025-1029
Gastonia 1030-1032 (1030, 1031)*
Greensboro 1033-1081 (1062)*
Greenville 1082-1084
Hamlet 1085-1087
Haw River 1088-1089
Hickory 1090-1091
High Point 1092-1094
Jacksonville 1095-1096
Jamestown 1097
Kenansville 1098
Kings Mountain 1099*
Kinston 1100*
Laurinburg 1101
Lexington 1102-1103*
Louisburg 1104
Lumberton 1105-1106*
Manteo 1107-1113
Mars Hill 1114-1119
Misenheimer 1120
Monroe 1121*
Montreat 1122-1123
Morganton 1124*
Mount Airy 1125
Mount Olive 1126
Murphy 1127
New Bern 1128*
Newton 1129-1130
Oxford 1131
Raeford 1154
Raleigh 1132-1152 (1141, 1151)*
Rockingham 1153-1157
Rocky Mount 1158-1160 (1158)*
Salisbury 1161-1166
Southern Pines 1167
Sylva 1168
Tarboro 1169
Troy 1155
Tryon 1170
Wadesboro 1153
Wake Forest 1171-1179
Washington 1177-1179
Wentworth 1180
Whitesville 1181-1183
Wilkesboro 1184-1185
Wilmington 1186-1187
Wilson 1188-1189*
Winston-Salem 1190-1203

SOUTH CAROLINA 1204-1395

Aiken 1204-1205
Anderson 1206-1207

Beaufort 1208-1211
Bennettsville 1212
Camden 1213*
Central 1214
Charleston 1215-1267
Clemson 1268-1280
Clinton 1281-1282
Columbia 1283-1313 (1304)*
Conway 1314*
Denmark 1315
Due West 1316-1319 (1318)*
Duncan 1320
Easley 1321-1323
Florence 1324-1327
Georgetown 1328-1329
Greenville 1330-1351 (1349)*
Greenwood 1352-1354 (1352)*
Greer 1355
Hartsville 1356
Lancaster 1357*
Laurens 1358-1360
Marion 1361*
Newberry 1362-1364
Orangeburg 1365-1369 (1367)*
Rock Hill 1370-1375*
Spartanburg 1376-1386 (1380)*
State Park 1387
Sullivan's Island 1388-1390
Sumter 1391
Union 1392-1393*
Walterboro 1394*
Winsboro 1395

TENNESSEE 1396-1726

Arnold Air Force Station 1396
Athens 1397
Blountville 1398*
Chattanooga 1399-1405 (1399, 1400)*
Clarksville 1406-1407*
Cleveland 1408-1409
Collegedale 1410-1411
Cookeville 1412-1415
Elizabethton 1416
Gainsboro 1417*
Gatlinburg 1418-1419
Greeneville 1420-1421
Harrogate 1422
Henderson 1423
Jackson 1424-1428 (1424)*
Jefferson City 1429-1430*
Johnson City 1431-1433
Kingsport 1434-1435 (1434)*
Knoxville 1436-1494
Lookout Mountain 1495
Madison 1496

Martin   1497
Maryville   1498-1499 (1498)*
McKenzie   1500-1503 (1502)*
Memphis   1504-1576 (1512)*
Murfreesboro   1577-1579 (1577)*
Nashville   1580-1714 (1647)*
Savannah   1715
Sewanee   1716-1724
Shelbyville   1725*
Tallahoma   1726

VIRGINIA 1727-1931

Accomac   1727
Alexandria   1728-1732
Amherst   1733
Appomattox   1734
Arlington   1735-1740
Ashland   1741-1743
Blacksburg   1744-1747
Bristol   1748*
Bridgewater   1749
Charlottesville   1750-1787
Chesapeake   1788*
Danville   1789-1790*
Emory   1791
Fairfax   1792-1794
Falls Church   1795-1796
Fort Belvoir   1797
Fort Monroe   1798
Fredricksburg   1799-1801
Gloucester Point   1802
Hampton   1803-1804 (1803)*
Harrisonburg   1805-1806*
Hollins College   1807-1808
King George   1809
Lancaster   1810-1811*
Lawrenceville   1812-1813 (1812)*
Lexington   1814-1817 (1815)*
Linden   1818
Locust Grove   1819
Lynchburg   1820-1827 (1820, 1822)*
McLean   1828-1829
Manassas   1830-1831
Martinsville   1832-1833

Middleburg   1834-1837
Mount Vernon   1838
Newport News   1839-1841 (1840)*
Norfolk   1842-1847 (1846)*
Petersburg   1848-1850 (1849)*
Portsmouth   1851-1855 (1851, 1853, 1855)*
Quantico   1856
Radford   1857-1958
Reston   1859-1862
Richmond   1863-1895
Roanoke   1896-1898
Springfield   1899-1902 (1899)*
Staunton   1903-1906
Sweet Briar   1907-1908
Vienna   1909
Virginia Beach   1910-1911
Warrenton   1912*
Warsaw   1913*
Waynesboro   1914*
Williamsburg   1915-1926
Winchester   1927-1928
Wise   1929-1930*
Wytheville   1931

WEST VIRGINIA 1932-2022

Athens   1932
Beckley   1933
Bethany   1934-1940
Bradley   1941
Buckhannon   1942-1944*
Charleston   1945-1974 (1966, 1974)*
Elkins   1975-1976
Glenville   1977
Harpers Ferry   1978-1979
Huntington   1980-2001 (1986, 1993, 1996)*
Kearneysville   2002
Keyser   2003-2004*
Morgantown   2005-2013
Parkersburg   2014-2015
Philippi   2016
South Charleston   2017
West Liberty   2018-2019*
Wheeling   2020-2022*

II

CORPORATE INDEX

American Patent Law Association   1736
Amherst County Public Library   1733
Anclote Psychiatric Center   340
Andalusia Public Library   3
Anderson County Library   1206
Andrew L. Todd Library   1579
Andrew S. Thomas Memorial Library   1946-1947
Anna Emma Kresge Memorial Library   1495
Anniston and Calhoun County Public Library   4-9
Anson County Public Library, See Sandhill Regional Library System
Appalachian Bible Institute   1941
Appalachian State University   947
Appomattox Court House National Historical Park   1734
Archbold Biological Station   234
Argie Cooper Public Library   1725
Arlington County Department of Libraries   1737-1739
Aro, Incorporated   1396
Art Museum of the Palm Beaches   341
Asa H. Gordon Library   545
Asbury Theological Seminary   755-756
Ashland Public Library   558-559
Association for Research and Enlightenment Library   1910
Athens Regional Library   354-356:555
Athens State College Library   10
Atlanta Christian College   499
Atlanta College of Art   397
Atlanta Historical Society   398-402
Atlanta Public Library   403-408
Atlanta Regional Commission   409
Atlanta University   410-417
Atlantic Estuarian Fisheries Center Library   939
Auburn University   13-17
   Archives   19-27
Augusta College   466
Augusta Regional Library   467
Austin Peay State University   1406-1407
B. L. Fisher Library   755-756
Babcock & Wilcox Library   1824
Baer Memorial Library   85
Barry College Memorial Library   258-259
Bascom Palmer Eye Institute   245
Base Library (Columbus Air Force Base)   781
Bates Leach Eye Hospital   245
Beaufort County Library   1208-1210
Belhaven College   804
Belknap Campus, University of Louisville, Library   712-722
Bell Laboratories   529
Bellamine College Library   664-665

Belmont Abbey College   940-942
Bendix Corporation, Avionics Division, Library   191
Bennett College   1033-1035
Berea College   565-567
Berry College Library   528
Bertha Smith Library   226
Bessemer Hall of History   28
Bethany College   1934-1940
Bethel College Library   1500
Bienenstock Furniture Library   1092
Biloxi Public Library   765-767
Birmingham Museum of Art   29
Birmingham Public Library   30-32
Birmingham-Southern College   33
Black,Crow, and Eidsness Library   202
Black Heritage Research Center   1388-1390
Blazer Library   608-609
Blount County Historical Society   126
Blount County Library   1498
Blue Mountain College   770
Blue Ridge Regional Library   1832
Boatwright Memorial Library   1873-1874
Boca Raton Public Library   169-170
Bolivar County Library   775
Bowling Library   84
Boynton Beach City Library   172-173
Braille Circulating Library   1863
Breckinridge County Public Library   613-614
Brenau College   504
Bristol Public Library   1748
Brooks Memorial Art Gallery   1504
Broward County Library   192-194
Brown & Williamson Tobacco Corporation   666
Brunswick-Greensville Regional Library   1812-1813
Brunswick Junior College   471
Buckeye Cellulose Corporation   1570
Burrow Library   1572-1573
C. G. O'Kelly Library   1203
Cabell County Public Library   1980
Calloway County Public Library   729-730
Campbell College   948
Campbellsville College Library   583
Cape Fear Technical Institute Learning Resource Center   1186
Cape Hatteras National Research Library   1107-1111
Captain John Smith Library   1839
Carl S. Swisher Library   224-225
Carmichael Library   108
Carnegie Library (Rome, Ga.)   531-532
Carol Grotnes Belk Library   947
Carol M. Newman Library   1744-1747

Dolley Madison Library, See Fairfax County
Public Library
Dorothy Wightman Library (Duplin
County)   1098
Dover Library   944-946
Draughon Library   13-18
The Duckworth Libraries   557
Duke University   996-1013
Dulin Gallery of Art   1436
duPont Ball Library   187
Durham County Library   1014
E. C. Blomeyer Library   343
E. Lee Trinkle Library   1800
EMR Telemetry Systems, Technical Information
Center   296
Earl Gregg Swem Library   1915-1918
East Carolina University   1082-1083
East Tennessee State University   1431-1432
Eastern Air Lines Corporation   247
Eastern Fish Disease Laboratory Library   2002
Eastern Kentucky University   751
Eastern Mennonite College   1805
Eastern Shore Public Library   1727
Edgecombe County Technical Institute   1169
Edward Waters College   220
Eglin Air Force Base Library   188-189
Elbert Ivey Memorial Library   1090-1091
Electronic Communication, Incorporated   291
Elizabeth City State University   1020
Elizabeth Jones Library   789
Elizabethton Public Library   1416
Elon College Library   1024
Emmanuel College Library   503
Emmet O'Neal Library   122
Emory and Henry College   1791
Emory University   420-435
Environmental Systems Corporation   1437
Erskine College Library   1316-1319
Ethel Mueller Barrat Library   747
Eufaula Heritage Association   59
Eula Dees Memorial Library   771
Eva B. Dykes Library   76
Evans Memorial Library   758-762
Everett Library   983-984
Everglades National Park Reference
Library   218
F. D. Bluford Library   1064
Fairchild Tropical Garden   248
Fairfax County Public Library   1899-1902
Fairfield County Library   1395
Fairhope Public Library   61
Falls Church Public Library   1796
Fauquier County Public Library   1912
Federal Reserve Bank of Atlanta   436-437
Felix G. Woodward Library   1406-1407
The Filson Club   668-687

Fishburn Library   1807-1808
Fisk University Library   1584-1609
Flint River Regional Library   506
Florence-Lauderdale Public Library   62
Florence Museum   1324
Florida Agricultural and Mechanical
University   302
Florida Bureau of Coastal Zone Planning   303
Florida Historical Society, See University of
South Florida
Florida Solar Energy Center Library   174
Florida Southern College   236-237
Florida State Department of Natural
Resources   293
Florida State University   304-325
Florida Technical University Library   265-266
Foreign Mission Board   1865-1866
Forsyth County Public Library   1190
Fort Monroe Casemate Museum   1798
Fort Valley State College   500-502
Foundation Library   408
Frances Carrick Thomas Library   631
Francis Marion College   1325-1327
Frederick T. Kelly Library   1791
Freed-Hardeman College   1423
Furman University   1330-1347
G. A. Pfeiffer Library   1120
G. R. Little Library   1020
Gadsden Public Library   68-69
Gainsboro Branch Library see
Roanoke Public Library
Gardner-Webb College   944-946
Gaston County Public Library   1030-1032
General Electric Company   688
Ground Systems Department   185
Geological Survey of Alabama   157
George C. Marshall Research Foundation
Library   1814
George C. Marshall Space Flight Center   86
George C. Wallace Heritage Association
(Library)   52
George Coon Public Library   749-750
George H. and Laura E. Brown Library   1177-
1179
George Mason University   1792-1794
George W. Armstrong, Judge, Library   877
Georgetown County Memorial Library   1328
Georgetown University   610
Georgia College   523-526
Georgia Conservancy   438
Georgia Department of Archives and
History   440-446
Georgia Department of Education   439
Georgia Historical Society   534-541
Georgia Institute of Technology   447-448
Georgia Mental Health Institute   449

III

GENERAL INDEX

An attempt has been made to indicate parenthetically the date of those titles published prior to 1900.

Gregg, Cissy, Cook Book Collection   587
Gregory, Noble J., Collection   735
Grenada, Ms.   789
Gresham, Mary, Collection   203
Gresham, Perry Epler, Collection   1938
Grider, George, Collection   1545
Griffin, Alonzo Mercer, Collection   826
Griffin, Charles H., Collection   868
Grimke, Thomas Smith, Collection   1235
Griswold, Rufus Wilmont, Collection   1629
Grogan, Elmira Farnham   509
Grogan, Florence, Collection   509
Grosse, Sir Edmund W.   999
Guatemala   180
Guide to the Study of Augusta and Richmond County   466
Guignard Family   1304
Guilford County (N.C.) History, Collection   1097
Gulf Coast history   766
Gullah dialect   1390
Guthrie, James, Collection   675
HUD   See U.S. Department of Housing and Urban Development
Hackney, Priscilla Benbow, Collection   1049
Haebler's Incunabula   1807
Hahn, Walter A., Collection   1090
Haiti   210
Hale, Wiley Pope, Collection   1546
Haley, James A., Collection   237
Halifax County, N.C.   1100
Hall, Gertrude   359
Hall, Lloyd Augustus, Collection   152
Hallandale, Fla.   217
Halle, A. Arthur, Collection   1523
Hall-Stakely Family   1457
Hamblett, Theora   778
   Collection   916
Hamilton County, Tn.   1452
   Collection   1400
Hamilton, William Franklin   788
The Hamlet   816
Hammett, Evelyn   777
Hammett, Horace Greely, Collection   1337
Hammond Family   1304
Hammond, James H., Collection   1305
Hampshire County, Va.   1964
Hampton Family   1304
Hampton, Va.   1803
Hampton, Wade, Collection   1305
Hancock County, Ky.   619
Hancock County, Ms.   881
Hancock, Joy Bright, Collection   392
Hand, James, Collection   776
Handicapped children   1860
Handy, W.C.   412

Hanes Collection of Incunabula   957
Hanes Collection of the History of the Book   956
Hanna, Hilton E., Collection   137
Harden-Jackson-Carithers   389
Harden, William   544
Hardin County, Tn.   1715
Hardwood   1740
Hardy, John   132
Hare, Butler B., Collection   1305
Hargrett Library, Collection   394
Harlan, John Marshall, Collection   676
Harper's Ferry   411, 1979
Harrell, Costen J.   427
Harris Collection   94
Harris, Corra   359, 422, 459
Harris County, Ga.   511
Harris, Joel Chandler, Collection   423
Harris, John Brice, Collection   1547
Harris, Julia Collier   422
Harris, L.M., Collection   1233
Harris, Roy, Collection   691
Harris, William Julius, Collection   373
Harrison, Byron Patton, Collection   917
Harrison County, Ky.   588
Harrison County, Ms.   765
Harrison, William Henry, Collection   603
Harrold Brothers   429
Hart, General Franklin A.   20
Hart, Oliver, Collection   1305
Hartman, Robert S.   1485
Harvey, William   661
Hassidism   246
Hastings, Robert J., Collection   1662
Hatch, Alden   212
Hatfields and McCoys   744
Hattiesburg **American**   795, 800
Haun, Mildred, Collection   1630
Havens, B.B. and Jonathan, Collection   1179
Hawesville, Ky.   619
The Hawk's Done Gone   1630
Haworth Family, Collection   1050
Hay, William Perry, Collection   215
Haygood, A.G.   427
Hayne, Paul Hamilton, Collection   1005, 1233, 1305
Haynes, George Edmund, Collection   1598
Haynesworth Family   1304
Hays, Brooks, Collection   1663
Hays, Francis Bacon, Collection   1131
Hays, William Shakespeare, Collection   578
Hazard, Ky.   620
Hazelius, Louis, Library, Collection   1289
Health   409, 418
Heard, Alexander   1622
Hearn, Lafcadio, Collection   163, 718

Holland, Ga. 507
Holloway, William H., Collection 137
Hollowell, Miss Frank, Collection 1698
Holmes County, Ms. 857
Holmes, David, Collection 849
Holmes, Mary J. 726
Holmes, Oliver Wendell, Collection 44
Holmes, Zelotes Lee, Collection 1360
Holston Conference Archives,
 Collection 1791
Holston Methodism 1791
Holt, Hamilton, Collection 344
Holt, Homer Adams, Collection 1954
Holt, Margaret McConnell, Collection 1081
Holt, Roland, Collection 960
Holtby, Winifred Collection 1600
Holzhauer, Emil, Collection 262
Home Moravian Church, Salem, N.C. 1196
Homes, Historic 354
Hondius, Jodocus 167
Hope, James Barron 1915
Hopkins, Alden, Landscape Architecture
 Collection 1923
Hopkins, Pauline, Collection 1601
Hopkinsville, Ky. 623
Hopwood, Joseph, Collection 1575
Horn, Stanley 1648
 Collection 1611
Horowitz, Charles, Collection 888
Horowitz, Israel 1850
Horry County, S.C. 1277, 1314
Horry County (S.C.) Historical Society 1314
Horse racing 626, 650, 1836
Horsemanship 264
Horses 264, 575, 626, 1834
Horticulture 248, 271, 1129, 1678
Houk, John Chiles 1441
Houk, Leonidas Campbell 1441
House construction 292
Housing 409, 435
Housing and urban development 464
Howell, Clark 385
Howie, Bob 796
Howland, Marie, Collection 61
Howorth, Lucy S., Collection of Women's
 Studies 1826
Hoyt, William Henry, Collection 961
Hudson, Arthur Palmer Collection 918
Hughes, Dudley M. 374
Hughes, Langston 412, 1588
Hughn, Hugh Higbee, Collection 1524
Huguenot Society of South Carolina
 Transactions 1243
Huie, William Bradford, Collection 49, 57
Hull, Marie 778
Human engineering and genetics 67, 449

Hungarian language 1900
Hunter, Dard 1807
Hunter, R.M.T., Collection 1756
Hunter Research Library 1499
Hunter, William Washington,
 Collection 1549
Huntington, WV. 1982
Hunt-Morgan Family, Collection 638
Huntsville, Al. 71
Hurlburt, J.S. 1408
Hurricanes 206
Hurston, Zora Neale 212
Huske, May Catherine, Collection 1029
Huth, Henry 1834
Hutterite groups 1805
Huxley, Julian, Collection 919
Hyde, Charles R. and Anne Bachman,
 Collection 1403
Hydraulics 929
Hymnals without tunes 1193
Hymnody Collection 1383
**Hymns and Hymn Writers of the
 Church** 1642
Hymns and Hymnals 314, 477, 1291, 1341,
 1383, 1631, 1741
I Chose to Die 1612
I, Priscilla 777
I Saw England 1279
Icelandic literature 435
Ichthyology see Fish
Ideas Have Consequences 1645
I'll Take My Stand 1623
Illiteracy 656
Illyrian Provinces 311
In My Father's House 821
In Search of a Husband 459
The Incredible Mr. Limpet 171
Incunabula 104, 957, 1101, 1307, 1807
Independent Republic Quarterly 1314
**Index to Maps of North Carolina in Books and
 Periodicals** 1112
"Indian Books" 1298
Indigo 1264, 1329
Indian affairs 1611, 1679, 1684
 Wars 440
Indians 35, 83, 240, 306, 310, 332, 403, 487,
 489, 531, 590, 710, 773, 937, 1119, 1127,
 1371, 1374, 1460, 1611
 See also names of individual tribes
Industrial chemistry and packaging 1320
Information Sciences, Collection 1828
Ingram, Annie Blythe, Collection 1153
Ingram, Henry 1768
Insects 234
Insurance, Collection 711
International relations 87

McHenry Coal Mine Collection 579
McIntyre, Florence, Collection 1526
McIver Family, Collection 1343
McKean, Thomas J., Collection 832
McKellar, Kenneth D., Collection 1509
McKendree, William, Collection 1632
MacKenzie, Roderick D., Collection 101
McKinney, B. B., Collection 1669
McKnight, Captain John, Collection 1729
McKowen, Emmett C., Collection 701
McLemore, Richard Aubrey, Collection 817
McMaster Family 1304
McMillan, Louise 512
McMillan, Thomas M., Collection 102
McMurtrie, Douglas, C., Collection 37
McNeer, May 304
McNutt, Alexander B. Plantation
    Collection 827
McQueen, Alexander Stephens 556
McTeer, Will A. 1465
McTyeire, Holland N., Collection 1633
McVitty, Lucy Winton, Memorial
    Collection 1807
Macon County, Al. 26, 83
Macon County, N. C. 1168
Macon, Ms. 859
Macon **Telegraph** 493
Madden, David 1480
Madgett, Naomi Long, Collection 1604
Madison County (Al.), Collection 73
Madison County, Tn. 1424
Madison Family 1986
Madison, James 1888, 1915
    Collection 1756
Magrath, William J., Collection 1305
Mahaffey, Pearl, Collection 1939
Mahan, Joseph B., Jr. Collection 487
Mahan, Katherine Hines 480
Malcolm X 414
Mallory, James 25
Malone, Blondelle, Collection 1305
Malone, Kemp, Library Collection 435
Malone, Walter, Collection 1510, 1534
Mammouth Cave, Ky. 568
Management 529, 689, 711
Manassas, Civil War battles 1830
Manigault Collection 1224
Manigault Family 1304
Manley, Basil, Collection 1304
Manley, Basil, Jr., Collection 1341
Manley, Effa, Collection 1605

Mann, Delbert, Collection 1634
Manning Family 1304
Manning, Reg 796
Manning, Richard I., Collection 1305
Manning, Wyndham M., Collection 1305
Manual of Railroads 173
Maps 28, 31, 35, 40, 87, 157, 167, 197, 222,
    249, 250, 275, 278, 282, 318, 326, 335, 350,
    357, 393, 430, 435, 531-532, 716, 986, 1028,
    1222, 1227, 1302, 1303, 1325, 1452, 1727,
    1769, 1821, 1823, 1841, 1861, 1864, 1894,
    1918, 1920, 1966
    Collection 975
Maps, fire 166
Marengo County, Al. 25
Mareno, Dr. Francisco, Library,
    Collection 285
Marine sciences 216, 255, 293, 297, 303, 547,
    667, 939, 1107
    Collection 181, 879, 1244, 1802
Marion County, Fla. 197
Marion, Francis 1216, 1327
Marion, S. C. 1361
Maritime history 1841
Marius, Richard 1480
Markart, John 1290
Marlboro County (SC.), Collection 1212
Marquart, John 1290
Marsh, Blanche 354
Marshall County, Ky. 564
Marshall, General George C. 1814
Marshall, John 1888, 1915
    Collection 1940
Marshall Plan 1814
Marshall University Oral History
    Collection 1992
Marshall, Zona Idella 859
Martin, Cecilia (Jackie), Collection 1975
Martin, Charles D., Collection 1015
Martin, John, Collection 1527
Martin, Thomas W., Memorial Library,
    Collection 41
Martin, Zenas L., Collection 1056
Martinsville, Va. 1832
Marxism 886
Mason, Benjamin 19
Massenet, Jules Emile Frederic 1233
"The Master of Doro Plantation" 777
Materials science 529
Mathematics 688, 714
Mather, Cotton, Collection 1771

Tree, L.C., Collection   1427
Trent, Josiah C.
   Collection on Walt Whitman   1010
   History of Medicine Collection   1006
Trescott, William H., Collection   1305
Trials   1385
Troisieme Voyage de Cook   546
Tropical botany   248
Tropical storms   177
Troup County, Ga.   508, 511
Troy, Al.   139
Truett, George W., Collection   478
Tuberculosis   1257, 1387
Tuck, William M.   1915
Tucker Collection of Early British Books for
   Children   1870
Tucker Family   1915
Tucker, George, Collection   1765
Tumors   1252
Tupelo, Ms.   899
Turner, F. Hill, Collection   1643
Turner, John Clyde, Collection   1176
Turnpikes   1965
Tuscaloosa, Al.   143
Tusculum College   1420
Tuskegee Institute Lynching Reports,
   Collection   155
Tutwiler Collection   30
A Twentieth Century Congress   1486
Twiggs County, Ga.   396
A Two-Party South?   1622
Tyler, James Hoge, Collection   1744
Tyler, John   1915
   Collection   2012
Typewriters   625
Tyson, Lawrence Davis   1445
UDC   See United Daughters of the
   Confederacy
Uncle Bob   812
Uncle Tom's Cabin   1422
Underwood, Joseph Rogers, Collection   574
Underwood, Oscar Wilder, Collection   115
Underwood, Thomas Rust, Collection   657
Union County, N.C.   1121
Union County, S.C.   1392-1393
United Baptist Church of Mayslick (Ky.)   724
United Brethren Church, Virginia   1928
United Daughters of the Confederacy   759,
   1872
United Lutheran Church   1363
United Methodist Church   33, 120, 236, 1142,
   1713-1714, 1791, 1943
   Heritage Center, Collection   739
   See also Methodist Church
United Presbyterian Church minutes,
   U.S.   1122

See also Presbyterian Church
U.S. Air Force   88, 769
U.S. Army Forces, Headquarters,
   records   1844
U.S. Bureau of Mines   158
U.S. Corps of Engineers   929
U.S. Environmental Protection Agency   438
U.S. Geological Survey   1894
U.S. Lifesaving Service   1111
U.S. Marine Corps history   1856
U.S. Navy   392
U.S. Textile Machinery Patents,
   Collection   1321
University of the South   1717
U.S.S. **Atlanta,** Collection   402
U.S.S. **Mississippi,** Collection   837
Up and Down the River   517
Up from Slavery   147
Upcountry (S.C.)   1357
Upshur County (WV.), Collection   1944
Urban Land Institute   1351
Urban management   542
Urban planning and development   464, 630,
   1143, 1351
Urbanization   407
Ushers Temple C.M.E. Church   500
Utopia   1011
Utopias, Collection   1011
Valdosta, Ga.   553
Valentiner, Wilhem R., Collection   1132
Valtman, Ed   796
Van Noppen, John and Ina   947
Van Zele Collection   167
Vance County, N.C.   1131
Vanderbilt University   1641
Vardaman, James K.   927
Vegetables   271
Veneer   1740
Venezuela   180
Vermillion and Kittredge, Collection   1561
Verner, Samuel P., Collection   1305
Vero Beach, Fla.   197
Vertebrates   234
Veterinary medicine   418
Vicksburg riots   842
Vicksburg, Siege of   930
Vicksburg Under Glass   930
Vietnam War   886
Vietnamese refugees   283
Vinson, Frederick Moore, Collection   641
Violins   1922
Virginia Baptist Historical Society   1873
Virginia Beach, Va.   1911

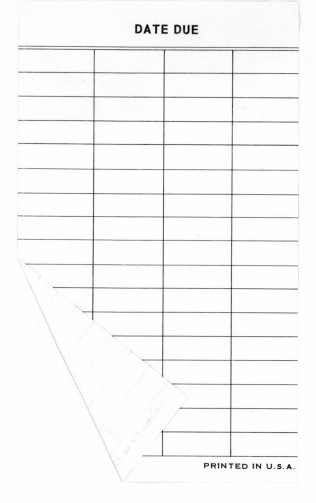

DATE DUE

PRINTED IN U.S.A.